CONCEPTS
AND METHODS OF
ARITHMETIC

by MARVIN C. VOLPEL

Chairman, Department of Mathematics
Towson State College, Towson, Maryland

DOVER PUBLICATIONS, INC. · NEW YORK

Published simultaneously in Canada by McClelland and Stewart, Limited.
Published in the United Kingdom by Constable and Company, Limited, 10 Orange Street, London W.C.2.

Concepts and Methods of Arithmetic is a new work, first published in 1964 by Dover Publications, Inc. This book is based in part on an earlier, shorter version published as lithoprinted notes in 1960 under the title *Fundamental Concepts of Arithmetic*.

Library of Congress Catalog Card Number: 64–16337

Manufactured in the United States of America

Dover Publications, Inc.
180 Varick Street
New York 14, New York

PREFACE

The past few years have seen many changes in the teaching of arithmetic. Foremost among these changes is the emphasis upon understandings and meanings. The modern philosophy of the teaching of arithmetic stresses the "why" of the operation as much as the "how." Arithmetic learnings take place when the learner understands the arithmetic processes. Rote learning—learning by rule—has been relegated to the past and the discovery technique has become the accepted mode of instruction.

Because arithmetic has become a respectable subject for students at all levels, and because there is great need for improvement in the teaching of arithmetic in the public schools today, the writer believes that a course in arithmetic which will develop concepts, clarify principles, and explain the structure of the numeration system should be a requirement for all teachers.

Teachers must know the meaning of such ideas as area, interest, decimal fraction, division, million, per cent, and so on. They must understand the principle of equal additions, the law of commutativity, the Golden Rule for fractions, the distributive law with respect to multiplication, and significant figures. They must develop an appreciation of the various algorisms for the operations involved with numbers, the values of approximation and estimation in solving problems, and above all, an awareness of the new approach to the interpretations of numbers and operations with them.

A course which stresses the new philosophy cannot be completely devoid of suggestions for teaching arithmetic. However, the primary function of this text is to explain concepts and principles and rationalize operations with numbers and to suggest ways of learning arithmetic. Since it is difficult to divorce techniques from subject matter, naturally some suggestions have crept into the text. The text is exhaustive in its treatment of topics in order that the reader will grasp a fuller meaning of the concepts with which he may have only a meager understanding. It is not intended that teachers, in turn, should

v

compel students to learn all of the material presented about particular topics or to solve all of the exercises. Topics are treated fully as background material for the teacher and to show the reader that there are other ways of doing examples.

The text attempts to present arithmetic in a new setting with attention given to the laws which permit operations with numerals and at the same time provides rationalization of mechanical processes. Throughout the text the author reiterates these laws in new and different settings; this re-use of these principles enables the reader to secure a greater grasp of the ideas which are basic to arithmetic.

Some of the features of the book are:

1. It is written in an easy-reading style.
2. It contains clear and logical interpretations of processes and operations.
3. It contains an abundant number of illustrations of operations.
4. It incorporates many suggestions for teaching arithmetic.
5. It provides for maintaining skills already established.
6. It is arranged logically.
7. It stresses the use of laws and principles throughout.
8. It provides numerous checks for testing results.
9. It contains many challenging exercises.

The text was written especially for those who are preparing to enter the teaching profession, but it is suitable for use in secondary schools and colleges where there is a demand for a respectable course in arithmetic presented from an advanced point of view.

MARVIN C. VOLPEL

Towson, Maryland
January, 1964

CONTENTS

CHAPTER 1

NUMBER

CHAPTER 2

ADDITION AND SUBTRACTION WITH WHOLE NUMBERS

CHAPTER 3

MULTIPLICATION OF WHOLE NUMBERS

CHAPTER 4

DIVISION WITH WHOLE NUMBERS

CHAPTER 5

OPERATIONS WITH COMMON FRACTIONS

CHAPTER 6

OPERATIONS WITH DECIMAL FRACTIONS

CHAPTER 7

PERCENTAGE

CHAPTER 1

NUMBER

1.1 Introduction

In primitive times man had few possessions and no system of number names was necessary to number them. There was no reason to count picks, boulders, skins, bowls, and artifacts of his environment. But as man progressed along the scale of civilization he became more prosperous and he found it necessary to enumerate and classify his possessions.

We find it reasonable to believe that when shepherd boys of old took their masters' sheep out to pasture they placed in a pile one pebble for each sheep in the flock. When they returned later with their flock they checked by removing a pebble from the pile of stones to see if there was one sheep for every stone. This concept of a one-to-one correspondence gave the shepherds a form of accounting—did all of the sheep return?—but did not answer the question, "How many sheep did return?"

This process of accounting for all the sheep is likened to the army corporal who must check his men each night, to account for all the men assigned to his barracks. At midnight he makes the rounds, flashlight in hand, to see if there is a man in every bunk. If so, he can be reasonably sure that all of his men are accounted for, and all is well. He does not have to assign a name to the number of men present. And when he checks the attendance the next morning and finds all men present, he is likely to report to his superior officer at reveille, "Sir, all present and accounted for!"

Our number system of assigning number names and number symbols to represent quantities has been taken from the Hindu and Arabic cultures and has come to us through a very interesting evolutionary process. Before we discuss the Hindu-Arabic system of notation let us glance at some of the systems established by older cultures. Our purpose in doing this is twofold: (1) to enable the reader to understand better and appreciate the number system which he uses, and (2) to give the reader a sense of appreciation of the

1

difficulties school children encounter in learning a number system as intricate as ours.

Since words and symbols are a necessary adjunct to a system of communication, it becomes necessary to assign words to quantitative ideas regardless of the system under consideration. Let us assume that in any system the number of items which will have a one-to-one correspondence to —) and —) will be the word "two." The word which will express the quantitative aspects of and will have a one-to-one correspondence with the symbols Y Y Y Y Y Y Y will be "seven" whether that quantitative idea is expressed with the symbols $\underline{PR}$ or □ △ or ⟨⟨ j or III or 7 or any other symbol. Thus when we say "twenty-five" we are thinking of the number of pennies which are equivalent in value to our quarter (of a dollar); the word "five" will represent the number of toes man has on each foot; the word "thirty-six" will represent the number of inches in a yard whether that amount is expressed symbolically 36, XXXVI, ∩∩∩ ⁞⁞⁞ , □△ , or in any other way. So when we use the expression "twenty-nine" we identify this number of things by mentally establishing a one-to-one correspondence with the number of days in the month of February every leap year, or with some other grouping of that many things.

Symbols carved on stone in caves and on tombs and pyramids and found written on clay tablets and on skins and papyrus lead us to conjecture that early civilizations had numeration systems, but we do not know if they used this form of notation to perform what we call the fundamental operations. However, there has been evidence uncovered which leads us to believe that the Romans did perform additions and subtractions.

1.2 The Egyptian System

One of the earliest systems of notation was that used by the Egyptians, which has been traced back to several hundred years before the birth of Christ. The Egyptian system was based on groups of tens—a symbol was used for one and then a new symbol was used for each new power of ten. Thus it was not necessary to have a symbol for zero.

The Egyptians made use of the two principles of repetition and addition. The number two was represented by two vertical strokes, 1 1—one and one more; the quantity three by three vertical strokes 1 1 1; the quantity nine by that many vertical strokes. There existed a one-to-one correspondence between items counted and vertical strokes. The symbols were repeated and added to find the total amount. Then a new symbol was introduced (a heelbone) to represent the quantity ten, ∩ . Two of these would represent our number twenty, and seven heelbones would be needed to represent seventy

Symbol	Name	Our number equivalent
I	Vertical staff	1
∩	Heelbone	10
𝒢	Scroll or coil	100
🪷	Lotus flower	1000
∬	Pointed finger	10,000
☜	Polliwog	100,000
👤	Man in astonishment	1,000,000

EGYPTIAN HIEROGLYPHIC NUMERALS

(which we write with only two symbols). The symbols could be written in any order, for by addition the numbers 1 1 1 ∩∩∩ and ∩∩∩1 1 1 both represent forty-three, but it became common practice to write the higher orders first. The Egyptians placed not more than four symbols in any one group. If there were more than four, these were placed on two or more lines as follows:

1 1 1

1 1 1

1 1 1

A few illustrations of Egyptian numbers are given here with their Hindu-Arabic counterparts.

∩III 10 + 3   13

∩∩∩IIII 10 + 10 + 10 + 1 + 1 + 1 + 1   34

𝒢 𝒢 II 100 + 100 + 1 + 1   202

🪷𝒢𝒢∩∩I 1000 + 100 + 100 + 10 + 10 + 1 1221

∬🪷𝒢 𝒢∩ 10,000 + 1000 + 100 + 100 + 10 11,210

EXERCISES

SET 1

1. Write the following with Egyptian hieroglyphic numerals:

43	791	5000	300,700
67	988	10,307	1,004,791

2. An Egyptian numeral is composed of 3 scrolls, 5 pointed fingers, and 2 lotus flowers. Express this number in Hindu-Arabic numerals.
3. Write a number in Egyptian hieroglyphics and then transcribe it to Arabic notation.
4. How many symbols would be necessary to write 9,654,321 in Egyptian hieroglyphics?
5. How would you express the present population (in millions) of the United States in Egyptian hieroglyphics?
6. In what way is the Egyptian system like the Hindu-Arabic system?
7. Why was there no need for the symbol for zero in the Egyptian system?
8. Express the following in Hindu-Arabic numerals:

1.3 The Roman System of Notation

The Roman system is thought to have originated from the practice of marking or tallying items, this record of quantities being made in clay, on sticks, or on tablets of stone. We find evidence leading us to believe that numbers were recorded as follows:

It is believed that the symbol for five as used in the Roman system has been taken from the stroke representing one and the diagonal stroke representing the fifth one, ⱶⱦ. This symbol is also said to represent the "vee" between the thumb and the four fingers of the hand when they are held closely together: ⱱ

In any event the quantity five is now represented by the modern capital "V."

It seems logical to conjecture that the symbol for ten (two times five) was formed by reversing the diagonal stroke, forming the capital "X," ✕, while some historians claim that the X represented the arms placed in a crossed position. Someone has suggested that since ten is the result of making two fives, maybe the symbol for ten was formed by using two "V's," one in the normal position "V" and one in the inverted position "Λ," thus✕ which when joined together at the tips will form the capital "X."

The Roman system makes use of a compound scale sometimes called the quinary-binary scale, for it introduces new symbols for five groups and every two sets of those five groups. Five ones are represented by V, and two V's become X or one ten. Five tens are represented by L, and two L's become C or one hundred. Five hundreds are represented by D, and two D's become M or one thousand.

IIIII	becomes V	The value of 2 V's becomes X
XXXXX	becomes L	The value of 2 L's becomes C
CCCCC	becomes D	The value of 2 D's becomes M

The Roman system makes use of the principle of addition, with the largest values written first; XXI represents 10 + 10 + 1 and LX represents 50 + 10, but it was not until recent years that the principle of subtraction was introduced. It is believed that the clockmakers of Europe, in order to use less space on a clock face shortened the Roman IIII to IV (representing one from five) and the Roman VIIII to IX (representing one from ten). This idea was then extended to include all fours and nines.

4 is one from five   IV
9 is one from ten   IX

      40 is ten from fifty   XL
      90 is ten from one hundred   XC

            400 is one hundred from five hundred   CD
            900 is one hundred from one thousand   CM

The student will observe that the values of the symbols for 1, 10, and 100 can be subtracted only from the two higher valued symbols. A "1" should never be subtracted from 100 to represent 99 nor 10 from 1000 to make 990.

$$1 \quad \text{from} \quad 5 \text{ is IV and } 1 \quad \text{from} \quad 5 \times 2 \text{ is } \text{ IX}$$
$$10 \quad \text{from} \quad 50 \text{ is XL and } 10 \quad \text{from} \quad 50 \times 2 \text{ is } \text{XC}$$
$$100 \text{ from } 500 \text{ is CD and } 100 \text{ from } 500 \times 2 \text{ is } \text{CM}$$

Use of Subtraction in the Roman System

The Roman system indicates multiplication by the use of horizontal and vertical bars. A horizontal stroke over a symbol multiplies that number by 1000. Thus $\overline{X}$, which could also be written with ten M's, represents 10,000. In like manner $\overline{LX}VII$ represents 60,000 + 7 or 60,007. It is believed that the use of vertical bars [ ] about a number symbol multiplied its value by 10,000 and that the use of both the vertical and the horizontal bars $\overline{[\ ]}$ multiplied the number within by 100,000. It is fairly safe to conclude that the ancient Romans had little use for such large numbers, and that they were seldom used. However, symbols other than those in use today have been discovered; the Romans did possess symbols for use in the extension of their number system. Illustrations of numbers written in the Roman system follow:

36	XXXVI	43,496	$\overline{XLIII}CDXCVI$
39	XXXIX	600,312	$\overline{DCCCCXII}$ or $[\overline{VI}]$ CCCXII
799	DCCXCIX	1956	$\overline{M}CMLVI$
3001	MMMI or $\overline{IIII}$	22,038	$\overline{XXII}XXXVIII$

The Roman system can be likened to our money system with the 25-cent piece and the \$2 bill excluded, the unit of the system being 1 cent.

1¢	5¢	10¢	50¢	100¢	500¢	1000¢
penny	nickel	dime	half	dollar	five dollars	ten dollars

5 pennies = 1 nickel
2 nickels = 1 dime
           5 dimes   = 1 half dollar
           2 half dollars = 1 dollar
                        5 dollars   = 1 five-dollar bill
                        2 five-dollar bills = 1 ten-dollar bill

Most of the calculations performed by the Romans were done by using the two fundamental processes of addition and subtraction. Multiplications were performed by the process of repeated additions, and divisions were performed by repeated subtractions.

1.4 The Abacus

The aforementioned systems of notation were a satisfactory means of recording numbers but did not lend themselves conveniently to forms of computation. The origin of the *abacus* is unknown but it is believed that its origin stems from designs made in the sand with pebbles in grooves to represent ones, tens, hundreds, and so on. Most ancient systems used a base (size of basic group or set) of ten, but the abacus (a calculative device) can be constructed with any number for its base. When ten pebbles had been accumulated in the ones column (the groove on the right) these were removed and re-placed by a pebble in the column adjacent to the left. When ten pebbles had been accumulated in this tens column they were removed and a new pebble was placed in another column to the left, and so on. Thus the number 472 (as we know it in the Hindu-Arabic system) would be shown in the sand with the following arrangement of pebbles:

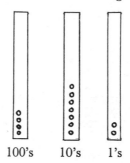

100's   10's   1's

Now if we wanted to add 219 to this amount we would put 9 stones in the column to the right, 1 pebble in the tens groove, and 2 pebbles in the hundreds groove. We then would remove 10 pebbles from the right-hand groove and replace them with one pebble in the adjacent groove. Then we would have a picture representation as follows for a combined total of 691:

```
                    *
                    *
                    *              o
            *       *              o
            o       *              o
    *       o       *          o   o
    *       o       *          o   o
    o       o       *          o   o
    o       o       *          o   o
    o       o       o          o   o
    o       o       o          o   o   o
  100's   10's   1's    =    100's 10's 1's
         472 + 219                  691
```

An early form of the Roman abacus was a metal plate with two sets of parallel grooves in it, one set directly below and with grooves longer than the other. A pebble in the upper groove was worth five times as much as a pebble in the lower groove directly beneath it. With this type of abacus the Romans needed only one pebble in each of the upper grooves and only four pebbles in the lower grooves. With these pebbles one could designate any quantity, illustrations of which are given below.

D L V	D L V	500 50 5	500 50 5
o o o	o o	o o	o
	o	o	o o
o	o	o o	o o o
o	o	o	o o
o o o	o o	o	o
o o	o o	o o	o
o o	o o o	o o o	o
o o o	o o o	o o o	o o
			o o o
C X I	C X I	100 10 1	100 10 1

THE NUMBER 3   THE NUMBER 7   THE NUMBER 26 (2 TENS + 5 + 1)   THE NUMBER 376 (300 + 50 + 20 + 5 + 1)

EXERCISES

SET 2

1. Write the following in Roman numerals:

73	406	4900	3838	19,000	176,050
96	888	9090	7000	39,066	900,048

2. Transcribe the following to our Hindu-Arabic system:

XIX MIX LXXVI $\overline{\text{CC}}$XLIV DCCCXIII CCLXXVIII

CCC LIX $\overline{\text{MM}}$DII CDXLIV MMMDCCCL $\overline{\text{VIII}}$DVIII

3. Which of the following are numbers in the Roman system?

CXLX   IVLX   CCCLII   DILL $\overline{\text{IV}}$IX   IICII   ID

4. Which of the Roman numerals should not be repeated (used more than once) in writing a numeral?

5. Draw a picture of the early Roman abacus and on it show our number 2517.

6. Sketch an abacus to the base seven and pattern it after our base ten number system.

7. Show on the abacus just drawn the representation of three sevens and four ones.

8. Using dollars, dimes, and pennies, show how to express with these coins our number 738.

9. Using dollars, half dollars, dimes, nickels, and pennies, show how to set up our numbers 345, 278, and 999 with the fewest coins.

10. Using only quarters, nickels, and pennies, show how to represent 16, 21, 26, 29, 33, 51, and 113 with the fewest coins.

11. With sets of paper disks whose values are 81, 9, and 1, show how to represent the following with the fewest disks possible: 29, 68, 80, 93, 226, 324, and 728.

12. If I can package eggs by the gross, dozen, and in singles, what is the minimum number of boxes I would need in order to package the following number of eggs: 45, 120, 168, and 1309?

13. Copy and complete the following chart:

Arabic numeral	Egyptian	Roman	What principles used?
76			
529			
1003			

1.5 The Hindu-Arabic System

Man was born with several fingers on each hand. The number of fingers on each hand was called "five" and the total number of fingers of the two hands was called "ten." This number "ten" was taken as the base (size of grouping) of the Hindu-Arabic system and all numbers in the system can be expressed in terms of tens. The use of the base "ten" was not uncommon among the early cultures. The numeral for the concept of "ten" is written with two symbols, a *one* (1) to denote a ten and a *zero* (0) to denote an absence of single units. To show the meaning of a ten to the children of an elementary school we ask them to count out a bundle of ten straws, or sticks, or tickets, or some similar objects and wrap them or tie them in a "bundle." This bundle idea permeates the arithmetic class-room of the elementary school, and a group of ten is often symbolized thus, ⊕, representing a bundle of sticks with a rubber band around them.

If we have a group of ten objects and then one more we have an array which looks like this: ********** * or ten and one. We call this amount "eleven," the name coming from the Teutonic *ainlif* which means "one left." Ten and two more can be represented like this: ********** **. We call this amount "twelve," which is also taken from the Teutonic *twalif* which means "two left." The number system is extended to include one more unit for a total of ten and three which could be called "ten-three" but which has been (un-fortunately) labeled "thirteen." One more item added to the collec-tion would give us a total of "fourteen" ("ten and four"). We continue to count to fifteen, sixteen, seventeen, eighteen, nineteen, and then to ten-and-ten or two tens, or twenty. If the teen numbers were first introduced as ten and three, or ten and four, etc., there would be less confusion in understanding and writing them.

Numerals beginning with twenty and extending to twenty-nine are composed of two groups of tens and some single units. The number expression 27 means two groups of ten and 7 single units. When this number name refers to one's age it signifies 27 single and distinct years but when it refers to cents it can signify 2 dimes (tens) and 7 pennies (ones), as well as 27 pennies.

Numerals can be thought of as having two connotations, namely, quantitative representation which we call the *collectional* aspect, and serial or geometric representation which we call the *linear* aspect. If we think of the symbolic expression 36 as representing the number of inches in a yard or the number of eggs in three dozen eggs, or just outright 36 students in a class, we are using the collectional aspect of number. We can interpret this amount as composed of 3 sets of twelve in each set, or 4 sets with nine in each set, or 3 sets of ten and 6 single units left over.

The geometric interpretation is all too prevalent in the minds of students, for if one asks the question: "What does 36 mean to you?" he is likely to receive the following response: "It's the next number after 35." The responder sees numbers in a sequence and after 35 he sees 36, and after 36 he sees 37, and so on. He does not think in terms of amounts but in terms of position on a number line. He is not entirely incorrect in his thinking, but he does not sense the full meaning of the number name, "thirty-six." He must be able to visualize "36" as an amount and as a location with respect to other numbers located on a number line.

1 1 1 1 1 1 1 1 1 1
1 1 1 1 1 1 1 1 1 1
1 1 1 1 1 1 1 1 1 1
1 1 1 1 1

29 30 31 32 33 34 35 36 37 38 39 40 41
+—+—+—+—+—+—+—+—+—+—+—+—+—+
×

QUANTITATIVE ASPECT OF 36

POSITIONAL REPRESENTATION OF 36

Computations with numbers will usually make use of the quantitative aspect or the collectional theory. If one has learned to count single items, or ones, he should be able to make use of the same skill in counting things no matter what their size or designation. He should be able to count stones, books, dozens, years, halves, or quantities of any description including tens. Thus the symbolism 10, 10, 10 should represent 3 tens, and the symbol 10 written ten times ought to represent 10 tens. A set of 10 tens is called one *hundred*. The number of days in a year can be expressed as 36 groups of 10 days each and 5 days remaining. Now these groups of tens can be regrouped into 10 tens, another group of 10 tens, and still another group of 10 tens with a group of 6 tens and 5 ones remaining. In other words we will have 3 groups of ten-tens (hundreds) and 6 groups of ten and 5 ones.

Then 365 = 3 hundreds + 6 tens + 5 ones

	hundreds	tens	ones
or 365 =	3	6	5

Since 10 tens represents a square arrangement of items we designate 10 tens as 10×10, or 10 squared, or 10^2 (read "the second power of 10" or "10 squared").*   A number written without any exponent is considered to be used once as a factor; it could be written with the exponent "1."   Thus 8^1 means 8 and n^1 means just plain n.   But it is not necessary to write the one as an exponent, for when no exponent is written we assume an exponent of 1.

Thus we see that each member or element of the smallest group of whole numbers is 1, that the size of the next larger collection is 10×1, that the size of the next larger group is 10×10; then we can assume that the size of the next larger group would be $10 \times 10 \times 10$ which we have named *thousand*.   This feature of place value—each symbol or number in a column or place has a value which is ten times the value it would have if it were in the column to the right— is a unique feature and the most outstanding characteristic of our numeration system.   The places (or columns) mentioned here may take the following headings:

Thousands	Hundreds	Tens	Ones
$10 \times 10 \times 10$	10×10	10	1
10^3	10^2	10^1	10^0
Base^3	Base^2	Base	1
1000	100	10	1

It should be apparent then that our number system consists of adjacent columns or places and that when we write numerals to represent quantities we do this by writing symbols or digits in their proper columns or places to represent the desired quantities.   If we wish to record a total of 6 groups of tens and 7 ones we must write the 6 (six) in the tens column and the 7 in the ones column.   We could write the 7 first in a place, name it the ones place, and then put the 6 in a column immediately adjacent to the left of the ones column.

* The little number ^{2} written a little to the right and a little above the number (called the base) is called an exponent and indicates the number of times that number (base) is to be used as a factor.   Thus 4^2 means 4×4 or 16, 8^3 means $8 \times 8 \times 8$, or 512.   In like manner 10^3 means $10 \times 10 \times 10$, or 1000.

This number, written as 67, represents sixty-seven things and is rationalized as follows:

Tens (10)	Ones (1)
6	7

67 = 6 tens and 7 ones

= 67 ones

The number which is composed of 13 tens and 5 ones can be thought of as being composed of 1 group of a hundred, 3 groups of ten, and 5 ones.   This would mean writing the number 1 in the place for hundreds, the number 3 in the place for tens, and the symbol 5 in the place for ones.

Hundreds (100)	Tens (10)	Ones (1)
1	3	5

The number represented by the symbols 1, 3, and 5 in the box above is read as "One hundred thirty-five."

One of the most practical illustrations of the meaning of 100 is derived from the use of cross-section paper cut into 10 by 10 squares. We designate one small square as representing one unit, then a strip of 10 of these units as representing 10, and 10 of these strips as representing 10 tens or 100.   Then it would follow that the next larger unit of measurement should be 10 hundreds or one thousand which can be represented pictorially by ten 10 × 10 squares.

Then it should follow that a number composed of 4 digits or symbols must represent a certain number of thousands, for it represents at least 10 hundred and 10 hundred is equivalent to one thousand. The number represented by four 5's, 5555, represents 5 groups of thousands, 5 groups of hundreds, 5 groups of tens, and 5 single units.

Thousands	Hundreds	Tens	Ones
5	5	5	5

1.6   The Role of Zero in the Hindu-Arabic System

At this time the reader should become better acquainted with the symbol representing the absence of quantity.   Our system makes use of the zero to represent a null or void, an absence of units whether they be ones, tens, hundreds, or what-nots. We know that the number expression 30 means 3 groups of tens and *no* ones. In the number 607 the 6 denotes 6 hundreds, the symbol 0 (zero) denotes no tens, and the symbol 7 represents that many ones. The zero must be written in the place when there are no groups of that size. Of course there are no hundreds in the number 37 but the use of the zero is not necessary as a prefix to show no hundreds. But the number "Six hundred seven" needs a zero when written in numeral form.

Hundreds	Tens	Ones
6	0	7

In the linear representation of number the symbol 0 has a place on the number scale for it represents the point at the very beginning of the scale. Most thermometers have a point *zero* on their scale to represent the division point between measurements in degrees above zero and measurements in degrees below zero. The zero indicates the point on the number scale which is halfway between the points which we indicate as negative 1 (-1) and positive 1 ($+1$). In other words, zero is a reference point.

$$-2 -1 \quad 0 \quad 1 \quad 2 \quad 3 \quad 4 \quad 5 \quad 6 \quad 7 \quad 8 \quad 9$$

The reader should take note of the fact that counting numbers (natural numbers) follow a sequence (by rote) along a number line increasing to the right. Such counting numbers have no bearing upon place-value representation, which increases by places to the left. The numbers 997, 998, 999, 1000, 1001, etc., are increasing in size as we count to the right but the addition of another place of higher value is made to the left.

The zero, then, is a numeral used to indicate a quantity or really an absence of quantity. There are many times when the zero is needed to answer the question, "how many?" Suppose a boy is playing ring toss and throws five rings in each of four trials. He scores 2 on the first attempt, zero the next time, then zero again, and then 3 on his last trial. What was his total score for the four trials? When the record is made of his successes and written in the vertical form we find a total of five rings in four attempts. The zeros are needed to help us determine that the participant had four chances.

$$
\begin{array}{r}
2 \\
0 \\
0 \\
3 \\
\hline
5
\end{array}
$$

When a baseball team wins a game by a score of 7 to 0 we say "seven to nothing." We mean that one team scored 7 runs and that the other team scored zero runs—no runs at all. If a baseball player is at bat 4 times in one game and fails to get a safe hit, the scorer records this fact as "0 (oh) for 4," meaning zero hits in 4 times at bat. Zero is a number and is needed to express quantity or absence of quantity.

Thus there are two distinct meanings to be developed for the symbol 0:

(*a*) Zero is a number denoting absence of quantity.

(*b*) Zero is a starting place or reference point on a number scale.

1.7 Extension of Our Number System

Once the base (size of grouping) of a system has been determined, the system can be extended indefinitely to include the entire set of natural or counting numbers. We are concerned in this chapter with positive integers only, but the system provides for non-integral numbers along the positive scale and for both negative whole numbers and negative fractions measured to the left of zero on the number scale. Numerals of a single digit refer always to ones, that is, "4" refers to four ones. However, if the numeral 4 is placed in the column adjacent (on the left) to the ones column it would refer to 4 tens. Then it would become a number of the second order, a number whose unit is ten; if it were in the next column to the left, it would represent a number of a higher order or hundreds, and so on. If this number 4 is placed to the left in a new place, its new value is ten times its old value. Four hundred is 10 times the value of 4 tens. Four thousand is 10 times the value of 4 hundred. Each new place or column to the left has a value ten times that of the adjacent column.

This accounts for the regular pattern of number names beginning with ones.

ones	1	
ten ones	10	*Ones*
hundred ones	100	
thousand	1000	
ten thousand	10,000	*Thousands*
hundred thousand	100,000	
million	1,000,000	
ten million	10,000,000	*Millions*
hundred million	100,000,000	
billion	1,000,000,000	
ten billion	10,000,000,000	*Billions*
hundred billion	100,000,000,000	

Though there is little need to learn the number names beyond the billion, since all larger numbers could be expressed in terms of smaller ones, our civilization in the near future might demand the use of other more convenient number names. For convenience in reading and writing large numbers we mark them off in groups of 3, beginning with the ones place and proceeding to the left every third number. This group of three digits is called a *period* and then its proper unit of reference is attached. Thus the symbols 237, in the same period, are always read "two hundred thirty-seven" whether they represent millions, thousands, or ones. Each period is assigned a name as indicated in the accompanying charts and these periods follow in this order: ones, thousands, millions, billions, trillions, quadrillions, quintillions, sextillions,. . ., each new period being 1000 times the value of the preceding period.

ones	10^0	written with a 1 and no zeros
thousands	10^3	written with a 1 and 3 zeros
millions	10^6	written with a 1 and 6 zeros
billions	10^9	written with a 1 and 9 zeros
trillions	10^{12}	written with a 1 and 12 zeros
quadrillions	10^{15}	written with a 1 and 15 zeros

Since 10^9 represents a billion, then 10^{10} (one more 10 as a multiplier) represents 10 times one billion and 10^{11} represents 100 times ($10^2 \times 10^9$) one billion. Each unit of measurement or period is multiplied by 1, 10, or 100 and accounts for all our number names and hence for the reading of numerals of any magnitude.

	Trillions			Billions			Millions			Thousands			Ones		
	100	10	1	100	10	1	100	10	1	100	10	1	100	10	1
(a)					5	0	3	0	0	0	0	6	0	7	0
(b)			1	0	0	3	4	0	6	0	2	1	9	0	8
(c)						4	0	3	1	7	0	0	0	0	3
(d)				4	2	1	0	0	0	0	6	2	5	0	0
(e)					1	8	4	7	3	6	5	4	9	8	7

Number (*a*) is read: Fifty billion, three hundred million, six thousand, seventy.

Number (*b*) is read: One trillion, three billion, four hundred six million, twenty-one thousand, nine hundred eight.

Number (*c*) is read: Four billion, thirty-one million, seven hundred thousand, three.

Number (*d*) is read: Four hundred twenty-one billions, sixty-two thousand, five hundred.

Number (*e*) is read: Eighteen billion, four hundred seventy-three million, six hundred fifty-four thousand, nine hundred eight-seven.

(Note that in reading whole numbers the use of the word "and" is unnecessary and hence omitted. Though the number is read as being made up of several different kinds of units—millions, thousands, and ones—we restrict the use of the word "and" to the reading of decimal fractions. This is good mathematics and good pedagogy. However, in teaching the meaning of numbers to school children we stress the fact that numbers are composed of hundreds, tens, ones, and so on. We show children that 43 is composed of 4 tens and 3 ones and even write it as 4 tens + 3 ones. Therefore it seems a bit inconsistent to the writer to deny students the right to say "and" when reading numbers. If the meaning is clear, I see no reason why a person cannot say, "Fourteen hundred and twenty-seven." The writer is not one who would restrict the use of the word "and" only to the reading of decimal fractions. Try to read these numbers without using the word "and": $6\frac{1}{4}$ $.7\frac{1}{2}$ $9.4\frac{1}{2}$.)

Thus the number 23,456,789,121 would be read as follows: 23 billion, 456 million, 789 thousand, 121.

billions	millions	thousands	ones
⌃	⌃	⌃	⌃
23	456	789	121

The number 13,429,816,275 is composed of

$$
\left.\begin{array}{r} 10 \\ 3 \end{array}\right\} \text{billion} \quad \left.\begin{array}{r} 400 \\ 20 \\ 9 \end{array}\right\} \text{million} \quad \left.\begin{array}{r} 800 \\ 10 \\ 6 \end{array}\right\} \text{thousand} \quad \left.\begin{array}{r} 200 \\ 70 \\ 5 \end{array}\right\} \text{ones}
$$

or

13 billion, 429 million, 816 thousand, 275 ones.

To write a number in symbols if it has been presented in words (to transcribe a given amount into symbolic form) we need only remember the periods in order from right to left, and then place the numerals in their proper columns. Thus the number two hundred thousand would be written "200" for the two hundred and then these digits would be placed in the period for thousands:

thousands, ones
200,

and all other places or spaces would be filled in with zeros to designate absence of those units. The number *two hundred forty-five million, three hundred seventeen* suggests the two sequences of digits 245 and 317. The former is placed in the period for millions and the latter in the period for ones. Other spaces are filled with zeros.

millions	thousands	ones	
245	000	317	245,000,317

The number *ten billion, three thousand, four* suggests that we must put the numerals 10, 3, and 4 in the proper columns in their respective periods.

Billions			Millions			Thousands			Ones		
	1	0	0	0	0	0	0	3	0	0	4

The number 67,589,432,617 is composed of

6 groups of ten billion	or	60,000,000,000
7 groups of billions		7,000,000,000
5 groups of hundred millions		500,000,000
8 groups of ten millions		80,000,000
9 groups of millions		9,000,000
4 groups of hundred thousands		400,000
3 groups of ten thousands		30,000
2 groups of thousands		2000
6 groups of hundreds		600
1 group of tens		10
7 groups of ones		7
		67,589,432,617

and is read: "Sixty-seven billion, five hundred eighty-nine million, four hundred thirty-two thousand, six hundred seventeen."

The English system of reading numbers is somewhat different from the United States system, for the English divide their numbers into groups of six digits. Numbers composed of nine digits or less are read alike in both systems, but beginning with the tenth place there is a difference in nomenclature. The English billion is equivalent to the million million in the American system, and a trillion is equivalent to a million million million in the American system; billion means two one millions multiplied together and a trillion means three one millions multiplied together.

Term	American Interpretation	English Interpretation
million	10^6	10^6
	1,000,000	1,000000
billion	10^9	10^{12} (1,000000 × 1,000000)
	1,000,000,000	1,000000,000000
trillion	10^{12}	10^{18} (1,000000 × 1,000000 × 1,000000)
	1,000,000,000,000	1,000000,000000,000000

In London the number 23456,800500 would be read: "Twenty-three thousand four hundred fifty-six million, eight hundred thousand five hundred." The number 3,005044,002001 would be read by Londoners as: "Three billion, five thousand forty-four million, two thousand one."

EXERCISES

SET 3

1. Write the following numbers in words:

   (a) 309   (g) 4,000,004,004
   (b) 1276   (h) 40,005,000,050
   (c) 34,007   (i) 809,098,070
   (d) 700,034   (j) 1,101,403,016
   (e) 1,005,403   (k) 167,854,793
   (f) 200,200,200   (l) 302,061,101

2. Write the following expressions in symbols:

   (a) Three thousand twenty-seven
   (b) Twelve hundred twelve
   (c) Two hundred two thousand six
   (d) Forty million, forty thousand, four
   (e) Two billion, two million, twenty thousand, twenty
   (f) Six billion, sixty-six million, six hundred six thousand, six

3. Write in words:

   (a) The number formed by seven consecutive ones.
   (b) The whole number formed by all ten symbols in order from the largest valued symbol to the smallest.

4. Obtain a recent estimate of the population of the United States and write it in words. Now multiply that number by two and write the new number in words.

5. Write the following numbers in words in both the American and English systems:

   (a) 345,683,450,256   (b) 21,305,000,707,888

6. Write the following numbers:

   (a) Seven and one quarter million
   (b) A half million
   (c) Three quarters of a million
   (d) One hundred less than a million
   (e) One hundred fifty more than half a thousand
   (f) Five ten thousands
   (g) A quarter of a billion
   (h) One and a quarter thousand
   (i) Twelve less than ten thousand
   (j) Three and one-half hundred thousand
   (k) Three and one-half billion

7. (a) Write the largest number you can think of using three twos.
   (b) Write five using only fours.

1.8 Interpreting Numbers

The number formed by the two digits 7 and 2 has the number name "seventy-two," which means 7 tens and 2 ones. However, it could be interpreted as seventy-two ones. If the quantity referred to money we could represent the amount with 7 dimes and 2 pennies or with 72 pennies.

$$72 = 7 \text{ tens} + 2 \text{ ones} \quad \text{or} \quad 72 \text{ ones}$$

The number represented by the three digits 456 is most often called or read, "Four hundred fifty-six." It is made up of 4 groups of 100, 5 groups of 10, and 6 ones. However, it might just as well be composed of 45 groups of 10 and 6 ones or even 456 ones. If this number referred to an amount of money it could be represented by $4 plus 56 cents, 45 dimes plus 6 cents, or by a single group of 456 pennies.

$$456 = 4 \text{ hundreds} + 5 \text{ tens} + 6 \text{ ones or } 45 \text{ tens} + 6 \text{ ones or } 456 \text{ ones}$$

Hundreds	Tens	Ones
4	5	6

4 hundreds plus 5 tens plus 6 ones

Hundreds	Tens	Ones
4	5	6

4 hundreds plus 56 ones

Hundreds	Tens	Ones
4	5	6

45 tens plus 6 ones

Hundreds	Tens	Ones
4	5	6

456 ones

The number 6700 is 67 hundred as well as 6 thousand 7 hundred. It is or can also be interpreted as 670 tens. And when we carry the interpretation into decimal or fractional parts we will discover other ways of reading the number, such as 67,000 tenths $\left(\dfrac{67,000}{10}\right)$. The ability to read numbers in different ways will be invaluable in learning to round off numbers and eventually in learning to make estimations in problem-solving situations.

The number represented by the four digits 6543 can be read in any one of several ways:

(1) 6 thousand 5 hundred 4 tens and 3 ones
(2) 65 hundred 4 tens and 3 ones
(3) 654 tens and 3 ones
(4) 6543 ones
(5) 65 hundred and forty-three ones
(6) 6 thousand five hundred forty-three

	Thousands ●	Hundreds ● ●	Tens ● ● ●	Ones ● ● ● ●
(1)	6	5	4	3
(2)	6	5	4	3
(3)	6	5	4	3
(4)	6	5	4	3

The student must keep the names of the places in mind and then visualize a movable indicator riding along the number names. Where the index stops, that's the name of the number.   To illustrate:

Read: 5489 as hundreds   *
Answer: 54 hundred eighty-nine   5 4 8 9

Read: 7368 as tens   *
Answer: 736 tens eight   7 3 6 8

Read: 40,391 as hundreds   *
Answer: 403 hundred ninety-one   4 0 3 9 1

Read: 6,000,000 as thousands   *
Answer: 6000 thousand   6 0 0 0 0 0 0

Another diagrammatic arrangement might prove helpful here. Let us express the quantity 3725 in various interpretations all of which are equivalent.

Thousands	Hundreds	Tens	Ones
3	7	2	5
	37	2	5
		372	5
			3725
	37		25
3		72	5
3			725
3	7		25

1.9   Approximate Numbers

It is often expedient to express number quantities both known and unknown as approximations.   When we count the tickets which have been taken at the door at a concert and find this number to be 587 we know that we have admitted exactly that many people by ticket but for the sake of convenience we express this number to the nearest number of hundreds, which in this case is 6.   We say that 600 people attended the concert.   When a man buys a shirt for $3.98 he might tell his friend that he has purchased a $4 shirt.   And when a woman buys a dress for $16.98 she might tell her friend that it cost $20 and she would be right if she is thinking of the cost of the dress in terms of ten-dollar bills.   The cost of the dress was nearer to $20 than it was to $10.   When we say that the population of the United States is 179,000,000 we do not mean exactly 179 million; we mean that in millions of people the total is nearer to 179 million than it is to 178 or 180 million.   When we read in the newspaper that the attendance at one of the World Series baseball games was 64,273 we might not be interested in the exact number; we just express the number of fans in attendance as (roughly) 64,000.   For our purposes we want to know a number somewhere in the neighborhood of the exact figure.

This practice of expressing the given quantity in terms of some larger group or denomination (different from single items) is called the "rounding-off process" and indicates that the final few digits are round numbers (zeros) or uncertain numbers.   Often we have a choice in the unit or denomination which we select.   We can express the weight of a man in units of one pound, in terms of one hundred pounds, or in terms of tens of pounds.   If a man weighed 162 pounds we could say that his weight is nearer 200 pounds than it is to 100 pounds; he is in the 200-pound class.   It would be more accurate and we would be closer to his actual weight if we called him a "160-pounder."   In terms of tens of pounds he weighs 160 pounds.   If a man were 5 feet $11\frac{1}{2}$ inches tall we would class him as a "six-footer."   The expression "6 feet tall" means that a man is almost 6 feet tall or that he is slightly over 6 feet tall, that his height is nearer to 6 feet than it is to 5 feet or to 7 feet.   His height expressed to the nearest integral number of feet is 6 feet.

When we say, "Express the weight of a chicken to the nearest pound," we merely want to know the approximate weight of the chicken.   We are not interested in the fractional part of a pound.   If the chicken weighed 4 pounds 11 ounces we ascertain whether this weight is nearer to 4 pounds or to 5 pounds. Since there are 16 ounces in a pound we find that the weight of the chicken is more than half a pound beyond the 4-pound weight. We would refer to the chicken as being a 5-pound chicken. Graphically this can be shown as follows:

4 lb.   5 lb.

| 0 1 2 3 4 5 6 7 8 9 10 11 12 13 14 15 0 1 2

The chicken weighed 4 pounds 11 ounces which is closer to 5 pounds than to 4 pounds.

Every number can be expressed on a number line and its quantitative value compared with neighboring values. On a number line the number 375 is nearer to 400 than it is to 300, so expressed in round numbers to the nearest hundred it would be 400.

Other illustrations follow:

400   421   450   500
 * | *   *

The number 421 is nearer to 400 than it is to 500, so rounded off to hundreds the number 421 becomes 400.

The number 3,663 is nearer to 4 thousand than it is to any other thousand.

3000   3663   4000
 * | *

The number 79 is nearer to 100 than to zero hundred but the number 34 expressed in hundreds would be zero hundreds.

0   34   79   100   200
 * | | *   *

If the ones digit of the number is 5 we usually round upward to the next higher number of tens. Thus 45 is rounded off to 50 (5 tens), and numbers like 785 and 1205 are rounded off to 790 and 1210 respectively. If there are no ones in the number and the tens number is 5, then we round upward to the next number of hundreds. The number 650 is rounded off to 700 and numbers like 250 and 1350 become 300 and 1400 when rounded off to hundreds. In other words, if a number is halfway between two given numbers and we must select one or the other as being the closer of the two numbers, we usually select the larger of the two. We know that $9\frac{1}{2}$ cents becomes 10 cents and that if we need $3\frac{1}{2}$ pies for company we will have to buy 4 whole pies. We know that 650 is halfway between 600 and 700 but we say that it is nearer to 700.

```
600              650              700
 *                |                *
```

1.10 Numbers in Exponential Form

Scientists and writers of scientific material find it more convenient to write very large numbers and small decimal numbers in exponential form rather than in the regular way. We have already developed the concept of an exponent and have shown some of its uses. Now we can make further use of the exponent to show multiples and powers of 10 which will enable us to write long number expressions in a short form.

$$10 = 10^1 \qquad \text{1 followed by 1 zero}$$
$$100 = 10^2 \qquad \text{1 followed by 2 zeros}$$
$$1000 = 10^3 \qquad \text{1 followed by 3 zeros}$$
$$10000 = 10^4 \qquad \text{1 followed by 4 zeros}$$
$$100000 = 10^5 \qquad \text{1 followed by 5 zeros}$$
$$1000000 = 10^6 \qquad \text{1 followed by 6 zeros}$$

A casual glance at both the number of zeros following the digit *one* and the exponent of 10 reveals the fact that there is perfect agreement between the number of zeros and the exponent. We can safely conclude, therefore, that a number consisting of a 1 followed by 19 zeros could be written in short form as 10^{19}. When n is a positive integer, 10^n should be written with a 1 followed by n zeros, and when a number is written with a 1 and n zeros, then that number can be expressed as 10^n. The special case of this rule will not be proved here, but it seems logical to assume that 10^0 should be written as a 1 with not any zeros after it, or that 1 with no zeros after it is equivalent to 10^0.

1.11   Scientific Notation

We have established that numbers can be rounded off to express certain integral quantitative units.   We have learned how to express 33,227 spectators at a football game as groups of tens, as hundreds, or as thousands to suit our desires or convenience.   We can specify that there were 33 thousand (33 × 1000) or that there were 3 ten thousand (3 × 10,000) people in attendance.   This number 33 × 1000 can be expressed as 33 × 10^3 for 1000 = 10^3 and the number 3 × 10,000 can be expressed as 3 × 10^4 for 10,000 = 10^4.

All rational numbers can be written in terms of powers of 10 or in terms of some multiple (either integral or fractional or both) of 10 or power of 10.

Thus

$$300 = 3 \times 100 \qquad\qquad = 3 \times 10^2$$
$$9000 = 9 \times 1000 \qquad\qquad = 9 \times 10^3$$
$$4{,}000{,}000 = 4 \times 1{,}000{,}000 \qquad = 4 \times 10^6$$
$$65{,}000 = 65 \times 1000$$
$$= 6.5 \times 10{,}000 \qquad = 6.5 \times 10^4$$

Numbers written in the above form are said to be written in *standard form* or in *scientific form* and can be more conveniently used by the scientist in this form than when written in the ordinary manner.   To write a number in its standard form, write it as *a number between 1 and 10 times a power of 10*.   In other words, place a decimal point after the first digit of the number and then multiply this times some power of 10.   The power of 10 must coincide with the power of 10 which will produce the units of measurement or the denomination.   Thus, to write 700 in standard form, put a decimal point after the first significant figure—this will be 7.   Now express 700 as 7.00 × *some power of ten*.   This other multiplication factor is 100 or 10^2.   Therefore 700 = 7 × 10^2.

$$3{,}000{,}000 = 3 \text{ million} = 3 \times 1{,}000{,}000 = 3 \times 10^6$$
$$26{,}000 = 2.6 \text{ ten thousand} = 2.6 \times 10{,}000 = 2.6 \times 10^4$$
$$875{,}000{,}000 = 8.75 \text{ hundred million}$$
$$= 8.75 \times 100{,}000{,}000 = 8.75 \times 10^8$$
$$4256 = 4.256 \text{ thousand} = 4.256 \times 1000 = 4.256 \times 10^3$$
$$245{,}000{,}000{,}000 = 2.45 \text{ hundred billion}$$
$$= 2.45 \times 100{,}000{,}000{,}000 = 2.45 \times 10^{11}$$

From the above illustrations we see that the exponent on the base 10 expresses the size of the denomination.   The sixth power of 10 indicated million, the fourth power of 10 indicated ten thousand, the eighth power of 10 indicated hundred million, the third power of 10 indicated thousand, and the ninth power of 10 indicated billion. After the number is written as a single-digit number plus something multiplied by a power of ten, the power of ten will be equal to the number of places in the number to the right of the decimal point.*

Complete decimal numbers like .6, .01, .00005, .000000000375, etc., can also be written in standard form by use of the same principles and the same rule as above. However, since this procedure with decimal numbers will involve the use of negative numbers as exponents the material will not be presented here.

$$16,000 \times 40,000 = 1.6 \times 10^4 \times 4 \times 10^4 = (1.6 \times 4) \times (10^4 \times 10^4)$$
$$= 6.4 \times 10^8$$
$$= 640,000,000$$

$$700,000 \times 800,000 = 7 \times 10^5 \times 8 \times 10^5 = (7 \times 8) \times (10^5 \times 10^5)$$
$$= 56 \times 10^{10}$$

EXERCISES

SET 4

1. Express the following as indicated:

    21 ounces as pounds   240 minutes as hours
    47 inches as yards   900 days as years
    70 cents as dimes   300 years as centuries
    84 items as dozens   6600 feet as miles

2. Express the following as tens (exact number of tens):

    40   170   3250   1900   37,000   540,000   5

3. Write several verbal expressions which are equivalent to:

    (a) One thousand thousand thousand   (b) one million

4. Express each of the following as hundreds:

    900   1100   32,100   550   800,000   927,000

---

* Students of trigonometry will recall the techniques employed for finding the logarithm of a number. Every logarithm consists of two parts, the characteristic and the mantissa. The former is found by inspection while the latter is found from prepared tables. One rule for finding the characteristic (part of a logarithm) of a whole number is to count the number of places in the number and decrease this amount by 1. If a number contains 4 digits, such as 5789, then the characteristic will be 3. This 3 would be the exponent of 10 if this number were written in standard form. The characteristic of the logarithm of 9,000,000 is one less than the number of places in the whole number. In this case it would be 6, which is the exponent of 10 if the number is put in standard form: $9,000,000 = 9 \times 10^6$.

5. Which of the numerals in exercise No. 4 has the smallest number of tens? The largest number of tens? Which of the numerals in exercise No. 2 has the largest number of hundreds?

6. Express each of the following in tens and in hundreds:

    65,000   71,800   931,000   29,000,000   250   503,760

7. Rewrite both in words and in symbols as indicated:

Eighty-one thousand	as tens
Fifty-two million	as thousands
Three and one-half hundred	as tens
Ninety-four thousand	as hundreds
One hundred one thousand	as tens
Seven and one quarter billion	as millions
Two million million	as billions
Sixty tens	as hundreds
One-half million	as hundred thousands
Twenty thousand	as tens of thousands

8. Write the following in standard form:

    8000   2100   7,650,000   38   7.2   82.5

9. Write the numerals of exercise No. 7 in standard form.

10. The distance from the earth to the sun is approximately 93,000,000 miles. Express this distance in scientific notation. Find three or more examples of the use of the standard form in science textbooks or scientific magazines.

1.12 Systems in Other Bases

If a group of 9 dogs and a group of 7 dogs will make a combined group of 16 dogs, what is the combined total when 9 and 7 both refer to inches? When they both refer to ounces? If both of them represent baseball players? If they both represent feet? If they both refer to quarts? If 9 and 7 represent musicians, how many trios can be formed? How many sextets? How many quartets? If 9 and 7 represent pennies, how else could the total amount of money be expressed?

The above questions are put to show that we don't always group things in sets of ten. We buy eggs by the dozen, candy by the pound, wheat by the bushel, coal by the ton, and so on. It is not always feasible to express these amounts in bundles of ten. The student, during his days in elementary school, has had much practice in wrapping sticks and straws in bundles of ten. He is well grounded in the collectional aspect of things when they are packaged in tens. Now he is made aware of, perhaps introduced to, collections of things in varying sizes. He is asked to think in terms of collections of varying sizes called *bases*.

Let us consider a money system which includes the penny, the nickel, the 25-cent piece, a bill whose value is equivalent to 125 pennies, and a bill whose value is equivalent to 625 pennies, and so on in powers of 5. The pieces of money have these values: 1, 5, 25, 125, 625, etc. These pieces of money could be assigned these names: penny, nickel, fi-five, fiver, five-spot, etc., and they would be used just as effectively as our present money system. We would be able to count out any amount of money with this new system just as well as we do with our system. In like manner, if we were to use our present money system exclusive of the nickel and the quarter and the five-dollar bill, we would also be able to operate quite efficiently in the business world. With pennies, dimes, dollars, and ten-dollar bills we can count out any amount of money.

In these systems 1733 cents would be represented by:

(*a*) 1733 cents = 2 five-spots, 3 fivers, 4 fi-fives, 1 nickel, and 3 pennies.
(*b*) 1733 cents = 1 ten-dollar, 7 dollars, 3 dimes, and 3 pennies.

When we devise a system with base five (groups of five) and pattern it after our decimal system, we discover that we need but five symbols to designate quantity. When we obtain five pennies we replace them by their equivalent, one nickel. When we accumulate five nickels we replace them by their equivalent, one fi-five. When we accumulate 1 fi-five and then 2 fi-fives and then 3 fi-fives and 4 fi-fives and finally one more fi-five, then we will have a new collection (5 fi-fives) which we have named "fiver." In the system which has five for its base we have no single symbol for five; five is written 10. Any system patterned after our decimal system will always have as many different symbols as the name of the base implies; that is, if the base is four, there will be four symbols: 0, 1, 2, and 3. If the base is five there will be five symbols: 0, 1, 2, 3, 4. The quantity five will be represented as a combination of two symbols 10 meaning one group of five (the base) and no single units remaining. When the base is seven there will be seven symbols and the number expression seven will be written 10. If the base is thirteen then the number expression representing thirteen will be written 10 and we will need thirteen symbols in the system. If the base is b then there will be b symbols in the system.

Let us analyze the above principle by using a concrete example. We know that a group of seven days represents one week. The single quantities or units are called *days*, and the collection of days (seven in number) is called a *week*.   We want to show that there is no symbol 7 in this system.

Let the X's represent days: Symbolic representation of quantity

	weeks	days
X X X X X		5
X X X X X X		6
X X X X X X X	1	0
X X X X X X X X	1	1
X X X X X X X X X	1	2
X X X X X X X X X X	1	3
X X X X X X X X X X X	1	4
X X X X X X X X X X X X	1	5
X X X X X X X X X X X X X	1	6
X X X X X X X X X X X X X X	2	0
X X X X X X X X X X X X X X X	2	1

From this array we see that the number names which represent quantities which are grouped in sets of seven with their corresponding symbolic representation will take the following form:

one	(1)	two sevens and one	(21)
two	(2)	two sevens and two	(22)
three	(3)	two sevens and three	(23)
four	(4)	two sevens and four	(24)
five	(5)	two sevens and five	(25)
six	(6)	two sevens and six	(26)
seven	(10)	three sevens	(30)
seven and one	(11)	three sevens and one	(31)
seven and two	(12)	three sevens and two	(32)
seven and three	(13)	three sevens and three	(33)
seven and four	(14)	three sevens and four	(34)
seven and five	(15)	three sevens and five	(35)
seven and six	(16)	three sevens and six	(36)
two sevens	(20)	four sevens	(40)

The numbering system above can be continued indefinitely.   Soon we shall come to the number 66 which means six sevens and six.   If we increase this amount by 1, that is, count to the next number, we will have six sevens and seven.   This is the same as having seven sevens. Now seven sevens will represent a new group of things which we will call a seven-seven or a forty-nine. This number would be represented in symbolic form as 100.

Symbol	Name	Symbol	Name
10_{ten}	Ten	100_{ten}	Ten-tens or Hundred
10_{five}	Five	100_{five}	Five-fives or Twenty-five
10_{seven}	Seven	100_{seven}	Seven-sevens or Forty-nine

1.13 The Duodecimal System

Let us use a second example which will be more familiar to most people. Suppose we are counting eggs in a grocery store and we are packaging them by the dozen. We would count out the eggs and soon reach one dozen. Then we'd have one dozen one, one dozen two,..., one dozen eleven, one dozen twelve or two dozen. There is no single symbol for twelve when the size of the group is twelve, neither are there symbols for ten and eleven. When the base is twelve then this number is written as 10 and we can use T for ten and E for eleven, or any other symbols to express these quantities. These numerals would represent the number of eggs up to two dozen: 1, 2, 3, 4, 5, 6, 7, 8, 9, T, E, 10, 11, 12, 13, 14, 15, 16, 17, 18, 19, 1T, 1E, 20. The last three symbols would represent respectively one dozen ten, one dozen eleven, and two dozen.

Now this system will proceed in order through groups of twelves to nine twelves (90), ten twelves (T0), and then to eleven twelves (E0). Counting from eleven twelves we reach eleven twelves and one (E1), eleven twelves and two (E2), ..., eleven twelves and ten (ET), and then to eleven twelves and eleven (EE). The next number would be twelve twelves which is the same as one twelve-twelve, one hundred-forty-four, or one twelve square, or one twelve squared—100.

COUNTING IN BASE THREE			COUNTING IN BASE FOUR				COUNTING IN BASE FIVE				
1	2	10	1	2	3	10	1	2	3	4	10
11	12	20	11	12	13	20	11	12	13	14	20
21	22	100	21	22	23	30	21	22	23	24	30
			31	32	33	100	31	32	33	34	40
							41	42	43	44	100

Mathematicians have long been aware of the fact that ten is actually a poor base for a number system for it has few exact divisions. The duodecimal system (base twelve) has a perfect half, third, fourth, sixth, and twelfth. If .5 represents five tenths in the decimal scale, then .5 represents five twelfths in the duodecimal scale. If .5 represents one-half when the scale is ten, then .6 represents the equivalent of one-half when the base is twelve. The Duodecimal Society of America has agreed upon the inclusion of the two symbols X and E to represent the quantities ten and eleven as we know them in the decimal scale. The X would be named *dek* and the E would be called *el*; the twelve would be *do* and written 10. The quantity one gross, or a dozen dozen (144 in base ten) is expressed as 100 and called *gro* for gross.

In summary, every system provides for a single object which we call one and when the number of ones is recorded we have established a ones place. Then the first column to the left of the ones place represents the base of the system. The number 15 represents one of the base and five single items. The symbols 34 represent 3 of something—size unknown but representing the base—and 4 ones. In the Table of Base Three above, 22 represents 2 threes and 2 ones, and in the Table of Base Five 43 represents 4 groups of five and 3 ones. Note that when the base is five then the last number in the square is written 100 to represent five-fives. And the next to the last numeral in the square is 44.

1.14 The Binary System

Before we close this discussion on number systems with bases different from ten let us discuss the system whose base is two. This is called the binary system and contains only two symbols, the 0 (for a void) and 1. This system is used in modern electronic computing machines found in many offices today. Since the computing is done electrically, all numbers put into the machine are inserted as electrical charges. Since a number to the base two is composed of only two different symbols, these numbers are easy to set in an electric machine; either put the charge in or leave it out. This system is likened to an adding machine which has only one long row of numerals or buttons on its face. To push the button down would print the numeral, failure to push the button would print a 0 in that place. To set the number 101 in the binary scale we would operate on only two buttons

ck at the binary system and show how our
numbers from 1 to 20 would be set in the electric machines:

Our number	Expressed in charges	Expressed on machine	Expressed in symbols
1	+	0000*	1
2	+0	000*0	10
3	++	000**	11
4	+00	00*00	100
5	+0+	00*0*	101
6	++0	00**0	110
7	+++	00***	111
8	+000	0*000	1000
9	+00+	0*00*	1001
10	+0+0	0*0*0	1010
11	+0++	0*0**	1011
12	++00	0**00	1100
13	++0+	0**0*	1101
14	+++0	0***0	1110
15	++++	0****	1111
16	+0000	*0000	10000
17	+000+	*000*	10001
18	+00+0	*00*0	10010
19	+00++	*00**	10011
20	+0+00	*0*00	10100

NUMBERS IN THE BINARY SYSTEM

Let us show how and why the numeral 19 (in the base ten) is
expressed as 10011 in the base two.   Begin with 19 single objects:

1 1 1 1 1 1 1 1 1 1 1 1 1 1 1 1 1 1 1

Group them by twos:

 1

Whenever we find a group of twos we form a new package. We will have 9 twos and 1. Now we group these twos by twos:

 1

Whenever we find two of anything we form a group. We find four two-twos and a two and a 1. Continuing, we find two groups of two two-twos and a two and a 1.

 1

With two of anything we form a new group. We find one group of two two-two-twos and a group of two and 1.

 1

Thus we see that 19 is composed of one 2^4 and one 2 and a 1. Another way of writing this is 19 = one $(two)^4$ and one (two) and one or 10011 (base two).

Base^4 Two^4 2^4	Base^3 Two^3 2^3	Base^2 Two^2 2^2	Base^1 Two^1 2^1	Base^0 Two^0 2^0
1	0	0	1	1

NINETEEN

Let us take another numeral such as 45 and see what it would become if expressed in base two. When 45 is regrouped in powers of two it becomes one group of 32 plus one 8 plus one 4 plus 1. In exponential form to the base two, 32 becomes 2^5, 8 is 2^3, 4 is 2^2, and 1 is 2^0. Thus $45 = 2^5 + 2^3 + 2^2 + 1$. Then in numeral form to the base two the number which we know as 45 becomes 101101 and is read, "One two to the fifth, one two cubed, one two squared, one."

2^5	2^4	2^3	2^2	2^1	2^0
1	0	1	1	0	1

FORTY-FIVE

Thus we see that the symbolic numeral expression equivalent to the number, "One two to the fifth power, one two to the third power, 1 two and 1," is represented by the numeral 101101.

1.15 Changing a Number in Base Ten to a Different Base

In order to comprehend the quantitative aspects of number expressions in bases other than ten it is necessary to transcribe given numbers into the language of the decimal system with which we are all familiar. The number *thirteen* represents the same number of individual items in any base though its symbolic representation will vary. In the base ten the number thirteen represents 1 group of ten and 3 ones. In the base twelve it means 1 group of twelve and a 1. In the base seven it means 1 group of seven and 6 ones and would be written 16. In the base five it represents 2 groups of five and 3 ones, 23. In the base four it would be 3 fours and 1. In the base three it would be 1 three squared, 1 three and 1 and would be written 111.

Every number expression in terms of ten can be written in terms of some other size group or package. For instance, the number 31 which we are accustomed to reading, "thirty-one," can be written in many ways, some of which are illustrated here:

31	Interpretation	Written	Base
	$1 \times 27 + 4$	14	twenty-seven
	$2 \times 14 + 3$	23	fourteen
	$2 \times 11 + 9$	29	eleven
	$3 \times 9 + 4$	34	nine
	$5 \times 6 + 1$	51	six
	$1 \times 5^2 + 1 \times 5 + 1$	111	five
	$1 \times 4^2 + 3 \times 4 + 3$	133	four

The process of changing a given number (base ten) to a number expression in any other base suggests the following question: "How

many groups of a given size can be formed from a given number?"
If I have a group of seventeen sticks of gum and wish to package them
in groups of five, how many packages can I form?

Thus the number seventeen can be written as 3 fives and 2 ones or
simply 32 (base five). How many baseball teams can be formed from
a group of 50 players? The number fifty contains 5 groups of nines
with 5 single ones remaining. Thus 50 in the base ten would be
written as 55 in the base nine. How many one pound packages of
candy are equivalent to eighty ounces of candy? The question
suggests the use of the subtraction process—to remove groups of
sixteen ounces until all the candy has been used up. When the
subtractions thus performed are of uniform size, the process becomes
the division process. Thus to find the answer to the above question
we can either subtract or divide to find the number of groups. If we
divide we find that 80 contains sixteen exactly five times with no
remainder. Since the base is sixteen we write 80 (base ten) as 50
(base sixteen).

When the rationalization of this process of changing from the base
ten to any other base has been fully understood, the student will
start searching for a short cut or a simple algorism (pattern for the
solution) which should be presented at this time.

Change 21 to base four.
How many groups of four are there in
21?   4) 21
(Divide 21 by 4)   5 — 1 remainder

Are there any groups of four-fours in
21?   4) 21
(Divide again by 4)   4) 5 — 1 remainder
                                                    1 (this is a four-
                                                      four with 1 re-
                                                      mainder)
In pure abstract form the algorism
looks like this: 4) 21
                                                 4) 5 — 1
                                                    1 — 1

From the algorism we see that 21 is composed of 1 group of four
squared and 1 group of 4 and 1 one. Thus 21 = 111 (base four).

For a second example let us change 82 to the base five. We must answer the question, "How many groups of five can be removed from 80?" The process:

Proceed in short division form dividing successively by five until you can no longer obtain an integral quotient. Write all of the remainders as whole numbers (which they are) and keep them properly aligned. These remainders become the digits of the new numeral; the first remainder is the symbol in the ones place, for it shows the number of ones which remain when the regrouping is effected. The remainders, written in reverse order, form the digits of the new numeral.

Examples:

(1) Divide 82 by 5:

$$5 \overline{) \, 82}$$
$$16 \text{ fives} \qquad 2 \text{ remaining}$$

Divide 16 fives by 5:

$$5 \overline{) \, 16 \text{ fives}}$$
$$3 \text{ five-fives} \quad 1 \text{ remaining}$$
(this is a five)

In the abstract form the example will look like this:

$$5 \overline{) \, 82}$$
$$5 \overline{) \, 16} - 2$$
$$3 - 1$$

Thus 82 will be written
312 (base five)

(2) Let us change 211 to the base seven

$$7 \overline{) \, 211}$$
$$7 \overline{) \, 30} - 1$$
$$4 - 2$$

The 4 represents 4 groups of 7^2 so 211 (ten) = 421 (seven)

(3) Change 71 to the base four.

$$4 \overline{) \, 71}$$
$$4 \overline{) \, 17} - 3$$
$$4 \overline{) \, 4} - 1$$
$$1 - 0$$

71 (base ten) = 1013 (base four)

(4) Change 113 to the base nine.

$$9 \overline{) \, 113}$$
$$9 \overline{) \, 12} - 5$$
$$1 - 3$$

113 (base ten) = 135 (base nine)

1.16 Changing Numbers to Base Ten

The problem of changing a number to the base ten, that is, from an unfamiliar base to the decimal scale, requires thorough knowledge of the positional or place value of the system.   Thus, if a number is already expressed in base six, then the denominations expressed by the symbols in that base represent different powers of the base six.   If the number 333 (base six) is to be converted to the decimal scale we find we have a total of 3 thirty-sixes, 3 sixes, and 3: $3 \times 36 + 3 \times 6 + 3$, or $108 + 18 + 3 = 129$.

If the base of a number system is five, then the first place or column to the left of the ones place designates fives, the next one to the left represents five squared, the next one to the left represents five cubed, and so on.   One need only to write the headings of the various columns in the given base, write the digits of the number in the proper columns, evaluate each place in terms of the decimal scale, and then add these values.   The result will be the value of the given number in the decimal scale.   Apply these rules to this number which is expressed in the base seven: 3236 (seven).

Headings	7^3	7^2	7	1
Given numerals	3	2	3	6

The number expression represents $3 \times 7^3 + 2 \times 7^2 + 3 \times 7 + 6$. This becomes $3 \times 343 + 2 \times 49 + 3 \times 7 + 6$ or $1029 + 98 + 21 + 6$ which equals 1154.

The number 11111 in the base five would represent $1(5^4) + 1(5^3) + 1(5^2) + 1(5) + 1$ or $625 + 125 + 25 + 5 + 1$ or 781.   As an exercise the student should prove that 781 can be converted to 11111 base five.

To find the decimal value of any number we first set up the headings of the system, write the given digits of the number in the proper columns, and then evaluate.   So to change 444 (six) to our decimal system of notation we write the fours in the proper columns and evaluate.   It is left as an exercise for the reader to show that 444 (six) $= 172$.

EXERCISES

SET 5

1. Count the students in your mathematics class by using the base five. Count them again using seven for the base.
2. Lay out a design of 51 toothpicks and group them by sets of three. Continue doing this to show that 51 consists of one group of three cubed, two groups of three squared, and two groups of three. How many are left over?
3. Rewrite the calendar for the month of December in the following bases:
   (seven)   (nine)   (thirteen)   (seventeen)
4. Change the following from the decimal system to the base indicated:
   111 to base seven   421 to base twelve   121 to base nine
   168 to base eleven   729 to base twelve   1281 to base twenty
5. Convert the following to the decimal scale:
   111 (four)   1120 (three)   222 (five)   2001001 (three)
   333 (seven)   2236 (eleven)   1234 (twenty)   100001011 (five)
6. Change 1122 from base eight to base ten. Then convert it to the base five.
7. Change 444 from base six to base seven, then to base eight, then to base nine.
8. 5252 is expressed in the duodecimal system. Express this amount in base eleven.   7007 (base fifteen) = ____ (base nine)
9. Write 707 (ten) in the duodecimal scale; in the scale of fifteen; in the scale of twenty; and in the scale of fifty.
10. Is it possible for 47 to represent an even number?
11. Prove the equivalence of the following expressions:
    444 (six) = 20101 (three) = 172 (ten)
12. From the following select those which are true number expressions:
    123   (seven)   4311 (three)   7294 (eleven)   4672 (five)
    910   (eight)   9999 (nine)   9999 (twenty)   112513 (four)
    TETE (thirteen)   9E5 (fourteen)   1164 (five)   123456 (nine)
13. From your selections in question No. 12 find the value of the smallest number and the largest number when converted to the decimal scale.

1.17 Different Concepts of Number

When we use number in its quantitative aspect to indicate how many, we are using number in its *cardinal* sense. If we use number to indicate a particular item of a group, to designate order or position, then we are using number in its *ordinal* sense. If I say that there are six grades in the elementary school I am using the number 6 in the cardinal sense, but if I say that Johnny is in the sixth grade I am using the number in the ordinal sense. If I say that I am reading from page 103 I am designating a particular page so 103 is used in the ordinal sense. How can I use that number in the cardinal sense? Could a number be used both as cardinal and ordinal at the same time?

Number names are used to express quantities of specific things. We say that there are 7 days in a week, 16 ounces in a pound, 37 students in a class, 245 pages in a book, 24 hours in a day, and so on. All numbers represent something—they designate quantities of things and though they might be written without any denomination or label they always refer to some specific unit. Generally speaking, all numbers in problem situations are said to be *concrete* because they refer to specific things. Teachers of primary children are painstakingly careful to label all numbers used in computation, to insist that when a group of 3 apples is combined with a group of 4 apples that a new group of 7 apples has been formed. That if 5 cookies are taken from a plate containing 12 cookies there will be 7 cookies left. Should one wish to find the number of dozen eggs there are in 1000 eggs he would use the division process: 1000 (eggs) ÷ 12 (eggs) or simply $12\overline{)1000}$. Since the question asks for the number of dozen, he would label his answer 83 dozen or write a sentence stating this fact. In performing computations one uses numbers in their *abstract* sense but recognizes that he is dealing with concrete things. In performing the division example just cited it becomes necessary to subtract 960 eggs from 1000 eggs for the first trial quotient is 80 dozen. (We remove 80 dozen eggs from the group first by the subtraction process.) In actual computation we merely write 8 in the proper place in the quotient space, multiply 12 by 8, write 96 as a partial product, subtract 96 from 100, write 4, and continue. We are working with concrete things, the numerals have labels, but we compute with numerals in their abstract form. Pure numerals which do not refer to any specific thing are *abstract*.

Quantities which are exact or specific are said to be *discrete* or *discontinuous*. If the reader counts the number of words on this line there should be no doubt in his mind as to the total number, and if he counts them again he should obtain the same number, there would be no variability. The number of words counted is discrete. When the teacher discovers that there are 36 students in his class he knows that there are 36, no more and no less. And when one specifies that he has solved 87 examples correctly he means exactly 87. These numbers can be located exactly on a number line or scale. Number quantities which are not of this type, numbers which represent measured quantities and not counted quantities are said to be *continuous*. When one reads the temperature as 72° he does not mean exactly 72° but a reading which is closer to 72 than it is to 73 or 71. When a man says that he is 5 feet 11 inches tall he means that he is nearer to that height than to any other height expressed in (integral) feet and (integral) inches. When one's weight increases from 156 pounds to 157 pounds then his weight has at some time been equal to every weight between those two values. If these numbers are represented on a number line then to pass from 156 to 157 it is necessary to pass through all values in between. This type of number is referred to as a continuous number and is best expressed on the number line. Such representation, the assignment of a number to a certain spot on the number line, illustrates the *linear* or geometric aspect of number. The number which comes after 48 is 49; in other words it is the forty-ninth division mark on the number line and if one passes through all of these division points (from 0 to 49) to arrive at the number 49, then we would ascribe the *quantitative* aspect to the number 49 and designate it as 49 units. If a number represents a specific quantity or amount we are using the number in a collectional sense.

Numbers which represent or specify whole entities are called *integers*. Integers are commonly called whole numbers for they always represent all of some one thing or things. Numbers like −12, −2, 0, 7, 41, 808, etc., are integers whether they represent concrete things or whether they are used in the abstract sense. All of the integers greater than zero (all of the counting numbers) are *natural* numbers. Numbers which represent the size of pieces or parts of a whole thing or of whole things are called *fractions*. Generally speaking, a fraction is thought of as the number property of a part of some whole thing, but in a later chapter other concepts of a fraction will be developed. Thus a piece of a pie might be of size one-fourth ($\frac{1}{4}$), or of size one-sixth ($\frac{1}{6}$), or of some other nonintegral size or denomination. These numbers are fractions. If a group is composed of whole things and some part or parts of whole things, then the number is called a *mixed number*. In the expression $6\frac{1}{2}$ days the numeral $6\frac{1}{2}$ represents a mixed number.

Like numbers are those which specify the same kind of thing or denomination; they have the same name or label. The numbers in the expressions 14 sheep, 17 sheep, and 31 sheep are called like numbers for they represent the same kind of things. Numbers referring to different kinds of quantities are called *unlike* numbers. Thus the numbers in the expressions 5 apples, 6 bananas, and 35 plums are called unlike numbers.

One of the most interesting facts about our number system is that numerals have both face value and place value. The number 7 refers to this many things: 1 1 1 1 1 1 1, regardless of the size or denomination of those things. Seven could refer to groups of baseball players (teams), to dollars ($1.00), to chains (100 feet long), or to some similar designation. In our number system, 7 can represent 7 hundreds, 7 tens, 7 ones, and so on. The decimal system can be extended indefinitely in either direction from the ones place to large numbers and small numbers and the 7 could represent that amount of any power of ten. Thus 70 represents 10 + 10 + 10 + 10 + 10 + 10 + 10 while 700 represents 100 + 100 + 100 + 100 + 100 + 100 + 100. The number 7 has a *face value* equivalent to a one-to-one correspondence with the days of the week. The number 7 is always seven whenever seen as such but it may have different *place values*. The place value of a numeral varies and is determined by the place or position it occupies in the whole number; its face value never changes.

Integers may be classified as either odd numbers or even numbers depending upon the remainder when the number is divided by 2. If an integer is exactly divisible by 2—has no remainder when divided into 2 parts or contains an integral number of groups of size 2—then the number is said to be an *even* number. Integers which do not fit this classification are called *odd* integers; they are not divisible by 2. All odd numbers and all even numbers differ by 2. Even numbers begin with zero, odd numbers with 1.

Even	odd	even	odd	even	odd	even	odd	even
0	1	2	3	4	5	6	7	8

odd	even	odd	even	odd	even	odd	even	odd
9	10	11	12	13	14	15	16	17

There are several other classifications of number such as *real* and *imaginary*, *rational* and *irrational*, *perfect* and *amicable*, *finite* and *infinite*, *constants* and *variables*, etc., which will not be discussed in this book.

Discoveries in the realm of mathematics are becoming rather common these days and new connotations and new number concepts are essential adjuncts to the classification of these new discoveries.

1.18 Some Properties of Numbers

1. The sum of two even numbers is another even number.
   If n represents an integer, then $2n$ will represent an even integer.
   If m represents an integer, then $2m$ will represent an even number.
   The sum of the two even numbers is $2n + 2m$ which is divisible by 2, hence the sum of the two even numbers is another even number. $2n + 2m$ when divided by 2 yields the quotient $n + m$.

2. The sum of two odd numbers is an even number.
   If $2n$ is an even number, then $2n + 1$ is an odd number.
   If $2m$ is an even number, then $2m + 1$ is an odd number.
   The sum of the two odd numbers is $2n + 2m + 2$. When this sum is divided by 2, the quotient is exact and there is no remainder. Hence the sum is even.

3. The sum of an even number and an odd number is an odd number. If n is an integer, the $2n$ is even and $2n + 1$ is odd. Their sum is $4n + 1$ which is not exactly divisible by 2. Hence the sum is odd.

4. The sum of three consecutive numbers is equal to the middle number multiplied by 3.
   Let n represent the middle or the second of three numbers. Then $n - 1$ represents the smaller and $n + 1$ represents the larger of the other two numbers. The sum of all three numbers is $(n + 1) + n + (n - 1)$ or $3n$.

5. The sum of consecutive odd numbers represents a number which is the square of an integer.

$$1 \qquad\qquad = 1 \quad \text{which is } 1^2$$
$$1 + 3 \qquad\quad = 4 \quad \text{which is } 2^2$$
$$1 + 3 + 5 \quad\ = 9 \quad \text{which is } 3^2$$
$$1 + 3 + 5 + 7 = 16 \quad \text{which is } 4^2$$

6. The square of an even number is an even number.
   If n represents an integer, then $2n$ will represent an even integer. The square of $2n$ is $4n^2$. Since this number is divisible by 2 it is an even number. $(4n^2 \div 2) = 2n^2$.

7. The square of an odd number is an odd number.

If we let $2n$ represent an even number, then $2n + 1$ will be an odd number.

The square of $2n + 1$ is $4n^2 + 4n + 1$. If this number is divided by 2, the quotient is $2n^2 + 2n$ with a remainder of 1; hence it is an odd number.

EXERCISES

SET 6

1. Write the largest number possible using only two fours.
2. Show that the sum of the cubes of 1, 2, and 3 is equal to the square of the sum of the three given numbers.
   Show that the sum of the cubes of 3, 4, and 5 is equal to the cube of 6.
3. Show that half the sum of any two numbers added to half the difference of the same two numbers is equal to the larger of the two numbers.
4. Write a number of three digits and then repeat these digits forming a six-digit numeral. Show that this new six-digit number is exactly divisible by 7, 11, and 13. Can you explain this?
5. Show that the sum of 5 consecutive odd numbers is equal to the middle number of the group multiplied by 5.
6. Show that if 1 is added to the product of any four consecutive numbers the number obtained will be a perfect square. (This can be proved algebraically.)
7. Are there any pairs of consecutive integers such that their product is equal to their sum?
8. Take any two integers and find their difference. Divide each number by the difference and show that the remainders are equal.
9. Using the numerals 5, 3, 1, and 7, write the smallest and the largest three-digit number. Write the smallest and the largest four-digit number using the same numerals.
10. Can you discover an interesting relationship which exists concerning numbers?

CHAPTER 2

ADDITION AND SUBTRACTION WITH WHOLE NUMBERS

2.1 Introduction

In the previous chapter we have been discussing the various interpretations of number; now we shall begin a discussion of the various things we do with number. Since number has already been defined as the property of a set of elements there must be some operations which enable us to find the number property of the sets when regrouping has taken place.

The operation which enables us to find the number property of 2 or more sets when combined into one set is the operation known as *addition*. If the sets are all of the same size the total amount can be found by *multiplication*. This regrouping process which asks one to put things of the same kind into a composite group is called the "synthesis" process.

The regrouping process which asks one to divide a composite group into one or more smaller groups is called the "analysis" process. The two operations which enable one to regroup into sub-groups are *subtraction*—the inverse of addition—and *division*, the inverse of multiplication.

Some addition operations can be performed by multiplication, but all multiplication operations can be done by addition. Some subtraction examples can be performed by division, but all division examples can be done by subtraction. Of the pairs of opposite operations each represents the "undoing" or "inverse" operation of the other. Subtraction is the inverse operation of addition, and division is the inverse of multiplication. Addition and multiplication operations are referred to as "putting together" operations, while subtraction and division are called "taking apart" operations.

THE REGROUPING PROCESS

I. Synthesis (putting together)

    A. Addition (groups may or may not be equal in size)

Example: 5¢ + 7¢ + 6¢ =
   B. Multiplication (groups must be of the same size)
      Example: 8¢ + 8¢ + 8¢ or 3 times 8¢ =

II. Analysis (taking apart, separation)
   A. Subtraction (taking away a group or groups of varying sizes)
      Example: 12¢ − 9¢ =
   B. Division (taking away groups of the same size)
      Example: 8¢ − 2¢ − 2¢ − 2¢ − 2¢ or:
      How many groups of 2¢ can be formed from 8¢: 8¢ ÷ 2¢ =

2.2 The Addition Operation

Addition can be defined as that operation with number groups which finds, without counting them, the total number of items there would be if the smaller sets were combined into one set. It consists of developing an ability or insight into seeing a composite group which is equivalent to two or more other groups. If Johnny has 3 dimes in one pocket and 5 dimes in another pocket he will still have the 3 dimes and the 5 dimes if he puts them all together in one of the pockets; he will have 8 dimes. If Mary spent 5 cents at one store and 4 cents at another store she might say she had spent 9 cents; this could be interpreted as 9 cents spent at one store for either one or two purchases. When Mr. Jones balances his books at the end of the month he finds that he has spent $63 for food. This in all probability is the result or total of several purchases each of which is less than $63. If Josey has 6 dolls and Sally has 4 little dolls and 2 big dolls, then Josey has just as many dolls as Sally. The number property which describes Josey's dolls is the same as the number property which describes Sally's dolls.

Addition should be thought of as a regrouping process. Either manually or visually one combines a group of 4 apples with another group of 4 apples to make a new group of 8 apples. The two groups of 4 apples each represent the same amount as a single group of 8 apples; in other words we say that "4 apples and 4 apples are 8 apples." These quantities of things have been put together into one collection to make a new group with a new number property. Sometimes it is impossible to put together or combine quantities such as we have just done. Then we must express a new number name which is equivalent to the other two (or more than two).

Suppose a man drives 400 miles in one day and then 500 miles on the following day. How far has he driven in the two days? We really can't put the 500 miles with the 400 miles as if they were apples or dolls or cookies; we must visualize a composite picture of 900 miles as representing the total distance traveled if all the miles were covered in one day (in one grouping). Perhaps this problem can best be illustrated on a number line. We mark off 400 miles to represent the distance traveled in one day and then mark off 500 miles more to represent the distance traveled the second day. The position at which we arrive or the number delineated on the number line will represent the total distance traveled.

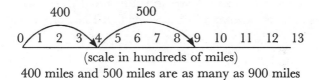

(scale in hundreds of miles)
400 miles and 500 miles are as many as 900 miles

The separate items which are added are called *addends* and the total or answer is called the *sum*.

2.3 Principles of Addition

There are three basic principles which govern our work with addition:

1. The principle of likeness. Only numbers of the same kind can be added. This means that a quantity of sheep can be combined only with another quantity of sheep to produce a third quantity of sheep. A pile of 8 books can be combined with a pile of 7 books to make a pile of 15 books. Tens are combined with tens, beads combined with beads, and children combined with children to form a new set of children. Naturally a weight of 5 pounds can be combined with a weight of 8 ounces but this will make a combined weight of 5 pounds and 8 ounces. A line 3 yards long extended a length of 2 feet will have a total length of 3 yards 2 feet. The total is not 5 units for only like units can be combined to obtain a single number property of the composite set.

2. The principle of commutativity. This law states that the order or addition does not affect the sum. The addition of 4 and 5 is the same as that of 5 and 4. If a baseball team scores 4 runs in one game and 5 in another, we can add 4 + 5 or 5 + 4 to obtain the total number of runs scored.

The law of commutativity states that

$$a + b = b + a.$$

The law can be illustrated by the baker who combined 5 pounds of sugar with 10 pounds of flour. Sugar can be combined with flour and vice versa with the same result. Likewise snow mixed with water will have the same effect or result as water mixed with snow. And pork and beans are the same as beans and pork.

3. *The principle of associativity.* This law states that 3 or more addends may be grouped or associated in any manner and the sum is not affected. If 3 and 4 are added first and their sum is added to 5, the result is the same as if 3 is added to the sum of 4 and 5.

$$3 + 4 + 5 = (3 + 4) + 5 = 3 + (4 + 5)$$
$$3 + 4 + 5 = \quad 7 \quad + 5 = 3 + \quad 9$$
$$3 + 4 + 5 = \quad 12 \quad = \quad 12$$

This principle can be illustrated by the coffee drinker who has his coffee with sugar and cream. Certainly coffee + sugar + cream will give the same result if the coffee and sugar are combined first and then added to the cream as if the sugar and cream are added first and then combined with the coffee.

$$(coffee + sugar) + cream = coffee + (sugar + cream)$$

A property of addition, which might be a property of other operations with numbers, is the property of *closure*. We know that if we add two integers the sum will be an integer, that is, the answer will be a number of the same kind. Thus we say that the set of all integers is closed with respect to addition. Closure is that property of a set of numbers which under a given operation will produce a number of the same set. The set of positive even numbers is closed with respect to addition. Why? The set of positive odd numbers is not closed with respect to addition. Does the set of powers of two have the property of closure with respect to addition? With respect to multiplication?

2.4 Structure with Respect to Addition Examples

There are many forms or classes of examples involving addition. To begin with, we classify all the sums of two single-digit numbers as the first class, a class of primary combinations. If we include the zero combinations (which the writer feels should receive greater emphasis) there will be 100 primary addition facts.

Examples:

$$
\begin{array}{cccccc}
1 & 6 & 4 & 5 & 8 & 9 \\
+1 & +2 & +0 & +6 & +7 & +9
\end{array}
$$

If we are to find the sum of three or more single-digit numbers we refer to this type of example as one in column addition. Emphasis is placed on this type of example first before the student is introduced to column addition of two-, three-, or four-digit numerals.

Examples:

$$
\begin{array}{cccc}
5 & 2 & 7 & 8 \\
3 & 2 & 0 & 2 \\
+4 & +2 & +6 & +4
\end{array}
$$

One of the most difficult types of addition example is the type which asks one to add a single-digit number to a two-digit number. This type of example is one of two classes, either an example which will produce a sum in the same decade (as the two-digit addend) or which will produce a result in the next higher decade. This type of example is referred to as an example in higher-decade addition. And for purposes of convenience we begin each new decade with the integral number of tens. The sum of $23 + 4$ gives an answer in the same decade (same number of tens as the larger addend), while $23 + 7$ gives us an answer in the next higher decade.

Examples of decade addition:

$$
\begin{array}{cccccccc}
34 & 45 & 78 & 21 & 68 & 83 & 55 & 71 \\
+2 & +3 & +1 & +7 & +3 & +9 & +8 & +9
\end{array}
$$

The process of passing from one decade into the next higher decade is referred to as *bridging the decade.*

Then there is the type of example which asks one to combine 2 two-digit numbers; some of the examples may not involve carrying while others will. The solution of the easier ones requires only the knowledge of the basic primary addition facts, while the solution of a problem involving carrying requires the ability to change the form of the sum, that is, to express the sum of $8 + 9$ as 1 ten and 7 ones, the sum of 4 tens and 7 tens as 1 hundred and 1 ten. This is commonly referred to as a regrouping process. The sum of 27 and 32 can be found in one of two ways: combining the separate like terms and jumping places along a line diagram. The first method:

27   2 tens and 7 ones

32   3 tens and 2 ones

Then the sum will be 5 tens and 9 ones. Thus 27 + 32 = 59.

To show how we find the sum by using the linear representation of number we first locate the number 27 on a number line. Then from this position we lay off 3 decades (jumps of 10) and then 2 ones. The picture representation would look like this:

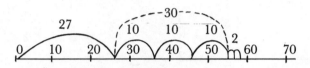

This type of addition is sometimes referred to as the double-column type of addition in which the computer begins with the first addend; then he adds to it the number of tens represented in the second addend; then he adds in the units digit. For instance, the addition of 47 and 35 would be done as follows:

47   47

35   30

          5

47 plus 30 gives us 77; 77 plus 5 gives us 82. Thus 47 + 35 = 82.
Practice this method in doing the following additions:

23	71	31	51	46	76	84	75	19	62
43	26	47	23	26	26	17	49	24	72

The enlargement of this latter type of example constitutes the highest form of addition example. There is really no limit as to the size of the addend (the number of digits in the addend) and certainly no restriction of the number of addends. Generally speaking, if a student can add effectively a column of 5 five-digit numbers it is not necessary to give him practice in adding longer columns of larger numbers.

Long and difficult examples in addition are encountered in the business world, but the solution is usually accomplished with the help of a computing machine.

EXERCISES

SET 7

1. Find the sum of the first 15 consecutive counting numbers.
2. Find the sum of all the whole numbers beginning with 51 and ending with 67.
3. Add 2969 + 4567 + 5116 + 2487 + 1904.
4. The temperature readings at noontime on seven consecutive days were 72°, 81°, 78°, 76°, 67°, 84°, and 83°. Make up and solve a problem which will require the addition of these temperature readings.
5. During successive weeks Mrs. Brown spent these amounts of money: $57.08, $34.45, $9.65, $14.95, and $7.55. What was the total amount of her purchases?
6. Which is the larger sum: (a) 43 + 54 + 76, or (b) 53 + 77 + 42?
7. If each of three addends is increased by 150, what effect does this have upon the original sum?
8. If one of two addends is increased by 450 and the other decreased by 310, what is the effect upon the original sum?
9. If one addend is increased by X and a second is increased by Y, what is the effect upon the original sum?
10. If one of two addends is increased and the other one is decreased, what is the effect upon the original sum?
11. The sum of $a + b + c$ is e. What happens to e if a is increased by r and c is decreased by s?
12. Find the total population of the seven largest cities in the United States (according to the most recent census). Express your answer to the nearest hundred thousand.
13. Begin with the number 17 and continue adding 9 until you pass 100. Begin again with 17 and keep adding 7 until you pass 100: Begin again and keep adding 5 until you reach the sum which is nearest 100.
14. Find the total number of days in the first six months of this year. Then find the total number of days in the last six months of this year.
15. Define: analysis, synthesis, regrouping, operation, and algorism.
16. (Optional) Ascertain the total surface area (in square miles) of the five Great Lakes.
17. (Optional) Find the total number of paid admissions to the most recent World Series.

2.5 Toward More Effective Addition

The 100 primary addition facts must be mastered thoroughly (and it is desirable to have this accomplished at the end of the third grade or certainly no later than upon completion of the fourth grade in the elementary school). Facts whose sums are 10 or less than 10 are reasonably easy to learn. Such devices as a tens peg board, domino charts, and a number line are especially helpful. With concrete materials (rings, pegs, etc.) students place objects on the peg board and discover through counting that 3 and 5 are 8.

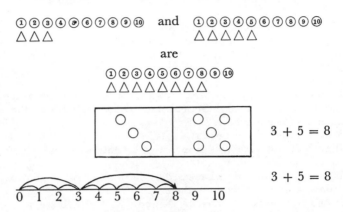

$$3 + 5 = 8$$

$$3 + 5 = 8$$

The teacher of arithmetic in the primary grades has numerous techniques for developing addition facts. The learning of the more difficult facts can be facilitated through the use of the following techniques:

1. *Use of the doubles combinations.* Most children find little difficulty in learning the doubles combinations. These facts should be useful in discovering new facts closely related to them. Each doubles combination has two near neighbors, one to the left (smaller) and one to the right (larger). If a child learns $6 + 6 = 12$ he ought to be able to see that $6 + 5 = 11$ (one less than 12) and that $6 + 7 = 13$ (one more than 12).

<table>
<tr><td colspan="3" align="center">Known fact</td><td colspan="3" align="center">Known fact</td></tr>
<tr><td>5</td><td>5</td><td>5</td><td>8</td><td>8</td><td>8</td></tr>
<tr><td>+4</td><td>+5</td><td>+6</td><td>+7</td><td>+8</td><td>+9</td></tr>
<tr><td>9</td><td>10</td><td>11</td><td>15</td><td>16</td><td>17</td></tr>
<tr><td colspan="3" align="center">Related facts</td><td colspan="3" align="center">Related facts</td></tr>
</table>

2. *Use of the tens combinations.* Perhaps the most useful information which the student can possess for the performance of the addition operation is the set of addition facts whose sums are 10. In the first

stages of the development number meanings the student is exposed to the meanings of the set of single-digit numbers and finally to the collection of ten objects (the base of the system).   He learns that 6, for example, is the same as 5 and 1, 4 and 2, etc., and that 7 is the same as 6 and 1, 5 and 2, etc., and so on to 10 which is the same as 9 and 1, 8 and 2, etc.   If he masters these ideas and facts then, when he sees the example 8 + 6 he may rationalize as follows: "8 + 6 is the same as 8 + 2 + 4 or 10 and 4 which is 14."

Step 1	Step 2	Step 3	Step 4
8	8	$8 \brace 2$ 10	10
	−2		
+6	4	4	4
			14

The steps in the thought process might take this form:

$$8 \quad + \quad 6 = ?$$
$$8 \quad + (2 + 4) =$$
$$(8 + 2) + \quad 4 =$$
$$10 \quad + \quad 4 = 14$$

So when one sees the combination, 6 + 9, he might think: "6 and 4 make 10 and since I have used 4 of the 9 there are 5 yet to be used. Therefore the sum is 10 and 5 or 15."

3. *Use of groups of five.*   Let us set up each of any two given addends as 5 plus so many ones.   Thus 8 is 5 + 3 and 9 is 5 + 4.   Therefore the sum of 8 and 9 must be equal to the sum of 5 + 3 and 5 + 4. The use of the associative law permits us to combine the two fives first and then the 3 and 4 for a sum of 10 + 7 or 17.   Thus 8 + 9 = 17.

$$
\begin{array}{ll}
8 = 5 + 3 & \quad 5 \qquad 3 \\
+\,9 = 5 + 4 & +\,5 \text{ and } +\,4 \\
& \overline{10 \text{ and } 7} \qquad \text{10 and 7 are 17.}
\end{array}
$$

This technique can be shown effectively with the use of a 20-bead frame consisting of two wires of 10 beads each.   Five beads on each wire should be black and 5 should be white.   The use of this type of learning device facilitates the establishment of mental images of quantitative representations of numbers. Thus the example, 6 + 8, would be pictured as follows on a bead frame:

$$\begin{array}{ccc} ***** 00000 & 6 & ***** 0 \ \ 0000 \\ ***** 00000 & +\ 8 & ***** 000 \ \ 00 \\ & & \text{10 and 4 are 14.} \end{array}$$

4. *Use of pure memorization.* The least desirable method, from the writer's point of view, of teaching addition combinations is that of pure memorization. This method suggests that when a child is exposed to the stimulus 6 + 8 he should memorize the automatic response 14. If he is shown the previously explained rationalizations he will have learned the combinations or at least will have been exposed to some simple rationalizations which will enable him to arrive at the sums without resorting to pure memorization.

In learning the fact that 6 and 8 is the same as 14 the student must be made aware of the fact that whenever 6 and 8 appear as a sum, the number in the ones place will always be a four. Thus 16 + 8, 26 + 8, 56 + 8, and 86 + 8 will all have a 4 in the ones place in the sum. The student should think, "There will be one more ten than in the given two-digit number, and the ones digit of the sum will be 4."

This method is commonly referred to as "adding by endings" and its usage should be preferred to the carrying method. Students should be encouraged to see whether the sum will be in the same decade or the next higher decade and should respond with the tens number first. Thus 27 + 5 should be 30 (we know it will be in the next decade) plus 2.

Examples:
$$\begin{array}{ccc} 36 & 48 & 62 \\ +\ 7 & +\ 4 & +\ 5 \end{array}$$
Forty(something)   Fifty(something)   Sixty(something)

The left-to-right approach to addition examples of this type is often called "front end" arithmetic and should be encouraged.

Many examples occur in addition which involve adding 9 to a two-digit number. Since 9 is one less than 10 we can first add 10 to the number and then subtract 1. If we are adding 9 to 27 we first add 10 and obtain 37 for the sum; then we subtract one and obtain 36 for the true sum. We thus know that the sum will be in the next decade and that the digit in the ones place will be one less than the ones number in the two-digit number. Examine the line diagram to see just how this thinking takes place with the use of a horizontal scale:

$$27 \qquad 36 \; 37$$

$$20 \ldots \ldots \ldots 30 \ldots \ldots \ldots 40 \ldots \ldots \ldots 50$$

In adding 9 to a number we see that the tens digit is one more than the tens digit of the original number and the ones digit is one less than the ones digit of the original number.   Keeping this in mind it should be easy to add 9 to the following numbers: 47, 53, 62, 78, 56, and 49.

2.6   Column Addition

The next type of addition example is the type which involves the combining of 3 or more single digits followed by the general class of combining 3 or more numbers of any size.   Column addition presents difficulties to children because of the "unseen" combinations involved in the solution.   In the example

$$
\begin{array}{r}
4 \\
3 \\
+\ 2 \\
\hline
\end{array}
$$

the pupil must retain the unseen 7 in his mind and then combine the 2 with it.   This difficulty is magnified in more involved addition examples.

The topic of column addition brings up the controversial subject of adding up or adding down.   Most writers are of the opinion that consistency of operation is more important than the direction of operation.   Many educators state that the pupil should be taught to add in one direction and then to add in the opposite direction for a check upon his results.   In theory this is sound but we have no way of knowing that the pupil will do this; he is more likely to rewrite his original sum and thus "force" the check.   The writer believes that there are arguments in favor of the "adding down" technique. Because addition suggests an accumulation of items, and because these are usually written in a column from the top down, the additions should be down the column.   When subtraction, the inverse of addition, is thought of as a taking-away process it is usually done up the column; therefore addition should be downward.   However, consistency of performance is more important than the direction itself.

The solution of addition examples of 2 or more two-digit numbers offers difficulties which can be surmounted if the problem is developed meaningfully. In performing the addition operation we must stress the principle that only like things can be added. Since every two-digit number is composed of tens and ones we must add the tens together and add the ones together. In the problem which asks us to find the total cost of a loaf of bread for 23 cents and a quart of milk for 25 cents we visualize the 23 cents as

	2 dimes and 3 pennies
and the 25 cents as	2 dimes and 5 pennies
so it is easy to see the total of	4 dimes and 8 pennies or 48 cents.

If one is given an example of adding 36 and 43 (in the abstract), he should visualize

36 as 3 tens and 6 ones and the
43 as 4 tens and 3 ones for a total of
7 tens and 9 ones or 79.

This application can be carried over into the addition of three-digit numbers with comparative ease. Consider this problem: "On Friday night 354 people attended the School Circus and on Saturday night there were 341 in attendance. How many people in all attended the School Circus?"

		H	T	O		
354	300 + 50 + 4	3	5	4	3 hundreds 5 tens 4 ones
+ 341	300 + 40 + 1	3	4	1	3 hundreds 4 tens 1 one
	600 + 90 + 5	6	9	5	6 hundreds 9 tens 5 ones

Thus we can easily establish the fact that 354 people and 341 people are 695 people.

This analysis is extremely valuable when introducing carrying or changing the form of the grouping. Suppose the student is asked to find the total cost of a pound of lard at 19 cents and a loaf of bread for 23 cents. He visualizes the

19 cents as 1 dime and 9 pennies and the
23 cents as 2 dimes and 3 pennies and then adds them together.

He adds the pennies first and obtains 12 pennies and then he adds the

dimes and finds a total of 3 dimes. Thus the total cost of the purchases was 3 dimes and 12 pennies. Now since the sum of 12 pennies
is equivalent to 1 dime and 2 pennies he changes the form of his sum
to 4 dimes and 2 pennies or 42 cents. Solutions:

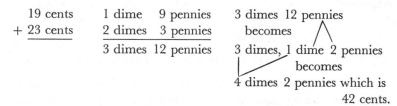

When the problem is solved symbolically the algorism might look like
this:

      19 cents
 + 23 cents
      12 cents (9 cents and 3 cents are 12 cents)
      30 cents (10 cents and 20 cents are 30 cents)
      42 cents (12 cents and 30 cents are 42 cents)

Then at the next level of thinking it might be interpreted as follows:

      19 cents   9 cents and 3 cents are 12 cents. Write 2 in
 + 23 cents   the ones place and carry 1 (one ten) into the
                      tens column.

      1
      19 cents   Now add the numbers in the tens
 + 23 cents   column and write the 4 in the tens
         2   place. The sum is 42 cents.

         1
      19 cents
 + 23 cents
      42 cents

Now the most advanced level of learning suggests that the one
(which has previously been carried to the top of the tens column)
is now carried "in the head" until such time as it is used or combined
with some of the numbers in the tens place. The student should be
encouraged to perform addition operations without the use of a
crutch but if he needs the crutch he should be permitted to use it.

The idea of carrying can be enhanced through the use of denominate numbers. Suppose Johnny spent 4 weeks and 2 days of the summer vacation with his uncle and 3 weeks and 6 days visiting his grandfather, how many weeks and days did he spend visiting his relatives?

$$\begin{array}{r} 4 \text{ weeks } 2 \text{ days} \\ + \ 3 \text{ weeks } 6 \text{ days} \\ \hline 7 \text{ weeks } 8 \text{ days which is equal to 8 weeks 1 day} \end{array}$$

Similarly we can show that a cord 4 feet 7 inches long, tied to a cord 5 feet 9 inches long, is equal in length to a cord 10 feet 4 inches long.

```
    1
4 feet  7 inches
5 feet  9 inches
────────────────
   16 inches   7 inches and 9 inches = 1 foot 4 inches.
    4          Write 4, carry 1 (foot)
```

Now 1, 4, and 5 are 10 (feet). Illustrations like these ought to be used to supplement the development of the regrouping process known as "carrying."

2.7 Checking Addition Examples

One of the primary objectives of the arithmetic program in the elementary school is to give children the opportunity to make judgments. This opportunity is provided in the last step in the solution of any type of example. Since we are interested in this chapter in the process of synthesis through addition we should be concerned with the establishment of the validity of the sums; in other words we should endeavor to find some way to check our addition to determine whether the sums are right. The simplest way is to write the addends in some other form and perform the addition again. The following example illustrates:

456	400 + 50 + 6	23
278	200 + 70 + 8	180
+ 569	500 + 60 + 9	1100
1303	1100 + 180 + 23	1303

Another suggestion for checking an addition example is the use of the commutative and the associative laws. The addends are written again without the first addend (it has been omitted). These addends should be totaled and then to their sum be added the first addend. If the sum is the same as the previous result we conclude that the addition is correct. The check just suggested is illustrated here:

```
423
356        356
201        201        1372
815        815         423
────       ────       ────
1795       1372       1795
```

In general the method can be stated as follows: Find the sum of 4 (or more) addends, A, B, C, and D. Formulate another example using B, C, and D, as addends and find their sum. Then add A to this last sum. Compare the sums. This procedure makes use of the principle that additions may be performed in any order without altering or affecting the result.

After students have been introduced to the subtraction operation they can use this process as a check of their addition examples. If the sum of three numbers, a, b, and c, is equal to d, then d decreased successively by c and b should give a remainder of a or when then decreased by a would give zero remainder. If $4 + 5 + 6$ is equal to 15, then $15 - 6 = 9$; $9 - 5 = 4$ (the first addend), and $4 - 4 = 0$. This check when applied to more difficult addition examples would operate as follows:

```
Add:  2345    The check:    9889    the sum
      5423               −  2121    the last addend
      2121                  ────
      9889                  7768    the sum less the last addend
      ────               −  5423    the second addend
                            ────
                            2345    the sum less two addends
                         −  2345    the first addend
                            ────
                               0
```

Since we have reached zero in the reverse process we can conclude that the sum 9889 is correct.

Another method of checking which was formerly taught in the elementary grades and which seems to be gaining favor again for use in grades 5 and 6 is the method called "casting out nines." Strangely enough that is exactly what the student does: he crosses out or casts out nines or numbers whose sum is nine from both the addends and the sum. And if the number left in the addends is the same as the number left in the sum he will assume that his sum is correct.   It can be shown intuitively that the excess of nines in any number is the sum of its digits.   The number 31 when divided by 9 has a remainder of 4 (the sum of 3 and 1), and when 45 is divided by 9 the remainder is 9 or zero (the sum of 4 and 5 is 9, which contains another 9, so it is discarded or cast out).   Should one divide 111 by 9 he ought to discover that the excess of nines is 3, the sum of 1 and 1 and 1.   In any number, the sum of the digits gives the excess of nines, the remainder when that number is divided by 9.

Let us find the excess of nines in the number 764

$$
\begin{aligned}
764 = 700 \quad &+ 60 \quad + 4 \\
7(100) \quad &+ 6(10) \quad + 4(1) \\
7(99 + 1) \quad &+ 6(9 + 1) + 4(1) \\
\underbrace{7 \times 99} + \underline{7} + &\underbrace{6 \times 9} + \underline{6} + \underline{4} \\
(\text{are divisible by } 9) &
\end{aligned}
$$

Since 7×99 and 6×9 are divisible by 9 we know that when 764 is divided by 9 there is a quotient with a remainder of $7 + 6 + 4$. But $7 + 6 + 4$ has another nine in it with a remainder of 8. So when 764 is divided by 9 there is an integral quotient with a remainder of 8.   This 8 is found by adding the digits of the original number and then, since the sum is a two-digit number, one must continue adding until a single digit is reached.   This accounts for the number 8.

Let us show that the excess of nines in a sum is equal to the sum of the excess of nines in the separate addends.

Addend A   = a certain number of nines plus an excess of nines (remainder).

Addend B   = a certain number of nines plus an excess of nines (remainder).

Sum A + B = a certain number of nines plus an excess of nines (remainder).

If the sum of the excesses of nines in the separate addends is equal to the excess of nines in the sum, then we can be reasonably sure that the original sum is correct.*

---

* The inclusion of one or more extra zeros in the sum, the inclusion of a nine, the reversal of digits in the product, or the improper placement of the partial sums will give a "check" by casting out nines but the sum will be incorrect. The casting out of nines as a check is not completely reliable.

Let us apply this method in the solution of an example:

```
Add  782   Analysis:  782   86 nines + 8   7 + 8 + 2 = 17 → 8
     443              443   49 nines + 2   4 + 4 + 3 = 11 → 2
     866              866   96 nines + 2   8 + 6 + 6 = 20 → 2
    ————                   ————————————————————————————————
    2091                   231 nines + 12 or 232 nines + 3   12 → 3
                                                 2 + 0 + 9 + 1 = 12 → 3
```

Now the sum of the 3 addends is 2091 which equals 232 nines and 3 left over. Since the sum of the excesses in the addends is the same as the excess in the sum we can conclude that the addition has been performed correctly.

If we add the digits in the first addend we get a sum of 17; now we add 1 and 7 to get 8. If we add the digits in the second addend we get a sum of 11; now we add 1 and 1 to get 2. If we add the digits in the third addend we get a sum of 20; now we add 2 and 0 to get 2. Now we add the 8, 2, and 2, to get 12: the sum of 1 and 2 is 3. Therefore 3 is the sum of the excesses of nines in the three addends. Now we find the excess of nines in the sum and hope that it will also be 3. The sum of the three addends is 2091. The sum of the digits 2, 0, 9, and 1 is 12; the sum of 1 and 2 is 3. Since we obtained the same excess (3) we will assume that the addition has been performed correctly.

Let us solve another example, one which will permit us to cast out nines in the addends.

```
Add 4523   The check  4̶5̶23   2 + 3 = 5 excess is 5 ⎫
    1127              1127   1 + 1 = 2 excess is 2 ⎬ excess is 7 ⎫
    6381              6̶3̶8̶1̶            excess is 0 ⎭             ⎬ Check
   ——————            ——————                                    ⎪
   12031             12031   1 + 2 + 0 + 3 + 1 = 7...excess is 7 ⎭
```

It is possible to cast out nines anywhere throughout the addends with the same degree of effectiveness. Let us add this column of numbers and then prove by "casting out nines" anywhere.

```
    4 2 1   Cast out the 4 and 5, the 2 and 7, the 1 and 8, the 8 and 1.
    5 3 7   This leaves the 3 for the excess on nines in the addends.
  + 1 8 8
  ———————
  1 1 4 6   1 + 1 + 4 + 6 = 12 ———→ 3
```

Now if we find the sum of the three addends we obtain 1146, the sum of whose digits is 12 and which hence has an excess of 3 when 1146 is divided by 9. Therefore since the sum of the excesses in the addends is equal to the excess in the sum we can be reasonably sure that the sum is correct.

A modification of the "excess of nines" rule has found its way into the elementary arithmetic classes in simplified form as the "one number" check and has been used effectively in some fourth-grade classes. The student adds digits until he reaches a two-digit number and then combines these two digits. He keeps adding digits so that he will always have a one-digit number. He is not at all concerned with number of nines or excesses of nines; he just adds and adds until he reaches a single-digit number. If the single digit he receives for the sum of the several digits in the addends is the same as the single number he receives from adding the digits in the sum he will assume that his answer is correct. Let us illustrate:

$$
\begin{array}{lr}
\text{Add} & 47 \\
& 24 \\
& 31 \\
\text{Sum} & \overline{102}
\end{array}
\qquad
\begin{array}{l}
4 + 7 \to 2 \\
2 + 2 + 4 \to 8 \\
8 + 3 + 1 \to 3 \\
1 + 0 + 2 \to 3 \quad\text{Check}
\end{array}
$$

If the pupil adds all the numbers 4, 7, 2, 4, 3, and 1 he obtains 21. Now $2 + 1 = 3$. This coincides with the sum of the digits in the answer so we assume accuracy of performance.

Let us do a more difficult sum and check for accuracy of performance:

$$
\begin{array}{l}
3\ 5\ 7\ 8 \\
2\ 9\ 6\ 5 \\
4\ 5\ 8\ 3 \\
3\ 9\ 5\ 4 \\
\overline{1\ 5\ 0\ 8\ 0}
\end{array}
\quad
\begin{array}{l}
3 + 5 + 7 + 8 = 23 \\
2 + 9 + 6 + 5 = 22 \\
4 + 5 + 8 + 3 = 20 \\
3 + 9 + 5 + 4 = 21 \\
1 + 5 + 0 + 8 + 0 = 14 \text{ and } 1 \text{ and } 4 = 5
\end{array}
\quad
\left.
\begin{array}{l}
2 + 3 = 5 \\
2 + 2 = 4 \\
2 + 0 = 2 \\
2 + 1 = 3
\end{array}
\right\} = 14;\ 1 + 4 = 5
$$

Check

Since there is agreement between the single number for the addends and the single digit for the sum we will assume that the addition is correct. For further verification the student should check by casting out nines.

A method of checking examples similar to the excess-of-nines check is the excess-of-elevens check. Since the base of our number system is ten, there are properties peculiar to the number 9 (one less than the base) and 11 (one more than the base). Every number can be written as a certain number of elevens and an excess or remainder. If we compare the excess of elevens in the sum with the sum of the excesses of elevens in the addends and obtain the same number, then we can conclude that the addition has been performed correctly. With the excess-of-nines check we found it possible to cast out nines to enable us to find the excess of nines. We cannot do this, however, for finding the excess of elevens in a number. To find the excess of elevens in a number we begin with the digit in the ones place, add to it the digit in the hundreds place, and then add to it the digit in the ten thousands place, and continue adding in every second digit to the left. Now we have added the digits in the odd-numbered places (first, third, fifth, etc.). From this sum we subtract the sum of the digits in the even-numbered places and the difference will be the excess of elevens in the number. If the minuend is smaller than the subtrahend we must add eleven or a multiple of eleven to the minuend before we subtract. Let us find the excess of elevens in 4567. Add 7 and 5 which gives us 12: 4567. From 12 subtract the sum of 6 and 4: 4567. This gives us a difference of 2 which is the excess of elevens in 4567. (When 4567 is divided by 11 there is a remainder of 2.)

Find the excess of elevens in 21,212,121. The sum of the digits in the odd-numbered places is 4 and the sum of the digits in the other places is 8. Since we cannot subtract 8 from 4 we add 11 to 4, then we subtract 8 from 15. The excess of elevens in 21,212,121 is 7.

The excess of elevens in any number (E_{11}) is equal to the sum of the digits in the even-numbered places (S_e) subtracted from the sum of the digits in the odd-numbered places (S_o), increased by a multiple of eleven if necessary.

$$E_{11} = S_o - S_e$$

Let us apply this rule in checking an addition example:

Add:

478	8 + 4	= 12		12 − 7 =	5
21339	9 + 3 + 2 = 14	3 + 1 =	4	14 − 4 =	10
15046	6 + 0 + 1 =	7	4 + 5 = 9	7 − 9 =	9 (add 11 to 7)
3325	5 + 3	= 8	2 + 3 = 5	8 − 5 =	3
6565	5 + 5	= 10	6 + 6 = 12	10 − 12 =	9 (add 11 to 10)
46753				Sum is 36;	6 − 3 = 3

In the sum 3 + 7 + 4 = 14, 5 + 6 = 11, and 14 − 11 = 3 — Check

Though this method of checking addition examples is not widely acclaimed, its use is recommended for it enables a student to gain further practice in combining single-digit numbers; it provides practice in addition in a new situation and thereby should strengthen control over the basic addition facts.

The rule of eleven can be shown intuitively using any number. Let's find the excess of elevens in 28,726. Express the number as a multiple of 11.

28,726

$$
\begin{aligned}
&= 20{,}000 + 8000 + 700 + 20 + 6 \\
&= 2(10{,}000) + 8(1000) + 7(100) + 2(10) + 6 \\
&= 2(9999 + 1) + 8(1001 - 1) + 7(99 + 1) + 2(11 - 1) + 6 \\
&= \underbrace{2 \times 9999} + 2 + \underbrace{8 \times 1001} - 8 + \underbrace{7 \times 99} + 7 + \underbrace{2 \times 11} - 2 + 6
\end{aligned}
$$

L——— All are exactly divisible by eleven ——J

Therefore 28,726 equals a certain number of elevens $+ 2 - 8 + 7 - 2 + 6$. The excess of elevens in the number is found by adding the digits in the odd-numbered places and then from this sum subtracting the sum of the digits in the even-numbered places. The excess of elevens in 28,726 is 5.

2.8 Addition in Different Bases

A study of the operation of addition as it is applied to different number systems ought to enhance the understanding of the decimal system of notation with which the students are somewhat familiar, and at the same time make the mature student aware of the difficulties children encounter when they are first presented with the learning of addition in the decimal scale.   Let us assume a number system in the scale of three.   The symbols of such a system would be 0, 1, and 2. The number 3 would be written as 10.   The numbers in serial order in this system would be 1, 2, 10, 11, 12, 20, 21, 22, 100, 101, 102, 110, etc. The primary addition facts in the scale of three would be

0	0	0	1	1	1	2	2	2
0	1	2	0	1	2	0	1	2
$\overline{0}$	$\overline{1}$	$\overline{2}$	$\overline{1}$	$\overline{2}$	$\overline{10}$	$\overline{2}$	$\overline{10}$	$\overline{11}$

+	0	1	2
0	0	1	2
1	1	2	10
2	2	10	11

THE PRIMARY ADDITION (AND SUBTRACTION)
FACTS IN BASE THREE

When we are working in the base three we are packaging or grouping in sets of threes; thus a group of 2 combined with another group of 2 and then combined with still another group of 2 will make 2 groups of three and in the base three this sum would be expressed symbolically as 20 (meaning 2 threes). If we add 2 threes and 1 with 2 threes and 1 we will get a group of 3 threes and a group of threes and 2 ones.

Similarly, 111 111 1 and 111 111 1 will make a group of 111 111 111 111 1 1 which in turn will make a group of 111 111 111 and a group of 111 and 1 and 1. This becomes a group of three-threes, 1 group of three, and 2 which would be written symbolically as 112 (meaning: 1 of 3^2 plus 1 of 3 plus 2 ones).

Add in the base three:

12	112	101	202	222	20101
10	110	202	121	111	11012

When we perform additions in the base 10 we usually "carry" tens or groups of tens into the adjacent column to the left. We follow the same practice in performing additions in any base. If the base is three, then when we reach a total of three in the ones column we carry that number into the base column; if we get three or more when we add the second column (the base column) we carry a number into the next column. Let us combine the following in the base three:

	3^3	3^2	3	1
1211				
2012	1	2	1	1
1110	2	0	1	2
	1	1	1	0

The 1, 2, and 0 make a three.

Write zero, carry one three. $\quad$ (1) | 0

The 1, 1, 1, and 1 make a three squared and one three.

Write 1, carry one three squared. $\quad$ (1) | 1

The 2, 0, 1, and 1 make a three cubed and one three squared.

Write 1, carry one three cubed. $\quad$ (1) | 1

The 1, 2, 1, and 1 make one three to the fourth power and 2 three cubed.

Write 1 2 (no carrying). $\quad$ 1 | 2

| 1 | 2 | 1 | 1 | 0 |

A similar example performed in base five would be solved as follows:

5^4	5^3	5^2	5^1	1	
	2	3	3	1	
	1	1	2	2	
	2	0	4	3	
			(1)	1	Write 1, carry one five
		(2)	0		Write zero, carry two five squared
	(1)	1			Write 1, carry one five cubed
(1)	1				Write 1 1 (meaning 1 5^4 and 1 5^3)
1	1	1	0	1	

Let us obtain greater insight into the mechanics of this operation through the solution of another example, this one in the base twelve.

Add 4 5 6 7 (twelve) — 4 great gross 5 gross 6 dozen 7 ones
$\underline{\text{2 7 9 T}}$ (twelve) — $\underline{\text{2 great gross 7 gross 9 dozen T ones}}$

$$
\begin{array}{rr}
\text{1 dozen 5 ones} & (7 + T) \\
\text{1 gross 3 dozen} & (6 + 9) \\
\text{1 great gross 0 gross} & (5 + 7) \\
\underline{\text{6 great gross}} & \underline{(4 + 2)} \\
\text{7 great gross 1 gross 4 dozen 5 ones} &
\end{array}
$$

$$
\begin{array}{cccc}
1 & 1\ 1 & 1\ 1\ 1 & 1\ 1\ 1 \\
4\ 5\ 6\ 7 & 4\ 5\ 6\ 7 & 4\ 5\ 6\ 7 & 4\ 5\ 6\ 7 \\
\underline{2\ 7\ 9\ T} & \underline{2\ 7\ 9\ T} & \underline{2\ 7\ 9\ T} & \underline{2\ 7\ 9\ T} \\
5 & 4\ 5 & 1\ 4\ 5 & 7\ 1\ 4\ 5
\end{array}
$$

Sometimes we might wish to find the base in which the additions have been performed. Should we want to know the scale in which $2 + 3 = 10$ we merely put the 2 and 3 single objects into one group with none left over, for the $2 + 3$ represent only one group (the base) and no ones.

$$2 = 1 \text{ and } 1$$

and $\qquad\qquad 3 = 1 \text{ and } 1 \text{ and } 1$

Then these single things put into one package will give us a package of size 5. Hence the base is five.

In what base will 7 plus 8 = 12? We see the 7 distinct things combined with 8 distinct things. Then these are grouped into one group with 2 single things left over. In other words, if we sort out the 2 single things first, we will have thirteen things which represent only one group; hence the base will be thirteen.

In what base would 9 + 9 equal 13? Since 9 and 9 represent 1 group of size unknown and 3 single things, then the size of the group must be fifteen: 111111111 11111111 = 111111111111111 111 = 1 fifteen and three = 13 (fifteen).

There is a very simple algebraic solution for the above examples. To find the scale in which 7 + 8 = 12 we begin by equating the new number system to the known sum in the base ten. Hence 7 + 8 = base + 2 = 15 (ten). Since $b + 2 = 15$, then $b = 13$. Therefore the base is thirteen. If 9 + 9 = 13 then base + 3 = 18 (ten). If $b + 3 = 18$, then $b = 15$. Hence 9 + 9 = 13 in the base fifteen. This type of solution will be beneficial in finding the base when the operation is a different one from addition. Let us find the base for this operation: 3 × 8 = 26.

Since we know that 3 × 8 is 24, then $26_{(?)} = 24_{(ten)}$

$$2 \times \text{base} + 6 = 24$$
$$\text{or} \qquad 2b + 6 = 24$$
$$\text{or} \qquad 2b = 18$$
$$\text{and} \qquad b = 9. \quad \text{Hence the base is 9.}$$

The principles of the checks which have been suggested for testing the addition examples in the decimal scale can be applied to the checking of examples which have been performed in any other scale. First, the additions can be performed in the reverse order. Secondly, one of the addends can be omitted and then later added in with the partial sum to get the whole sum. Thirdly, the sum can be checked by the use of subtraction—each addend can be subtracted successively until zero is reached. The excess-of-nines rule and the excess-of-elevens rule cannot be used as such, but the excess-of-nines rule as the "base less one" rule and the excess-of-elevens rule as the "base plus one" rule can be applied. If the base of an addition example is seven, then one can cast out sixes or find the excess of sixes just as one does when the excess-of-nines rule is applied to numbers in the base ten. The excess of sixes in 1412 (seven) is 2 for we can cast out 1, 4, and 1. If an example is performed in the base seven one can find the excess of eights (base plus one) in the same manner that he finds the excess of elevens when the base is ten, namely, the sum of the digits in the odd-numbered places minus the sum of the digits in the even-numbered places. The excess of eights in 1412 (seven) is $2 + 4$ minus $1 + 1$ or 4. If the subtrahend is larger than the minuend, then one must increase the minuend by the base plus one or multiples of it. Let's check this addition example which is performed in the base six.

$$\left. \begin{array}{l} 2214 \text{ excess of fives is } 4 \\ 4234 \text{ excess of fives is } 3 \end{array} \right\} \text{ excess of fives is 2 for } 4 + 3 = 11_{(six)};$$
$$\overline{10452} \text{ excess of fives is } 2 \qquad\qquad\qquad\qquad\qquad 1 + 1 = 2$$

If we cast out 2, 2, and 1 in the first addend we will have the 4 left. If we cast out the 2 and 3 in the second addend we will have 4 and 4 left. The excess of fives in 4 and 4 is 3. If we combine the 4 and the 3 (the two excesses) we will have a five and an excess of 2. Now if we cast out the 1 and the 4 and also the 5 in the sum we will have the 2 left. This excess agrees with the sum of the excesses of the addends.

Now if we check the same example by finding the excesses of sevens we add the digits in the odd-numbered places and from this sum subtract the sum of the digits in the even-numbered places;

$$\left. \begin{array}{l} 2214 \text{ excess of sevens } = (4 + 2) \text{ minus } (1 + 2) = 3 \\ 4234 \text{ excess of sevens } = (4 + 2) \text{ minus } (3 + 4) = -1 \end{array} \right\} \begin{array}{l} \text{sum of} \\ \text{excesses} = 2 \end{array}$$
$$\overline{10452} \text{ excess of sevens } = (2 + 4 + 1) \text{ minus } (5 + 0) = 2 \text{ — Check } \rule{0.5em}{0.4pt}\rceil$$

Since the excess of sevens in the sum is equal to the sum of the excesses of sevens in the addends, we can assume that the addition has been performed correctly.

The number 2234 is in the base six. If we want to find the excess of fives (one less than the base) we use the principles of the "cast out nines" rule. Therefore we cast out fives and have the 2 and 4 left. Their sum is six but when written in the base six becomes 10, which clearly indicates that the excess of fives is 1 for $1 + 0 = 1$. Take the number 45328 base twelve and find the excess of elevens by applying the principles of the "cast out nines" rule. Now $4 + 5 + 2$ make an eleven so they can be cast out; 3 and 8 make an eleven and can also be cast out. Therefore, the excess of elevens in the number 45328 (twelve) is 0, or in other words the number 45328 (twelve) is exactly divisible by eleven.

The use of the base-less-one rule is illustrated in checking the following addition examples:

Add in the base five and check by casting out fours:

2 1 3   excess of fours is 2 ⎫
1 1 4   excess of fours is 2 ⎬ make a four
2 2 2   excess of fours is 2 ⎫
2 1 4   excess of fours is 3 ⎬ make a four and 1 left over → 1 Check
‾1‾3‾2‾3‾   1 and 3 make a four, 2 and 3 make a four and 1 left over

Add in the base seven and check by casting out sixes:

3 5 6 1   Cast out 6 and the 5 and 1.   This leaves an excess of 3 ⎫ sum
2 2 6 4   Cast out 6 and the 4 and 2.   This leaves an excess of 2 ⎬ is 5
‾‾‾‾‾‾‾‾   Check

6 1 5 5   Cast out 6 and the 5 and 1.   This leaves an excess of 5

Now let us apply the principles of the base plus one rule in checking one of the previous examples. The numbers in this example are written in the base five; let's prove the example by finding the excess of sixes.

2 1 3   excess of sixes $= (3 + 2) - 1 = 4$ ⎫
1 1 4   excess of sixes $= (4 + 1) - 1 = 4$ ⎬ $4 + 4 + 2 + 3 =$
2 2 2   excess of sixes $= (2 + 2) - 2 = 2$ ⎪ $23_{(five)}; 3 - 2 = 1$
1 0 2   excess of sixes $= (2 + 1) - 0 = 3$ ⎭
‾1‾2‾1‾1‾   excess of sixes $= (1 + 2) - (1 + 1) = 1$ ——Check

EXERCISES

SET 8

1. Find the sums:

(a) 678	(b) 56,473	(c) 678,233	(d) 4,556,208
213	22,400	335,117	1,459,469
986	45,717	404,793	2,677,895
559	23,644	377,688	5,606,716
905	11,956	488,086	3,304,577

2. Check example 1 (d) by omitting the first addend, and then later adding it to the sum of the other four addends. Explain why this is so.
3. Use the excess-of-nines check to see if all the sums in question No. 1 are correct.
4. Use the excess-of-elevens check to ascertain if the sums in question No. 1 are correct.

5. Complete these series until you reach a number greater than 100.
   (a) 7   13   19.......
   (b) 8   17   26.......
   (c) 4   11   18.......
   (d) 2   11   20.......
   (e) 5   17   29.......
   (f) 1   14   27.......

6. Combine in the base four:

(a) 112	(b) 203	(c) 123	(d) 231	(e) 333
122	203	321	112	333
103	121	121	211	333

7. Repeat the additions above if the numbers are written in base five.

8. Find the sum of the four sums of Exercise No. 1.   Round off the sum to the nearest number of tens of thousands.

9. In what base or bases are the following additions performed?

(a) 258	(b) 333	(c) 123	(d) 456	(e) 21234
346	346	210	456	20554
615	1012	333	8E0	42232

10. Add and check by using the base-less-one rule.

(a) 284 (nine)	(b) 42617 (eight)	(c) 42452 (seven)	(d) 3232 (six)
163	32452	23016	2323

11. Add and check by using the base-plus-one rule.

(a) 412 (five)	(b) 5623 (seven)	(c) 8107 (nine)	(d) T0E1 (twelve)
304	4214	4456	10ET

12. Show that the last primary addition sum for any base is always twice the base less two.

13. You write a three-digit addend and then I'll write the second addend such that the sum of the digits in the respective columns will total 9.   Now you write another addend and I will write one such that the digits you just wrote plus mine will total 9.   Now you write a third addend.   The sum of the five addends will always be 2000 increased by your last addend diminished by two.   Can you show why this is so?

$$427 + 572 + 364 + 635 + 418 = 2000 + 418 - 2 = 2416$$

2.9   Interpretations of Subtraction

Addition has been defined as the combining of two or more groups of the same kind into one group.   The process is defined as synthesis.   The opposite operation of addition, the separation of a composite group into sub-groups when the size of one of the groups is known, is called subtraction and is defined as the analysis process.   Subtraction, then, is the operation which enables one to find a missing addend when the sum and the other addends are known and is defined as the "inverse" of addition. Since the operation is the reverse of addition we can assume that the basic principle of addition, namely, that only like things can be added, is equally true of subtraction.

The number representing the sum of the two or more numbers (this number is referred to as the larger one) is called the *minuend*; the given addend or the number or the amount which is to be subtracted is called the *subtrahend*; and the remaining addend, the one sought, is called the *difference* or *remainder*.

There are three basic interpretations of subtraction.

1. *The "How many left?" idea.* If Billy had 3 apples and ate 1 of them, how many did he have left?

2. *The "How many more?" idea.* If Johnny has 20 cents with which to buy a ball costing 39 cents, how much more money does he need?

3. *The "comparison" or difference-between idea.* If Jimmy weighs 85 pounds and Larry weighs 83 pounds, what is the difference in their weights?

The first type, the "how many are left" interpretation is the type of problem that is most common in the experiences of small children. Children visualize a certain number of things which they have in the beginning and give some of these things to a playmate. They should be interested in learning the kind of arithmetic (the operation) which will lead them to discover how many they have left (how many remain).

This type of problem can be effectively illustrated graphically. If Smitty had 4 apples and gave one to his sister, how many did he have left?

$$0\ 0\ 0\ 0 \qquad 0\ 0\ 0\ \cancel{0} \qquad 0\ 0\ 0$$
$$4 \qquad\qquad 4-1 \qquad\qquad 3$$

Another illustration is of the film-strip variety:

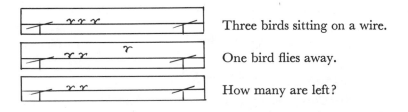

Three birds sitting on a wire.

One bird flies away.

How many are left?

This problem can be illustrated as a counting-backward operation. We can represent the given amount by a point on the number line and then count backwards, one at a time, until we have subtracted the required amount.   The abstract example, 9 − 3, will serve as an illustration.

1 2 3 4 5 6 7 8 9   nine things
1 2 3 4 5 6 7 8 9̶   nine things, take away one
1 2 3 4 5 6 7 8̶ 9̶   nine things, take away two
1 2 3 4 5 6 7̶ 8̶ 9̶   nine things, take away three leaves 6.

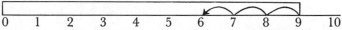

An illustration of the "how many more" idea of subtraction is the problem which takes the additive approach.   For instance, Eddie is saving money to buy a bicycle.   He has saved up $23 and he wants to buy a bicycle which costs $39.   How much more does he need? The idea expressed here is that Eddie will add to his savings until he has accumulated the required amount.   He visualizes more and more dollars being added to his savings until he has enough money to buy the bicycle.   He may visualize this addition in the following manner:

$23 and 10 more dollars will make $33.

$33 and   6 more dollars will make $39.

Since he needs 10 dollars more and 6 dollars more he will need 16 dollars more to make the total of $39.   The algorism would look like this:

$$\begin{array}{r} \$39 \\ - \ 23 \\ \hline \end{array}$$

and the thinking necessary to reach a solution suggests that we find a number of dollars which when added to $23 will make $39. Graphically the solution becomes:

```
*********     and how much more to make     *********
*********                                   *********
***                                         ***0000000
                                            000000000
```

$23 + $7 + $9 = $39.

Another illustration can be taken from the children's experiences. If the school bus will hold only 32 pupils and there are already 27 pupils on the bus, how many more students will the driver let on the bus? There are 5 more places to fill.

```
  32        *****00000
- 27        *********
   5        *********
            **
```

An illustration of the third type of subtraction, the "difference between" type, is the problem which asks, "How long does it take the train to get to Washington if it leaves New York at 8 P.M. and arrives in Washington at 11 P.M.?" The question is clearly one of finding the difference (there is no take-away) between the time of departure and the time of arrival. It is definitely a subtraction problem but the minuend is not diminished. We are interested in knowing how far apart these numbers are on a number line.

```
1  2  3  4  5  6  7  8  9  10  11  12  1  2  3
----------------------------------------------
         8 to 9    1 hour   |---|
         8 to 10   2 hours  |-------|
         8 to 11   3 hours  |-----------|
```

The time required for the trip from New York to Washington is 3 hours.

When two boys stand back to back to see how tall they are and to see how much taller one boy is than the other, the observer is making use of the comparison idea of subtraction. One does not subtract, he finds the difference by comparing the two numbers on the same number line. When we measure the two boys we see them measured along an imaginary stick which is graduated in inches. We see a difference in heights of 2 or 3 inches. We are using the subtraction operation though we really don't diminish the minuend.

Write the subtraction algorism for each of these three problems:

1. There are 18 boys in my class, 13 of whom went to the library. How many were left?

2. I want to organize two full baseball teams but I have only 13 players. How many more do I need?

3. I have 18 boys in my class; Miss King has 13 boys in her class. How many more boys are in my class than in Miss King's class?

2.10 The Subtraction Facts

Subtraction facts have meaning when they are associated with addition facts. It is easy to teach subtraction combinations along with the addition combinations. At the time one is learning that when 3 things are combined with 2 things of the same kind, the total is 5, it is comparatively easy and extremely timely to show that when 3 things are taken from a group of 5 things the remainder will be 2. There will be 2 left. Since subtraction, separating into sub-groups, is the opposite operation from addition, subtraction facts can be shown simultaneously with the addition example. Thus when a child learns that $4 + 3$ is 7, he should learn 3 companion facts, namely, $3 + 4 = 7$, $7 - 3 = 4$, and $7 - 4 = 3$. This teaching unit becomes a learning unit of 4 facts and is often referred to as "the whole story of 3, 4, and 7." The "take away" stories are usually read "seven take away three leaves four" and "seven take away four leaves three."

Since for every addition fact there is a subtraction fact, there should be as many subtraction facts as there are addition facts—100 including the zero combinations and 81 excluding the zero combinations. Though many teachers present zero subtraction facts as a group and lead children to generalize that "subtracting zero from a number leaves the same number" and "a number subtracted from itself leaves zero," young children should not be expected to generalize these facts.

The writer believes that computations involving zero contain more errors than computations with any other numeral. Hence operations involving the use of zero should be stressed as distinct number relationships. We must emphasize the fact that $6 + 0 = 6$ and that $7 + 0 = 7$, and also that $8 - 8 = 0$ and $9 - 9 = 0$. We must do more than merely generalize these zero facts.

The most difficult of the subtraction facts are those which contain a two-digit minuend. When 7 is subtracted from 16, what is the remainder? This fact should be taught at the time children are learning that 7 and 9 are 16. Thus the approach to the example

$$\begin{array}{r} 16 \\ -\ 7 \\ \hline \end{array}$$

is definitely additive; seven and how many more will make 16? Should the pupil fail to recall this fact there are several ways to show him how to arrive at the result. Show him that $16 = 10$ and 6 and then from the 10 subtract 7. This leaves 3, which, when combined with 6, gives an answer of 9.

$$\begin{array}{r} 16 = \quad 10 + 6 \\ -\ 7 = -\ 7 \\ \hline 3 + 6 = 9 \end{array}$$

The example can be solved by the use of the 20-board or the 100-bead frame in similar fashion.   The 16 items would be represented like this:

********** — — — — —
****** — — — — — — 0000

Now if 7 are removed from the group they can very conveniently be removed from the group of 10.   If so, the representation would now look like this:

*** — — — — — — *******
****** — — — — — — 0000

Now the student should see that the remainder consists of 3 and 6 or 9.

The example can be objectified once more by the use of money. Have the pupil lay out 16 cents in dimes and pennies and then ask him to give his neighbor 7 cents.   He should discover that in order to do this he must change the dime into pennies.   Now from the 10 pennies he can remove 7 pennies.   His remainder will again be 9 cents.

16 cents = 1 dime + 6 pennies
(10¢)   (6¢)
1¢ 1¢ 1¢ 1¢ 1¢ 1¢ 1¢ 1¢ 1¢ 1¢ 1¢ 1¢ 1¢ 1¢ 1¢ 1¢
− 7 cents   1¢ 1¢ 1¢ 1¢ 1¢ 1¢ 1¢
─────────────────────────────────
1¢ 1¢ 1¢ 1¢ 1¢ 1¢ 1¢ 1¢ 1¢

The example can be solved also by the use of the number line. Subtraction as a taking-away process can be represented by moving to the left along a number line.   So we represent 16 on the number line and then count backwards seven places.   First we count or move backward six places (either one by one or by six)—and we'll be at 10—and then we count back one more place.   Now we will be at 9. Thus 16 − 7 leaves 9.

0 1 2 3 4 5 6 7 8 9 10 11 12 13 14 15 16 17 18 19 20

A mastery of the 100 subtraction facts is necessary for performing decade subtraction.   Decade subtraction, similar to decade addition, is the subtraction of a single digit from a two-digit number.   Some of the subtraction facts are examples of decade subtraction though seldom called that because of the fact that those combinations are *basic* and are learned definitely through the additive approach. If we subtract a one-digit number from any two-digit number, the remainder will be a number in the same decade or the next lower decade. But first, one must learn the endings for the subtraction facts. Since we have learned that $16 - 7 = 9$, then we ought to see that $26 - 7 = 19$, $36 - 7 = 29$, $46 - 7 = 39$, and so on.

In summary we see that there are really two approaches to the subtraction operation, namely, the *take away* approach and the *additive* approach. In doing the example which asks one to subtract 8 from 15 one can say to himself, "15 take away 8 is (7)" or "8 and (7) are 15." Both approaches are equally sound but the additive is more difficult to show and prove when working with elementary school children.

2.11 Simple Subtraction Involving Large Numbers

Many subtraction examples encountered in daily living involve the subtraction of two- or three-digit numbers from numbers of the same order without any change in the minuend. We can very easily subtract 3 from 6, 45 from 48, 123 from 127, etc., for we can sense the difference between them when they are represented on the same number line. When these examples are set up in vertical form we see that they differ only in the ones place. In other words, we need subtract only the numbers in those places.

$$\begin{array}{ccc} 6 & 48 & 127 \\ -\,3 & -\,45 & -\,123 \\ \hline \end{array}$$

As in addition, the principle of likeness operates throughout the subtraction operation. We subtract ones from ones, tens from tens, hundreds from hundreds, and so on. Thus when we subtract 234 from 456 we are subtracting 4 ones from 6 ones, 3 tens from 5 tens, and 2 hundreds from 4 hundreds. In vertical form the example would look like this:

hundreds	tens	ones		
4	5	6	or	4 hundreds 5 tens 6 ones
2	3	4		2 hundreds 3 tens 4 ones
2	2	2		2 hundreds 2 tens 2 ones

When solving simple subtraction examples like the one above, a student might perform the operation from left to right doing what is called "front end arithmetic." Though there is nothing to prevent his doing them in this manner he ought to be encouraged to begin in the ones column as preparation for the more difficult or compound examples. In subtracting $45.60 from $58.80 a student might sense the difference between the amounts expressed in dollars as $13 and the difference between the amounts expressed as cents as 20 cents and immediately state the difference as $13.20.

2.12 Compound Subtraction by the Decomposition Method

Compound subtraction implies that one or more of the digits in the subtrahend are larger than the digit which occupies the same place in the minuend. The simplest illustration would be of the type in which the ones digit in the smaller number would be larger than the ones digit in the larger number. Such an example would be

$$42$$
$$- 27$$

When this problem is attacked like the simple problem in the preceding paragraph, the student meets an impossible situation for he cannot subtract the 7 in the ones place from the 2 in the ones place of the minuend. Some transformation or changing is necessary. With the use of manipulatory materials he has learned how to convert a group of ten into ten ones, he has seen that it has often become necessary to convert a dime into pennies before he could subtract or make change, and he has seen through his study of number that there are many ways to express numbers. He may approach the given example in any one of the following ways:

(a) Let the 42 represent 42 cents.

Subtract 27 cents from 42 cents.

Express 42 cents as 4 dimes and 2 pennies.
Express 27 cents as 2 dimes and 7 pennies.

In order to subtract one must convert one of the dimes into pennies. Then the written statement becomes

3 dimes and 12 pennies
2 dimes and 7 pennies

and the operation is very easy to perform.

(b) 42 = ooooooooo

ooooooooo   10 + 10 + 10 + 10 + 2

ooooooooo

ooooooooo   Now to subtract (take away 27) one must

oo   take away 2 tens and some from one of the
tens. That will leave 1 ten and 3 and 2
ones or a total of 15. The completed
operation would look like this:

ØØØØØØØØØØ   OOOOOOOOOO

ØØØØØØØØØØ   ØØØØØØØOOO   oo

or the algorism might look like this:

$$10 + 10 + 10 + 10 + 2$$
$$-\underline{(10 + 10 + \qquad 7 \qquad)}$$
$$10 + \ \ 3 + 2$$

(c) Since 42 = 30 + 12 we can subtract 27 from 30 + 12

30 + 12   and now the numerals in the subtrahend
20 + 7   represent smaller amounts and can be
subtracted from the numbers in the minuend.
The remainder will be 10 + 5 or 15.

(d) The regrouping process can be extended to include the bundle arrangements of numbers with which the present-day school child should be very familiar. The symbol ⸙ represents a bundle of ten sticks or straws with a rubber band around them—a group of ten ones. Thus the symbolic representation of 42 would take this form: ⸙ ⸙ ⸙ ⸙ 1 1. Now in order to take 27 distinct ones from this amount there must be some regrouping. One of the bundles of ten must be regrouped as ten ones. Then the symbolic representation of 42 would look like this: ⸙ ⸙ ⸙ 11111111111, and the 27 (the two tens and seven ones) can be removed from the group, can be taken away or subtracted.

(e) The operation can be performed along the number line. The difference can be obtained by counting backward the required number of units. Let us locate the number 42 on a number line and from it move 27 units to the left. First we will move 20 units by taking two large steps of 10 units each. We will then be at the point marked 22 on the number line. Now we must count 7 more units to

the left.   This places us at the point marked 15 on the number line.
Therefore 42 − 27 = 15.

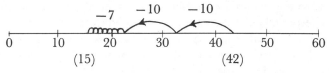

(15)   (42)

Many people perform subtraction examples with reference to a
number line.   If they do not count backward as we did in the preceding example then they count forward or use the additive approach.
Witness the thought process in doing this example:

$$207$$
$$- \; 149$$

If we find the difference in a piecemeal additive fashion we would
think: "From 149 to 150 is 1 unit, from 150 to 200 is 50 units, and
from 200 to 207 is 7 units.   Therefore the distance measured along
a number line from 149 to 207 is 1 + 50 + 7 or 58."

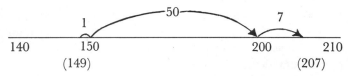

140   150   200   210
    (149)   (207)

(f) All of these suggestions are preliminary to the development of
the standard algorism for compound subtraction examples.   When
the digit in the ones place in the minuend is smaller than the ones
digit in the subtrahend it is necessary to decompose the minuend.
We do this by taking one of the tens and changing it into ten ones.
These ten ones we add in with the ones already in the ones place
and now we are ready and able to subtract.   The original example
would be written in this form:

tens	ones		tens	ones
4	2	becomes	3	12
− 2	7		− 2	7

Without the headings the algorism would look like this:

$$
\begin{array}{r}
3 \;\; \boxed{10} \\
\not{4} \;\; \boxed{2} \\
\underline{- \; 2 \quad 7}
\end{array}
$$

The 7 is subtracted from the 12 and the 2 is subtracted from 3; the remainder is 1 ten and 5 ones or 15. For convenience' sake the ten ones which are added to the number in the ones place are shown by prefixing a one to the number already in the ones place but lest it be interpreted as another number inserted in the midst of the given number it is usually expressed as a small stroke signifying ten. The changed minuend which still must be equal to 42 is now expressed as 30 and 12 and is written 3'2 or more generally

$$\begin{matrix} 3 \\ \cancel{4}\,'2 \end{matrix}$$

Then the most widely used algorism and the most widely accepted algorism looks like this:

$$\begin{array}{r} 4\ \ 2 \\ -\ 2\ \ 7 \\ \hline \end{array} \qquad \begin{array}{r} 3 \\ \cancel{4}\,'2 \\ -\ 2\ \ 7 \\ \hline 1\ \ 5 \end{array}$$

If the idea of decomposing a ten is thoroughly understood the pupil ought to be able to apply his understanding to larger numbers which would involve decomposition of hundreds and thousands into smaller denominations.

Then   423   becomes $\begin{matrix} 3 \\ \cancel{4}\,'2\ 3 \end{matrix}$ and   6 2 1 9   becomes $\begin{matrix} 5 \\ \cancel{6}\,'2\ 1\ 9 \end{matrix}$
　　　　 − 161　　　　　 − 1 6 1　　　　 − 4 3 0 7　　　　　　 − 4 3 0 7

and　　 500   becomes $\begin{matrix} 49 \\ \cancel{5}\cancel{0}\,'0 \end{matrix}$
　　　 − 264　　　　　 − 26　 4

The solution of the preceding examples can be accomplished through two distinct approaches. The student can make use of the take-away approach or the additive approach. When he takes the number quantity which appears in the subtrahend from the number in the corresponding place in the minuend he is using the take-away approach, but when he adds to the number in the subtrahend to make the number in the minuend he is using the additive approach. To illustrate:

The decomposition take-away approach:

```
 5
 6 '2 8     Thought process: Change one hundred into 10 tens.
 3  7 3     3 from 8 leaves 5
            7 from 12 leaves 5
 ‾‾‾‾‾‾
 2  5 5     3 from 5 leaves 2.  Answer: 255.
```

The decomposition additive approach:

```
 2
 3 '2 9     Thought process: Change one hundred into 10 tens.
 1  6 2     2 and 7 makes 9
            6 and 6 makes 12
 ‾‾‾‾‾‾
 1  6 7     1 and 1 makes 2.  Answer: 167
```

The reader may be disturbed over the use of the crutch illustrated here. Such devices are suggested for use with children to facilitate their understanding and their computation in the early stages of learning a new idea. Continued use of such devices is to be discouraged; when a student has reached the stage when such a gimmick is no longer necessary, he should discard it and perform the example in a conventional and mature manner. Then the example in subtraction

$$\begin{array}{r} 4056 \\ -\ 2828 \\ \end{array}$$

would be performed with complete understanding and competency and the remainder written as 1228. (The reader should note that the term "borrowing" has not been used in this chapter. Its use and its attendant connotation should not be tolerated.)

2.13 Compound Subtraction by the Equal-Additions Method

When some of the terms of the subtrahend are larger than the corresponding terms of the minuend there is another method of attacking this example; namely, by the *law of compensation*, or the law of equal adjustment. This law states that if both the subtrahend and minuend of a subtraction example are increased by the same amount the difference is unaffected. It should be obvious that if both the minuend and the subtrahend are increased by 1 or by any other number, then the difference will be the same as before. That is, if Joey has 5 apples and eats one of them he will have 4 left. The remainder would still be four if he had 6 apples (minuend increased by one) and ate 2 (subtrahend increased by one) of them.

5 apples	6 apples	23	24	35	45
− 1 apple	− 2 apples	− 19	− 20	− 17	− 27
4 apples	4 apples	4	4	18	18

This method of performing subtraction examples by adding equal amounts to both terms of the example is called the "equal additions" method. Let us see how it works when the ones digit only is larger than the ones digit of the minuend.

Example: 4 2
             − 1 8

Procedure: Add equal amounts to both the minuend and subtrahend. Add ten ones to the minuend and one ten to the subtrahend making them respectively, 40 and 12, and 28.

4 2	4 '2	8 from 12 is 4
− 1 8	− 2 8	2 from 4 is 2
		Answer is 24

The student will note that we have added a ten in the ones place in the minuend and a ten in the tens place of the subtrahend.

Let us solve an example of greater difficulty, one in which two or more numbers of the subtrahend are larger than the digits in the corresponding places in the minuend.

Example: 6 4 3
             − 3 7 8

Add in 10 ones making the minuend   6 4 '3
                                                 8
Add in 1 ten making the subtrahend   3 7 8   8 and 5 are 13
                                                 5

Add in 10 tens making the minuend   6 '4 '3
                                                 4 8
Add in 1 hundred making the subtrahend   3 7 8   8 and 6 are 14
                                             2 6 5   4 and 2 are 6

The remainder is 265.

Let us see how this method would apply to a more complicated subtraction example. From 5000 subtract 2364. The student should observe that one needs only to prefix a 1 to each of the zeros in the minuend making them tens and increasing all but the ones digit in the subtrahend.

thousands	hundreds	tens	ones
	10	10	10
5	Ø	Ø	Ø
3	4	7	
2	3	6	4
2	6	3	6

In summary the student should have observed that there are four ways to think through a compound subtraction example:

1. Decomposition—take-away
2. Decomposition—additive
3. Equal additions—take-away
4. Equal additions—additive

EXERCISES

SET 9

1. Write the remainders to these subtraction examples without copying them.

300	5200	4508	3700	3901	5700	56000	569004	280001
161	3900	3401	2308	3887	3207	23061	234072	160203

2. I traveled from New York to Washington by train, arriving in Washington at 1:38 P.M. If the trip required 3 hours and 51 minutes, find the time of my departure from New York. Do the problem two different ways.

3. Subtract: 5 years 3 months 3 weeks 2 days
             2 years 5 months 3 weeks 5 days

4. Write out two problems, on the adult level, illustrating the comparison interpretation of subtraction. Solve the problems.

5. Illustrate 56 − 32 linearly. Also show 71 − 29 by the use of a line drawing. Show 31 − 16 by use of the bundle idea.

6. Subtract   7 miles   65 rods 4 yards 2 feet 5 inches
             −3 miles 241 rods 5 yards 1 foot 7 inches

7. Show how many dozen eggs are represented by 99 eggs by the operation of repeated subtraction.

8. Be prepared to give a simple oral interpretation of this algorism:

$$
\begin{array}{r}
\overset{2}{}\;\;\overset{9}{}\;\;\overset{9}{} \\
\cancel{3}\;\;'\cancel{0}\;\;'\cancel{0}\;\;'7 \\
-\;1\;\;6\;\;4\;\;9 \\
\hline
1\;\;3\;\;5\;\;8
\end{array}
$$

9. Which of these subtraction examples has the largest remainder? (Determine without actually doing the subtracting.)

(a) 83455   (b) 84356   (c) 85643   (d) 82354   (e) 85643
    78894   79830   81079   77729   81088

10. The enrollment at Southern University one semester was as follows:

	Seniors	Juniors	Sophomores	Freshmen
Male	654	879	1204	1507
Female	321	278	547	469

Find the differences between the male and female enrollments by classes.

2.14 Subtraction in Other Bases

When the base is different from ten the algorisms just developed for subtraction problems in the decimal scale are equally applicable. We can perform the subtraction examples by either of the four methods previously outlined. Since we made use of the primary addition facts in base ten when performing subtraction examples, we will likewise make use of the primary subtraction facts when doing subtractions in bases different from ten. When we are working in the decimal scale and must subtract 8 from 13 we can approach the problem through the additive approach: 8 and what else equals 13? Similarly when we are working in any other base we use the same approach. What number added to 7 will give us a group of 9 and 2 ones? What number added to 5 will give us a group of eight and 4 ones? Eleven and how many more will make a group of thirteen and 7?

$7 +$ _____ $= 11$ (nine) $4 +$ _____ $= 13$ (five) $2 +$ _____ $= 11$ (three)

Reproduced below is the table of primary addition facts in the base of seven. The numbers within the table represent the sums of two addends, and the numbers in the top row and first column represent addends. The cell in the row headed 4 and the column headed 5 shows that their sum is 12. Conversely, if the numbers within the table represent minuends and a subtrahend is given, we can read to

the head of the row or column containing the given minuend to find
the remainder. If the minuend is 14 (seven) and we wish to subtract
5 from it we first find 14 in the table headed by 5. We read the
number in the head of the column which contains this number 14.
Thus $14 - 5 = 6$, and so $14 - 6 = 5$ in base seven. From the
table we see that there is no other primary subtraction fact in the base
seven whose minuend is 14.

+	0	1	2	3	4	5	6
0	0	1	2	3	4	5	6
1	1	2	3	4	5	6	10
2	2	3	4	5	6	10	11
3	3	4	5	6	10	11	12
4	4	5	6	10	11	12	13
5	5	6	10	11	12	13	14
6	6	10	11	12	13	14	15

PRIMARY SUBTRACTION AND ADDITION
FACTS IN BASE SEVEN

Compound subtraction in bases different from the decimal scale
can be performed in any one of the four methods outlined in paragraph
13 but a little practice with problems in different bases will soon convince the student that the additive approach is superior to the take-
away approach unless one has all of his subtraction tables available.
Let us subtract 237 from 463 in the base eight by the decomposition
method—additive approach.

$\begin{array}{c} 5 \\ 4\ \cancel{6}\ '3 \end{array}$ Change 6 eights into 5 eights and 1 eight. Combine the 1
eight with the 3, making 1 eight and 3.

2 3 7 7 and (4) make 1 eight and 3. Write 4 in the ones place.
2 2 4 The rest of the subtraction offers no difficulty. Answer: 224.

Let us do a more difficult compound example in base six.

$\begin{array}{l} \ \ 3\ 4\ 0\ 2 \\ -\ 1\ 4\ 2\ 5 \end{array}$ Change the 4 groups of thirty-sixes into 3
thirty-sixes and 1 thirty-six. This in
turn becomes 6 sixes.
$\begin{array}{l} \ \ \ \ \ \ \ 3 \\ 3\ \cancel{4}\ '0\ 2 \\ 1\ 4\ 2\ 5 \end{array}$

```
    3                                                          3 5
3 4'0 2    Change the 6 sixes into 5 sixes and 1 six.     3 4'0'2
           This makes the term in the ones place in
1 4 2 5    the minuend 1 six and 2.   Then 5 and          1 4 2 5
_____     (3) make 1 six and 2.                          _____
                                                                3
```

```
  3 5                                                     2 '3 5
3 4'0'2    The 2 can be subtracted from the 5.            3 4 0 2
           Write 3 in the base column.  Now 4
1 4 2 5    cannot be subtracted from 3 so we must         1 4 2 5
_____     change the 3 two hundred sixteens into 2       _____
    3 3    of them and 1 two hundred sixteen.             1 5 3 3
           When the latter is combined with the 3
           thirty-sixes already there, we have a
           term in the minuend consisting of 1 two
           hundred sixteen and 3 thirty-sixes.
           Now 4 thirty-sixes and (5) thirty-sixes
           make 1 two hundred sixteen and 3
           thirty-sixes.  Write 5 in the proper
           column.  Complete the subtraction.
```

Of course the student need not rewrite the example as he performs the successive steps. The entire subtraction can be done in just one written algorism. Some of the compound subtraction examples might become mutilated if the student continues to change and cross out numbers in the minuend. Let us do the above example again by the equal-additions method. The completed algorism would look like this:

$$
\begin{array}{r}
3'4'0'2 \\
2\ 5\ 3 \\
1\ 4\ 2\ 5 \\
\hline
1\ 5\ 3\ 3
\end{array}
$$

2.15   Checks for Subtraction Examples

(a) Since subtraction can be thought of as the operation which finds a missing addend, we must be able to check our subtraction example by the addition operation. If $25 - 12 = 13$, then the sum of 13 and 12 must be 25, or in more general terms, if $A - B = C$, then $C + B$ must equal A. The sum of the remainder and the subtrahend must equal the minuend; if not, then the subtraction has not been performed correctly. This rule applies regardless of the base involved.

(*b*) The subtraction operation asks us to find a missing addend when one of them is known. When this addend has been discovered and then subtracted from the minuend we ought to obtain the original addend. In other words, if we subtract the remainder which we have obtained from the minuend we ought to get the subtrahend. If $25 - 14 = 11$ then $25 - 11 = 14$. In general terms if $A - B = C$, then $A - C = B$. This rule applies regardless of the base involved.

(*c*) We can also check subtraction examples by the excess-of-nines and the excess-of-elevens rules when the examples have been performed in the base ten. The excess of nines (or elevens) in the subtrahend subtracted from the excess of nines (or elevens) in the minuend should equal the excess of nines (or elevens) in the remainder. If not, the remainder is probably incorrect.

Examples:

$$\begin{array}{ll} 42387 & \text{excess of 9's} = 6 \\ -17122 & \text{excess of 9's} = 4 \\ \hline 25265 & \text{excess of 9's} = 2 \end{array} \left.\begin{array}{l} \\ \\ \end{array}\right\} \; 6-4=2 \; \text{— Check} \quad \begin{array}{l} \text{excess of 11's} = 4 \\ \text{excess of 11's} = 6 \\ \text{excess of 11's} = 9 \end{array} \left.\begin{array}{l} \\ \\ \end{array}\right\} \; 11+4-6=9 \; \text{— Check}$$

(*d*) If the base is different from ten we can use the rules illustrated in the paragraph above in the form of the excess of base-less-one and the excess of base-plus-one just as we did in checking addition examples. Let us illustrate the check of a subtraction example done in base six.

$$\begin{array}{ll} 23134 & \text{excess of 5's} = 3 \\ -21053 & \text{excess of 5's} = 1 \\ \hline 2041 & \text{excess of 5's} = 2 \end{array} \left.\begin{array}{l} \\ \\ \end{array}\right\} \; 3-1=2 \; \text{— Check} \quad \begin{array}{l} \text{excess of sevens} = 1 \\ \text{excess of sevens} = 6 \\ \text{excess of sevens} = 2 \end{array} \left.\begin{array}{l} \\ \\ \end{array}\right\} \; \begin{array}{l} \text{seven} + 1 - 6 \\ = 2 \end{array} \; \text{— Check}$$

2.16   The Complementary Method of Subtraction

Four methods have been given for doing compound subtraction. Now we would like to discuss another method which can be used for either simple or compound subtraction examples. It is called the complementary method and makes use of both addition and subtraction in its execution. The complement of a number is the difference between the given number and its next higher power of ten. The complement of 7 is 3, of 86 is 14, of 678 is 322, and so on.

Then any number can be expressed as the difference between its complement and the next higher power of ten. 48 is equal to 100 − 52, so when 48 is to be subtracted from any number we can subtract its equivalent (100 − 52). This operation would be equivalent to subtracting 100 and then adding 52, and this operation can be performed in reverse order, adding 52 and then subtracting 100. If we add the complement of the subtrahend to the minuend and subtract the next higher power of ten we will have obtained the difference.

The example:

$$
\begin{array}{cccc}
83 & 83 & 83 & 83 & 83 \\
-\ 48 & -(100-52) & -100+52 & +52-100 & +52-100 \\
& & & & \overline{135-100} = 35
\end{array}
$$

Another example:

$$
\begin{array}{cc}
842 & 842 \\
-\ 329 & +671-1000 \\
& \overline{1513-1000} = 513
\end{array}
$$

The reader should observe that one finds the complement of the subtrahend and then adds. The result will be too large by some power of ten or a multiple of a power of ten if several subtractions are to be performed in an example. All one needs to do after the additions have been performed is to decrease the last digit to the left in the sum by 1 or a multiple of 1. The complement of a number can be found mentally and students who have studied logarithms have had much practice with complements. In finding the co-logarithm of a number, one subtracts the logarithm from 10.00000 − 10; the last digit in the logarithm is subtracted from 10, all others are subtracted from 9. To find the complement of 7462, for instance, we think: 8 and 2 are 10; 3 and 6 are 9; 5 and 4 are 9; 2 and 7 are 9. With a little practice students will be able to find the complements mentally and a subtraction example will be turned into an addition example. The example

$$
\begin{array}{r}
6337 \\
-\ 2584
\end{array}
$$

would be rationalized as follows:

Find the complement of the subtrahend and add: 6 3 3 7
The complement of the subtrahend: (7 4 1 6)
The subtrahend: 2 5 8 4
We add 7 and 6; 3 and 1; 3 and 4; 6 and 7. $\overline{1\ 3\ 7\ 5\ 3}$
Drop the 1 in the first or front place.   3 7 5 3
                                      the remainder

Another example: 86   Solution: 86
                 − 19   + 81 − 100
                 + 37   + 37
                 − 52   + 48 − 100
                              $\overline{252 - 200}$ or 52

In general: Minuend − subtrahend = difference
             Minuend − $(10^n$ − complement) = difference
             Minuend − 10^n + complement   = difference
             Minuend + complement − 10^n = difference
             (Minuend + complement) − 10^n = difference

EXERCISES

SET 10

1. Do the following subtraction examples using Roman numerals:
   (a)   35   (b)   48 (c)   91 (d)   500 (e)   678 (f)   2000
      −23   −32   −64   −155   −382   −1900

2. In what scales are the following subtractions performed?
   (a)   2222   (b)   8456   (c)   101001   (d)   3344
      −1246   −6527   −89899   −1255
       T87   1828   11102   2056

3. Subtract in the duodecimal system:
   (a)   456E0   (b)   77777   (c) 10456   (d)   90TE8
      −23488   −6008E   −9TE   −71E09

4. Prove 3 (a) and 3 (b) above by the excess of base-less-one rule.
5. Prove 3 (c) and 3 (d) above by the excess of base-plus-one rule.
6. Find the complements of the following numbers:
   (a)   31   524   789   11345   33509   3005678
   (b)   97   222   508   44503   51023   2560000

7. Subtract by the use of complements:

5673	9567	95,821	78,452	76,235
2674	2207	11,574	3,997	− 56,331
				− 11,496

$65.96	$56,873.06	$100,000.00
− 56.34	− 23,112.65	− 17,500.00
+ 23.09	− 19,405.30	− 32,750.00
− 14.56	− 3,002.00	− 14,472.50

8. Write a numeral composed of two different digits. Form a new numeral by reversing the digits. Show that the difference between the two numbers is exactly divisible by 9. Does this also work for a three-digit numeral?

9. Make up and solve four compound subtraction examples in base seven.

10. Decode the following puzzle as a subtraction example in base ten.

$$\begin{array}{r} P\,R\,E\,S\,T\,O \\ -\ H\,O\,C\,U\,S \\ \hline P\,O\,C\,U\,S \end{array}$$

CHAPTER 3

MULTIPLICATION OF WHOLE NUMBERS

3.1 Understandings

The second of the two operations describing the synthesis process is the operation called multiplication. If the addends which we are combining are all of the same size and if we know our multiplication facts we can write the algorism in a shorter form and obtain the result more expediently. Should a student wish to know the value of 3 fives he can count them by fives: 5, 10, 15, or he can add 3 fives: 5 + 5 + 5, or he can simply say that 3 fives are 15. If one uses an addend 3 times he can write the example as a multiplication example in either a horizontal manner

$$3 \times 5$$

(read: "three fives are") or in the vertical fashion

$$\begin{array}{r} 5 \\ \times\ 3 \\ \hline \end{array}$$

also read as "three fives are." Thus 4 × 7 is interpreted as the addend 7 used 4 times. This is a short way of writing 7 + 7 + 7 + 7. Each of the equal addends is called the *multiplicand* and the numeral which indicates the number of addends used is called the *multiplier*. In the horizontal form the first numeral written is used as the multiplier while in the vertical form it is always the lower number. The answer obtained in a multiplication example is called the *product*.

We pointed out that in addition the addends must represent concrete things and that the sum must have agreement in name with any one of the addends. If we add 5 sheep and 5 sheep and 5 sheep we expect the sum to be 15 sheep. Likewise, in multiplication, since the multiplicand is one of several equal addends it must represent concrete quantities and the product must have complete agreement in kind with the multiplicand. The multiplier always represents the number of groups. Then in the example which says "4 × 5" the 5 must represent something specific, something concrete like apples, dogs, cents, etc., and the 4 represents the number of groups of these things. If we solve the example, 7 × 5 cents, the product must be in cents, namely 35 cents. The product must agree in kind with the multiplicand.

$$\begin{array}{ll} \text{multiplicand:} & \text{12 eggs} \\ \text{multiplier:} & \times\ 3 \\ \text{product:} & \overline{\text{36}}\ \text{eggs} \end{array}$$

In the abstract sense 3 fours is equal in amount to 4 threes. The product of 3 and 4 is always 12 whether performed as 3 × 4 or 4 × 3. The end result is the same in both cases though the interpretations are different. Three fours should be exhibited as 4 + 4 + 4 or $xxxx + xxxx + xxxx$ while four threes will be shown as 3 + 3 + 3 + 3 or $ooo + ooo + ooo + ooo$. In the abstract the multiplications can be performed in any order, $a \times b$ is the same as $b \times a$. This is the *commutative* law applied to multiplication.

$$5 \times 6 = 6 \times 5 \quad \text{and} \quad 300 \times 16 = 16 \times 300 \quad 3 \times 7 = 7 \times 3$$

In the abstract sense either of the numbers (or both of them) can be used as the multiplier and these multipliers are called *factors* of the product thus produced. If the product is known to be 15, the factors are probably 3 and 5; if the product is 24, the factors might be 4 and 6, 3 and 8, 2 and 12, 1 and 24, or any set of non-integral factors like $\frac{1}{2} \times 48$ or $2\frac{1}{2} \times 9\frac{3}{5}$.

The product of a set of numbers is not altered regardless of the combinations of factors used to produce the number. Thus the factors 2, 3, and 5 will produce the product 30 regardless of the groupings or sets of factors used. The combination 2 × 3 multiplied by 5 will produce the same product as twice the product of 3 and 5. The selection of groups of sets of factors is permitted by the principle known as the *associative* law of multiplication. In general, this law states that if one is to find the product of $a \times b \times c$ he may multiply a by b and this product by c or multiply b by c and then by a.

$$a \times b \times c = (a \times b) \times c = a \times (b \times c)$$

The example 3 × $\frac{1}{2}$ × 4 can be done more conveniently if the last two terms are grouped and then their product 2 is multiplied by 3.

$$3 \times \tfrac{1}{2} \times 4 = (3 \times \tfrac{1}{2}) \times 4 = 3 \times (\tfrac{1}{2} \times 4)$$
$$\text{Also } 7 \times 4 \times 5 = (7 \times 4) \times 5 = 7 \times (4 \times 5)$$

In each case the latter multiplications are the easier to perform.

The multiplication operation permits us to perform compound multiplications with ease by use of a third law known as the *distributive law*. If one is to multiply a compound number by a single-digit number he may multiply the separate parts of the compound number by the single digit and then add the several products. The law stated formally says, "If one is to multiply a sum of numbers by another number, each number can be multiplied by the multiplier and then the products added" or "the several numbers may be added first and then the multiplications performed." If $x + y$ is to be multiplied by n the additions can be performed or the multiplications can be performed first: $n(x + y) = nx + ny$ (note that the multiplication symbol is not necessary before the parenthesis). This law is very important in our multiplication algorism, for if we multiply 26 by 3 we multiply the whole number 26 as the sum of 20 and 6 by 3 and then add the products.

$$3 \times 26 = 3(20 + 6) = 60 + 18 = 78.$$

This law, one of many governing operations, illustrates the distributive law of multiplication with respect to or distributed over addition.

3.2 The Multiplication Facts

Success in performing the multiplication operation is contingent upon knowing a set of multiplication facts. In addition and subtraction one had to learn a set of primary combinations—there are some facts the students must know and know readily. The same is true for multiplication. These multiplication facts must be learned, though they need not be memorized in table or serial order. When a child is learning that 4 sixes are 24 he can learn that 6 fours are also 24; when he learns that 5 sevens are 35 he can also learn that 7 fives are also 35. He does not necessarily learn a set of facts from memory but the organization of these facts into some kind of table form will help fix patterns and sequences of numbers which will aid or help the student in the recall of the learned fact. In the table which follows the numbers in the top row and the first column comprise a set of factors, either of which can be the multiplier, whose product is given in the proper box or cell within the table. Should one wish to know the product of 4 times 8 he would enter the table through the

column headed 8 and read down to the row which is headed 4. Thus
the product is 32.

×	0	1	2	3	4	5	6	7	8	9
1	0	1	2	3	4	5	6	7	8	9
2	0	2	4	6	8	10	12	14	16	18
3	0	3	6	9	12	15	18	21	24	27
4	0	4	8	12	16	20	24	28	32	36
5	0	5	10	15	20	25	30	35	40	45
6	0	6	12	18	24	30	36	42	48	54
7	0	7	14	21	28	35	42	49	56	63
8	0	8	16	24	32	40	48	56	64	72
9	0	9	18	27	36	45	54	63	72	81

THE 100 PRIMARY MULTIPLICATION FACTS

The harder facts are those combinations whose product is 30 or more.
Arranging these products in table form enables the student to visualize
the serial form of the products; he can more easily learn to count by
sixes, sevens, eights, or nines. Emphasis should be placed on those
sets of factors which produce a result equal to or greater than 30. In
other words, children should learn the sets of factors which produce
the following products:

30	40	54	63	72	81
32	42	56	64		
36	45				
	48				
	49				

Some of the multiplication facts can be fixed through the use of
unique techniques. Let us take the nines facts, for instance. One
can readily see from the table that in sets of nines the number in the
ones place decreases by 1 while the number in the tens place increases
by 1 and that the sum of the digits is 9. This latter fact is substan-
tiated by the excess-of-nines rule which has been explained elsewhere;
a number is divisible by nine if the sum of its digits is divisible by nine,
and conversely, if the excess of nines is zero then the number is exactly
divisible by 9. However, when one is groping for the product of
7 × 9 he can't take time to run through the whole table of nines so

that he might make use of this truth.   Since 9 × 7 has the same product as 7 × 9 we will approach the former multiplication example through the latter.   We know that 7 × 9 must be less then 7 × 10. Since 9 is one less than 10, the product of 7 × 9 must be 7 less than the product of 7 × 10, or 70 − 7 which is 63.

```
000000000X  10 − 1
000000000X  10 − 1
000000000X  10 − 1
000000000X  10 − 1      7 × 9 = 7 × (10 − 1) = 70 − 7 = 63
000000000X  10 − 1
000000000X  10 − 1
000000000X  10 − 1
─────────  ──────
  70 − 7    70 − 7
```

Then from this explanation 3 nines must be less then 3 tens or in turn must be less than 30.   So 9 threes must be less then 30, or shall we say in the twenties.   Then 5 nines or 9 fives must be in the forties, and the digit in the one's place must, when added to the digit in the tens place, give a sum of 9.

Thus 9 × 6 must be in the fifties: 9 × 6 = 5_   (four,...to make 9)
And 9 × 8 must be in the seventies: 9 × 8 = 7_   (two,...to make 9)

It should be apparent that when the multiplier is 9 the digit in the tens place is one less then the single-digit multiplicand: 9 × 4 = 3 tens + 6 ones.

This fact can be further illustrated by use of the number line from 1 to 10.   If we want to multiply any number by 9, we cover it up so as to count the number of numerals to the left of it and the number of numerals to the right of it.   Let us multiply 4 by 9.   We place our finger over the 4 and then count the digits to the left of 4—there will be *three* of them—and the number of numerals to the right of 4—there will be *six* of them.   Therefore the product is 36.

$$1\ 2\ 3\ \boxed{4}\ 5\ 6\ 7\ 8\ 9\ 10$$
$$\quad\ 3\qquad\qquad 6$$

In early civilizations man counted on his fingers.   We have every reason to believe that he also performed multiplication facts on his fingers.   Historians tell us that man learned his multiplication facts through 5 × 5 and then used his fingers to help him learn the harder facts. He numbered his thumbs 6, the first fingers 7, the middle fingers 8, the fourth fingers 9 and the little fingers 10. If he wanted to know the product of 7 times 8 he placed the 7 finger of one hand against the 8 finger of the other hand. He closed the fingers below. Then the sum of the fingers exposed was used as the digit in the tens place and the product of the closed fingers was used as the digit in the ones place. Thus 7 × 8 is equal to 50 + 6. The illustration given here illustrates the product of 8 × 8.

The product of 8 × 8 is 64

3 fingers exposed   3 fingers exposed 3 + 3 = 6
2 fingers closed   2 fingers closed 2 × 2 = 4

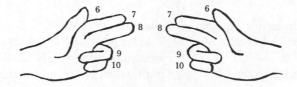

3.3 The Multiplication Algorism

After one has mastered the primary multiplication facts he is ready to perform more difficult multiplications involving multi-digit numbers. The first of these compound multiplications will involve multiplying a two-digit number by a single-digit number, an operation which can be shown by use of the addition algorism. Should the problem ask one to find the cost of 3 loaves of bread at 23 cents a loaf he can find the cost by using addition. The addend is 23 cents used three times. In other words we add the 3 threes and the 3 twenties and the algorism can be shown in any one of several ways.

23 cents	(20 + 3) cents	2 dimes + 3 pennies	(20 + 3) cents
23 cents	(20 + 3) cents	2 dimes + 3 pennies	(20 + 3) cents
23 cents	(20 + 3) cents	2 dimes + 3 pennies	(20 + 3) cents

$$
\begin{array}{cccc}
2\,d + 3\,p & (20 + 3)\text{ cents} & \begin{array}{cc}\text{tens} & \text{ones}\\ 2 & 3\end{array} & 23\text{ (cents)} \\
\times\ 3 & \times\ 3 & \times\ 3 & \times\ 3 \\
\end{array}
$$

The number 23 is a compound number and each of its component parts must be multiplied by 3. Thus both the 20 and the 3 must be multiplied by 3—the distributive law in operation. The student may think of "3 twenties and 3 threes," or 60 and 9 for 69.

$$\begin{array}{r} 23 \\ \times\ 3 \\ \hline 60 \\ 9 \\ \hline 69 \end{array} \qquad 3 \times (20 + 3) = 60 + 9 = 69$$

The same techniques can be applied to the multiplication of a larger number by a single-digit multiplier. Let us find the total number of people attending 3 basketball games if 322 people attended each game.

$$\begin{array}{cc} 322\ \text{people} & 300 + 20 + 2 \\ \times\quad 3 & \times\ 3 \qquad 3 \times (300 + 20 + 2) \end{array}$$

hundreds	tens	ones		
3	2	2	3 hundreds 2 tens 2 ones	3×300
		$\times\ 3$	$\times\ 3$	$3 \times\ 20$
				$3 \times\ 2$

The use of any one of the above algorisms would result in a total of 966 (people).

The next type of example necessitates regrouping (or carrying) in the product; the kind of example which gives us ten or more ones in the ones place, ten or more tens in the tens place, 10 or more hundreds in the hundreds place and so on. One of this type example should suffice.

Find the product of 7×467 $7 \times (400 + 60 + 7)$

$$\begin{array}{ccc} 400 + 60 + 7 & 4\ \text{hundreds}\ 6\ \text{tens}\ 7\ \text{ones} & \begin{array}{ccc} H & T & O \\ 4 & 6 & 7 \end{array} \\ \times\ 7 & \times\ 7 & \times\ 7 \end{array}$$

The multiplications can be done in any order and then the partial products can be added. The performance of the above multiplications gives us 28 hundreds, 42 tens, and 49 ones. The student should see that when these partial products are summed some regroupings can be made; 40 of the ones become 4 tens, 40 of the tens become 4 hundreds, and 20 of the hundreds become 2 thousand.

```
400 + 60 +  7      2800      49     467
          × 7       420     420     × 7
2800 + 420 + 49      49    2800      49      7 ×   7
                                    420      7 ×  60
                                   2800      7 × 400
                                   3269      7 × 467
```

These examples clearly reveal the use of the distributive law; we see that multiplication is distributive with respect to addition.

```
      400 + 60 + 7
               × 7
           40 + 9   (7 ×   7)
        400 + 20    (7 ×  60)
   2000 + 800       (7 × 400)
   2000 + 1200 + 60 + 9 = 3269
```

Multiplication with two-digit multipliers begins naturally with the multiplier 10. It has already been established that $a \times b = b \times a$. Therefore it ought to be easy to establish the fact that $10 \times N = N \times 10$. Since a certain number of tens will by addition give a sum of tens and zero ones, it follows that any number of tens would give a product whose end term (digit in the ones place) is zero. Two tens are 20, 10 twos are 20. Four tens are 40, thus 10 fours are 40. Twelve tens are 120, thus 10 twelves are also 120. To multiply any integer by 10, rewrite the multiplicand and annex one zero.

```
    17      28      48     789    6074   40609   891000
  × 10    × 10    × 10    × 10    × 10    × 10     × 10
   170     280     480    7890   60740  406090  8910000
```

The principle just developed can now be extended to multiplications with multipliers which are powers of 10. One can multiply an integer by 100 by annexing two zeros to the right of the multiplicand; to multiply by 1000 simply annex three zeros to the right of the integral multiplicand.

```
     6      17     678    5690       19     346      6784
 × 100   × 100   × 100   × 100   × 1000  × 1000    × 1000
   600    1700   67800  569000    19000  346000   6784000
```

Multiplying a number by 11 means to use the addend 10 times and 1 more time. Thus 11 × 45 means to use 10 forty-fives and 1 more forty-five.   Since $10 \times 45 = 450$ and 1×45 is 45 then $11 \times 45 =$ 450 + 45 or 495.

$$11 \times 45 = \begin{cases} 10 \times 45 = 450 \\ 1 \times 45 = \underline{45} \\ 495 \end{cases}$$

Then to multiply 729 by 11 we simply multiply the number by 10 and add it to itself:

$$10 \times 729 = 7290$$
$$1 \times 729 = 729$$

Therefore

$$11 \times 729 = 7290 + 729 \text{ or } 8019$$

The completed algorism for 11×729 looks like this:

$$\begin{array}{r} 729 \\ \times\ 11 \\ \hline 729 \\ 7290 \\ \hline 8019 \end{array} \quad \begin{array}{l} (\ 1 \times 729) \\ (10 \times 729) \end{array}$$

Multiplication by a two-digit multiplier can be rationalized through the use of a problem of this type: If the Coca-Cola salesman delivered 12 cases of Coca-Cola containing 24 bottles each to the school cafeteria, how many bottles of Coca-Cola did he deliver?   The solution of the problem can be rationalized through the following steps:

1. 24 bottles   12 times.   That means 24 bottles 10 times and 2 more times.

$$\left.\begin{array}{l} 24 \text{ bottles} \\ 24 \end{array}\right\} 2 \text{ times}$$

$$\left.\begin{array}{l} 24 \text{ bottles} \\ 24 \\ 24 \\ 24 \\ 24 \\ 24 \\ 24 \\ 24 \\ 24 \\ 24 \end{array}\right\} 10 \text{ times}$$

10 twenty-fours and 2 twenty-fours

2.   24 bottles   and   24 bottles   48 bottles
      × 10   × 2   + 240 bottles
     240 bottles   48 bottles   288 bottles

3. The standard algorism: 24 bottles   24 bottles
                              × 12   × 12
                                48   or   48
                               240   24
                               288 bottles   288 bottles

When students see the reason for indenting the second product then the algorism might take the final form though there is nothing imperative about it; they might continue to write the solution with the zero in the second partial product.

All the teen numbers can be used as multipliers in exactly the same way. Multiply first by the number in the ones place and then add to this product the product of 10 times the given number. Thus 16×248 means 10×248 and 6×248 or $6 \times 248 + 10 \times 248$.

```
 248
× 16
1488    6 × 248   the first partial product    1488 ones
2480   10 × 248   the second partial product   248 tens or 2480 ones
3968   16 × 248   the complete product
```

In the structural pattern of multiplication examples we pass now to multiplication by even decade numbers: 20 as 2 tens, 30 as 3 tens, etc. There are two approaches to this problem: (a) using the multiplier as tens, and (b) using the number as a distinct two-digit number. In the former case we teach that 34 multiplied by 2 tens gives 68 tens, and 111 multiplied by 40 gives 444 tens since 40 is the same as 4 tens. In the latter case we teach that since the digit in the ones place in the multiplier is a zero, there are no ones to multiply by. Hence we multiply only by the digit in the tens place and write the product in the proper place, the tens place.

If one follows the technique of using the multiplier as a two-digit number, he will write the example like this:

$$\begin{array}{r} 34 \\ \times\ 20 \\ \hline \end{array}$$

and in performing the computations will immediately write a zero below the 4 since there are no ones to multiply by. Then he proceeds

to multiply by the digit in the tens place, the 2, and writes the product
in the tens column thus:

$$\begin{array}{r} 34 \\ \times\ 20 \\ \hline 0 \end{array} \qquad \begin{array}{r} 34 \\ \times\ 20 \\ \hline 680 \end{array}$$

The 6 is written in the hundreds place because tens times tens gives
hundreds (2 tens × 3 tens = 6 hundreds).   The 8 is written in the
tens place because tens times ones gives tens (2 tens × 4 ones = 8
tens).   This approach is essential for an interpretation of the general
problem of multiplying a number by any two-digit number.   Let us
multiply 56 by 48.

In the interpretation of the example we find that 56 is to be multiplied by 48, that is, it is to be used as an addend 48 times.   That is the
same as saying that 56 is to be used as an addend 40 times (multiply
by 40) and 8 times (multiply by 8).   In other words, we have 56
used 40 times and 8 times.

$$\begin{array}{r} 56 \\ \times\ 40 \\ \hline 2240 \end{array} \quad + \quad \begin{array}{r} 56 \\ \times\ 8 \\ \hline 448 \end{array} \quad = \quad \begin{array}{r} 448 \\ 2240 \\ \hline 2688 \end{array}$$

In this analysis we see that 50 and 6 are to be used 40 times and also
8 times.   In other words, it is 50 + 6 multiplied by 40 and 50 + 6
multiplied by 8.

$$\begin{array}{r} 50 +\ \ 6 \\ \times\ \ 40 \\ \hline 2000 + 240 \end{array} \qquad \begin{array}{r} 50 +\ \ 6 \\ \times\ \ 8 \\ \hline 400 + 48 \end{array}$$

In a more complicated maze of multiplications the solution might
look like this:

$$\begin{array}{r} 50 +\ \ 6 \\ 40 +\ \ 8 \\ \hline 48 \\ 400 \\ 240 \\ 2000 \\ \hline 2000 + 640 + 48 \end{array}$$

(8 sixes)
(8 fifties)
(40 sixes)
(40 fifties)
(48 fifty-sixes)

In compact form the algorism
will look like this:

$$\begin{array}{r} 56 \\ \times\ 48 \\ \hline 448 \\ 2240 \\ \hline 2688 \end{array}$$

When students learn that the second digit in the multiplier represents tens and that the partial product will be in tens, the terminal

zero in the partial product may be omitted. However, students must know why it is being omitted and must never fill in the place with any other digit. When we multiply by a tens number in the multiplier we must set the first digit of the product in the tens place. This idea must be extended and incorporated in more difficult examples involving multiplication. Let us multiply 689 by 374.

$$\begin{array}{r} 689 \\ \times\ 374 \end{array}$$ $600 + 80 + 9$ are to be multiplied by 4 and by 70 and by 300.

$$\begin{array}{r} 600 + 80 + 9 \\ \times\ 4 \\ \hline 2400 + 320 + 36 \end{array} \ = \ 2756$$

$$\begin{array}{r} 600 + 80 + 9 \\ \times\ 70 \\ \hline 42000 + 5600 + 630 \end{array} \ = \ 48230$$

$$\begin{array}{r} 600 + 80 + 9 \\ \times\ 300 \\ \hline 180000 + 24000 + 2700 \end{array} \ = \ \begin{array}{r} 206700 \\ \hline 257686 \end{array}$$

$$\begin{array}{r} 689 \\ \times\ 4 \\ \hline 2756 \end{array}$$ The most common algorism

$$\begin{array}{r} 689 \\ \times\ 70 \\ \hline 48230 \end{array}$$ $\downarrow$

$$\begin{array}{r} 689 \\ \times\ 300 \\ \hline 206700 \end{array}$$

$$\begin{array}{r} 689 \\ \times\ 374 \\ \hline 2756 \\ 4823 \\ 2067 \\ \hline 257686 \end{array}$$

EXERCISES

SET 11

1. Define: multiplicand, partial product, multiplier, associative law, distributive law.
2. Prove by a diagram that 7 groups of 4 will be the same in quantity as 4 groups of 7.
3. The table of multiplication facts which begins $3 \times 1 = 3, 3 \times 2 = 6$, $3 \times 3 = 9$ is not really the "Table of Threes." Explain.
4. Show 5 different ways (different algorisms) to find the product of 3×241.
5. Write in words the complete solution of 5×5234.
6. Select one of these forms and defend its use before the class.

$$(a)\ \begin{array}{r} 127 \\ \times\ 300 \end{array} \qquad (b)\ \begin{array}{r} 127 \\ \times\ 300 \end{array}$$

7. Defend this statement: "Never use money as a multiplier."

8. Explain: "ones times ones = ones or tens"
   "tens times tens = hundreds or thousands"
9. Multiply

4382	9164	5098	7213	6677	4288
× 57	× 68	× 34	× 76	× 85	× 29

10. Multiply

789	687	566	928	354	907
× 246	× 375	× 536	× 928	× 527	× 480

11. Multiply

42,006	209,007	314,008	23,000,045
× 208	× 1006	× 21,006	× 1,003,400

12. About how many different multiplication examples can be devised with two-digit multipliers and two-digit multiplicands?
13. Show pictorially the meaning of 7 × 0 and the meaning of 0 × 7. Interpret 0 × 0.

3.4 Other Multiplication Algorisms

For purposes of enrichment as well as general interest one might be interested in other multiplication algorisms. It is believed that the predecessor to our present multiplication algorism was the method known as the *lattice method*. The lattice was a rectangular arrangement of squares (really formed by rows and columns) each of which was cut by a diagonal from right to left (with a positive slope). The multiplicand was written as a row of numerals across the top of the lattice and the multiplier was written along the right-hand side. The products of the separate factors were obtained and written in the corresponding square with the numeral representing ones written below the diagonal and the digit representing tens written above the diagonal. Thus 6 × 7 would be shown in the lattice as

Now when all of the multiplications have been performed the final product is obtained by adding the digits in the diagonals beginning with the diagonal in the lower right-hand corner and adding the numerals in the diagonals until all of the additions have been performed. Numerals are carried into the next diagonal row of numerals. The numerals thus obtained, from the respective sums of the diagonals, reading from left to right, represent the product of the two given factors.

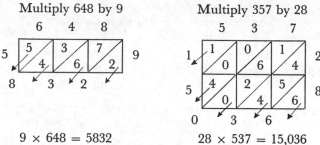

Multiply 648 by 9

$9 \times 648 = 5832$

Multiply 357 by 28

$28 \times 537 = 15,036$

Though the mechanical representation of multiplication (*à la lattice*) looks like a conglomeration of numerals, it is no more of a maze to the uninitiated than the modern algorism (with which the reader is familiar). The use of the lattice method or form is simple in its operation for it presumes only a knowledge of the primary multiplication facts and the ability to add. The use of this device makes all the operations simple ones, eliminates carrying in the internal structure of the solution, and assures proper alignment of numbers in their respective places in the partial products.

Show by use of the lattice that $375 \times 479 = 179,625$.

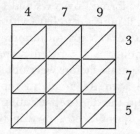

A very interesting old method of multiplication which finds some proponents even today is known as "successive doubling." It is based on the principle that every number can be expressed as the sum of powers of 2. Thus $3 = 2^1 + 2^0$, $9 = 2^3 + 2^0$, and $24 = 2^4 + 2^3$. (The student should recall that $2^0 = 1$.) Thus $78 = 64 + 8 + 4 + 2$ while 79 is just 1 more than that. This is precisely the problem of expressing numbers in base two.

Let us make use of this principle by multiplying 12×23.
We begin with 1×23 which is 23.
Then we find 2×23 which is 46.
Then we find 4×23 which is 92.
Then we find 8×23 which is 184.

Now since we want to find 12 times 23 we add the last two products: 92 + 184 or 276.

You see $4 \times 23 = \ \ 92$
and $8 \times 23 = 184$
Therefore $12 \times 23 = 276.$

Let us show how to multiply 37 by any number from 1 up to 37. Write 37 and then keep doubling the products in succession.

37	(1×37)	$3 \times 37 = \begin{cases} 37 \\ + 74 \\ \hline 111 \end{cases}$	$6 \times 37 = \begin{cases} 74 \\ + 148 \\ \hline 222 \end{cases}$
74	(2×37)		
148	(4×37)		
296	(8×37)	$5 \times 37 = \begin{cases} 37 \\ 148 \\ \hline 185 \end{cases}$	$7 \times 37 = \begin{cases} 37 \\ 74 \\ + 148 \\ \hline 259 \end{cases}$
592	(16×37)		
1184	(32×37)		
etc.			

Now let us skip some of the products and find 29×37. Since 29 is composed of the addends $16 + 8 + 4 + 1$ we select the corresponding factors from the column of doubled values. We select the products opposite these powers of 2, namely:

$$37 \text{ which is } \ 1 \times 37$$
$$148 \text{ which is } \ 4 \times 37$$
$$296 \text{ which is } \ 8 \times 37$$
$$\underline{592} \text{ which is } 16 \times 37$$

Now if we add we have 1073 which is 29×37.

The abbreviated form of this doubling technique is to write all of the successive doubles as far as needed and then discard or cross out all those products which are not needed. Thus to multiply 22×29 we write 29 and then proceed to double the successive results. The 1×29 and the 8×29 are not needed so these are discarded. We add 58, 116, and 464 for a total of 638. Thus $22 \times 29 = 638$.

1×29	29	~~29~~
2×29	58	58
4×29	116	116
8×29	232	~~232~~
16×29	464	$\underline{464}$
$(2 + 4 + 16 = 22)$		
22×29	=	638

A method analogous to the one just described, based on expressing a number as the sum of powers of two, is referred to as the Russian method. It consists of halving the multiplier (ignoring remainders) and doubling the multiplicand. Thus to multiply 22 × 29 we write the factors in two columns and take half of the multiplier (writing only integral quotients) and double the multiplicand.

$$22 \times 29 = \begin{array}{l} 22 \\ 11 \\ 5 \\ 2 \\ 1 \end{array} \left| \begin{array}{l} 29 \rightarrow \text{corresponds to } \ 1 \times 29 \text{ or } 2^0 \times 29 \\ 58 \rightarrow \text{corresponds to } \ 2 \times 29 \text{ or } 2^1 \times 29 \\ 116 \rightarrow \text{corresponds to } \ 4 \times 29 \text{ or } 2^2 \times 29 \\ 232 \rightarrow \text{corresponds to } \ 8 \times 29 \text{ or } 2^3 \times 29 \\ 464 \rightarrow \text{corresponds to } 16 \times 29 \text{ or } 2^4 \times 29 \end{array} \right.$$

Since 22 is composed of $16 + 4 + 2$ or $2^4 + 2^2 + 2^1$ we add the numbers in the second column which correspond to the respective products of these powers of two times the multiplicand, 29. We add

$$\begin{array}{ll} 58 & (\underline{2} \times 29) \\ 116 & (\underline{4} \times 29) \\ 464 & (\underline{16} \times 29) \\ \hline 638 \end{array}$$

To summarize this method we can presume that the ancient belief of even numbers being evil is still operative and we can cross out terms in the rows having even numbers in the first column. Thus in the above example we would cross out the rows containing the 22 and the 2 and then add the numbers remaining in the second column. Let us try this method in multiplying 29 × 33.

$$29 \times 33 = \begin{array}{l} 29 \\ 14 \\ 7 \\ 3 \\ 1 \end{array} \left| \begin{array}{l} 33 \\ 66 \text{ [half of 29 (ignoring remainder); } \text{ twice } 33] \\ 132 \text{ [half of 14;} \hspace{3.2cm} \text{twice } 66] \\ 264 \text{ [half of } 7 \text{ (ignoring remainder); } \text{ twice } 132] \\ 528 \text{ [half of } 3 \text{ (ignoring remainder); } \text{ twice } 264] \end{array} \right.$$

Now cross out the row headed by the 14; it is an even (evil) number, and add the numbers remaining in the second column. Add 33, 132, 264, and 528. The sum is 957. Therefore, 29 × 33 is 957.

Let us multiply 47 × 54 by the Russian method. The algorism would look like this:

$$47 \times 54 = \begin{array}{r} 47 \\ 23 \\ 11 \\ 5 \\ -\!-2\!-\!- \\ 1 \end{array} \left| \begin{array}{r} 54 \\ 108 \\ 216 \\ 432 \\ -864- \\ 1728 \\ \hline 2538 \end{array} \right.$$

There is an easy way of finding the product of two numbers which are both slightly less than some power of 10, that is, numbers slightly smaller than 10, 100, 1000, etc. This method is known as the "complement" method.* The complement of a number is the difference between the number and the next larger power of 10. Thus the complement of 7 is 3, the complement of 92 is 8, the complement of 987 is 13, etc. If we want to find the product of 7 × 8 by the complement method we write the factors and their complements as follows:

$$
\begin{array}{r}
8 \ - \ 2 \\
\times \ 7 \ - \ 3 \\
\end{array}
$$

Now we multiply the complements to obtain a numeral for the ones place, 3 × 2 = 6, and then subtract either complement from the numeral of which it is not the complement, that is, 3 from 8 or 2 from 7 for the numeral in the tens place. Thus the product of 7 × 8 is 56.

The product of 98 × 97 by the complement method would present the following algorism:

$$
\begin{array}{r}
97 \ - \ 3 \\
\times \ 98 \ - \ 2 \\
\hline
0 \ 6 \quad 2 \times 3 = 6 \\
95 \qquad 98 - 3 = 95 \ (\text{or } 97 - 2 = 95)
\end{array}
$$

Since there will be four places in the product we must insert a zero in the tens place; hence the product is 9506.

Examples:

$$
\begin{array}{r}
93 \ - \ 7 \\
\times \ 92 \ - \ 8 \\
\hline
8556
\end{array}
\qquad
\begin{array}{r}
99 \ - \ 1 \\
\times \ 94 \ - \ 6 \\
\hline
9306
\end{array}
\qquad
\begin{array}{r}
88 \ - \ 12 \\
\times \ 89 \ - \ 11 \\
\hline
(7700 + 132) \\
7832
\end{array}
\qquad
\begin{array}{r}
994 \ - \ 6 \\
\times \ 997 \ - \ 3 \\
\hline
991018
\end{array}
\qquad
\begin{array}{r}
999 \ - \ 1 \\
\times \ 999 \ - \ 1 \\
\hline
998001
\end{array}
$$

If two numbers are slightly more than a power of 10, their product can be obtained easily by what is called the "supplement" method. The supplement of a number is the difference between that number and the nearest (lower) power of 10. Thus the supplement of 12 is 2, of 111 is 11, of 1009 is 9, and so on. Let us multiply 12 × 13 by the

*The complement method is explained in Section 2.16.

supplement method.   The supplement of 12 is 2, of 13 is 3.   Write the numbers and their supplements:

$$
\begin{array}{r}
13 \;-\; 3 \\
\times\, 12 \;-\; 2 \\
\hline
\end{array}
$$

Multiply the supplements to obtain the digit of the ones place; add one of the supplements to the other number and write this sum in the tens place.   You should get 156. $(2 \times 3 = 6,\; 12 + 3 = 15)$. Find the product of 103×103.   In each case the supplement is 3. Thus we add 3 to 103 to get 106 and we multiply 3×3 to get 9. We know that 100×100 gives us a 5 place number so we must insert a zero between the 106 and the 9; our answer or product is 10609. To multiply 106 by 109 we write the numbers with their supplements:

$$
\begin{array}{r}
106 \;-\; 6 \\
\times\, 109 \;-\; 9 \\
\hline
\end{array}
$$

9×6 is 54, write 54. $109 + 6$ and $106 + 9$ are both 115.   Therefore the product of 109×106 is 11554.   (We know the product is a five-digit numeral.)

$$
\begin{array}{rrr}
104 \;-\; 4 & \qquad 107 \;-\; 7 & \qquad 113 \;-\; 13 \\
\times\, 106 \;-\; 6 & \qquad \times\, 103 \;-\; 3 & \qquad \times\, 107 \;-\; 7 \\
\hline
\end{array}
$$

Occasionally we have for a multiplier a number whose tens digit is a multiple of the ones digit such as the numbers 42, 63, and 84. When such is the case the multiplications become easy, for the second partial product is a multiple of the first partial product.   When one multiplies 768 by 42 he first multiplies by 2 and sets the partial product, 1536.   Then since the number in the tens place, 4, is twice the digit in the ones place, the second partial product is twice the first partial product (in tens, of course)..   Then instead of multiplying the 768 by 4 we simply multiply 1536 by 2 and set this product in the proper place.   Then we add the partial products.

$$
\begin{array}{r}
7\;6\;8 \\
\times\; 4\;2 \\
\hline
1\;5\;3\;6 \\
3\;0\;7\;2 \\
\hline
3\;2\;2\;5\;6
\end{array}
\qquad
\begin{array}{l}
\\
\\
2 \times 768 \\
2 \times 1536 \text{ (in tens, of course)}
\end{array}
$$

A second example:

```
  6 9 8          6 9 8
× 9 6 3        × 9 6 3
               ───────
                2 0 9 4      3 ×   698
              4 1 8 8        2 × 2094
            6 2 8 2          3 × 2094
            ───────────
            6 7 2 1 7 4
```

When the multiplier contains multiples of some number already a part of the multiplier but in mixed-up order, the system will still work but careful attention must be given to the correct placement of the partial products. The proper alignment of the partial products presents the only serious problem.   Multiply 579 by 428.

```
                                              5 7 9
                                            × 4 2 8
                                            ───────
2 × 579 = 1128; an answer in tens           1 1 5 8
4 × 579 or 2 × 1158; answer in hundreds    2 3 1 6
8 × 579 or 2 × 2316; answer in ones          4 6 3 2
                                           ───────────
                                           2 4 7 8 1 2
```

Sometimes when multiplying by a two-digit number it is convenient to factor the multiplier into two or more single-digit multipliers and then perform the multiplications.   If one needed to find the product of 16 × 45, he could arrive at the answer in one of several ways. He might first multiply 45 by 4 and then that product by 4 again, for 16 is equivalent to 4 × 4.   If one wished to multiply any number by 48, he could multiply first by 6 and then by 8, or he could multiply successively by 2, 2, 3, and 4 or by any combination of multipliers which makes 48.   To multiply by 49, multiply first by 7 and then by 7 again.   This method of multiplying by single-digit factors of a given multiplier simplifies the algorism and makes it possible for one to arrive at the answer with little or no pencil and paper work.

3.5 Relationships Inherent in the Multiplication Operation

It is desirable to know something about the relative size of the product of two or more numbers before the multiplications are performed. In the solution of a real problem situation involving multiplication (or any other process for that matter) we suggest that the student first estimate the answer. This will be easy to do if the student knows something about the size of the product in relation to the factors involved in producing that product. Therefore, let us discuss this situation briefly. If one multiplies a single-digit number by a single-digit number the product will contain either one digit or two digits. The smallest single-digit non-zero number is 1. 1 × 1 is 1. The largest single-digit number is 9. Therefore the largest possible product of two one-digit numbers is 9 × 9 or 81.

The smallest two-digit number is 10. Therefore the smallest possible product of the 2 two-digit numbers is 100. The largest two-digit number is 99 and the product of 99 × 99 is 9801. The smallest three-digit number is 100 and the largest is 999. Then the product of 2 three-digit numbers will range between 100 × 100, or 10,000, and 999 × 999, or 998,001. A comparison of the size of the products with the number of digits in the multipliers or factors reveals that the number of digits in the product is either equal to or is one less than the sum of the number of digits in the multipliers. Then the product of 2 one-digit numbers will produce a product with either 2 digits or 1 digit, the product of 2 two-digit numbers will produce a number with either 4 or 3 digits, the product of 2 three-digit numbers will produce a product with either 6 or 5 digits, and so on.

The student ought to be able to demonstrate the more general law that the number of digits in the product of any two numbers is equal to or is one less then the combined number of digits in the factors. Thus the product of 17 × 456 will produce either a 5- or a 4-digit number. What can you tell about the product of 1045 × 7056?

This fact will be extremely useful in helping to position the decimal point when multiplying decimal fractions. Thus 20.3 × 40.3 ought to be in the neighborhood of 800 for 20 × 40 is 800, and 5000.27 × 26.8 ought to have six places to the left of the decimal point in the product. Also this fact gives reason for the "grouping by twos" phase of the square-root process. The converse of the principle states that if the square of a number contains four places then the square root contains two and if the number contains seven places then the square root contains four.

There are many other relationships which exist between the factors and their product and a few of them will be discussed here. The serious student of arithmetic ought to be able to add to this set, all of whose examples illustrate the principle that if $a \times b = c$ then $ma \times nb = mnc$.

1. If the multiplicand remains constant and the multiplier increases, then the product grows larger.

68	68	68	68
× 2	× 13	× 47	× 98

2. If the multiplier remains constant and the multiplicand increases, then the product grows larger.

12	19	39	78
× 14	× 14	× 14	× 14

3. If the multiplicand is doubled while the multiplier remains constant, then the product is doubled.

22	44
× 4	× 4

The ratio between the products is 1 to 2.

4. If both the multiplicand and the multiplier are doubled then the product will be four times as great.

8	16
× 3	× 6

The ratio between the products is 1 to 4.

5. If the multiplier is doubled while the multiplicand remains constant, then the product is doubled.

17	17
× 3	× 6

The ratio between the products is 1 to 2.

6. If both the multiplier and the multiplicand are tripled, then the product is multiplied by 9.

11	33
× 10	× 30

The ratio between the products is 1 to 9.

7. If either the multiplicand or the multiplier is halved while the other remains constant, then the product will be halved.

66	33
× 10	× 10

The ratio is 1 to $\frac{1}{2}$.

8. If both of the factors in a multiplication example are halved, the new product will be one-fourth as great.

$$\begin{array}{cc} 44 & 22 \\ \times\,8 & \times\,4 \end{array}$$

The ratio is 1 to $\frac{1}{4}$.

9. If one of the factors is doubled while the other one is halved, then the product remains unchanged.

$$\begin{array}{cc} 40 & 80 \\ \times\,8 & \times\,4 \end{array}$$

The ratio is 1 to 1.

10. If the multiplier is 1, then the product is the same as the multiplicand. $1 \times N = N$. This is called the *identity* element in multiplication.

11. If one of the two factors is tripled and the other is divided by 3, the product remains unchanged.

$$112 \quad \text{is the same as} \quad 336$$
$$\times\,9 \qquad\qquad\qquad \times\,3$$

3.6 Checks in Multiplication

Since we have accepted the basic principle known as the commutative law in multiplication we can check our multiplication examples by performing the multiplications in reverse; that is, we can interchange the multiplier and the multiplicand.   The product of 27 × 34 is the same as the product of 34 × 27.   If we want to find the total number of pupils in the 27 classrooms containing on the average 34 pupils each, we multiply 27 times 34 (pupils).

$$\begin{array}{r} 34 \text{ (pupils)} \\ \times\,27 \\ \hline 238 \\ 68 \\ \hline 918 \text{ (pupils)} \end{array}$$

This would give us the same number of pupils as if we had 34 classrooms with 27 pupils in each room.   If we obtain the same product we shall assume that the original answer is correct.

It should be apparent that in the performance of the multiplications the same multiplication facts present themselves but in reverse order; there are different partial products to add, however.

A second method for checking multiplication examples is by use of the division process, which has not been discussed up to this point. In passing, let it be said that the product, divided by either of the given factors of a multiplication example produces the other. If $9 \times 12 = 108$, then 108 divided either by 9 or by 12 will produce the other factor. In the example given above, if we divide 918 by 27 and obtain 34 for the result, then we will assume that the original product is correct.

The excess-of-nines check which was so carefully explained in the chapter on addition is applicable to the checking of multiplication examples. The excess of nines in the product should be equal to the excess of nines in the product of the excesses in the factors. In other words, if $a \times b = c$ then the excess of nines in c should be equal to the excess of nines in a times the excess of nines in b. Let us prove or check a multiplication example by the use of this principle.

```
  4 2 6    the excess of nines is 3        3
× 4 7    the excess of nines is 2      × 2
2 9 8 2                                   6
1 7 0 4                                    |
2 0 0 2 2  the excess of nines is 6—Check
```

When the multiplications are completed we should find the excess of nines in the multiplicand and the multiplier and then in their product. Then we should find the excess of nines in the original product, and if the two products agree we shall be reasonably sure of accuracy in the original multiplication.

The excess-of-elevens check which has been discussed elsewhere can also serve us as a means of checking our multiplication examples. We find the excess of elevens in the multiplicand and the excess of elevens in the multiplier. Then we find the product of these excesses. We then find the excess of elevens in the original product and if the two numbers agree we assume accuracy. Example:

```
  2 4 3 8    excess of elevens (12 − 5) 7      7
× 1 5 7    excess of elevens ( 8 − 5) 3    × 3
1 7 0 6 6                                   21  excess of
1 2 1 9 0                                       elevens is
2 4 3 8                                          10
3 8 2 7 6 6
```

The student should show that the excess of elevens in the product is also 10.

EXERCISES

SET 12

1. Solve by the lattice method: 47 × 642, 746 × 839, 435 × 8376.
2. Why has the lattice method as an algorism become obsolete?
3. Show how to find 4 × 5 on a number line.   Also 9 × 3 and 3 × 8.
4. Find the products of the following by the successive doubling technique:

    11 × 18   17 × 63   21 × 79   37 × 43

5. Do the following by the Russian method:

    13 × 52   43 × 91   34 × 111   20 × 816

6. Multiply the following by the complementary method:

    92 × 93   94 × 96   98 × 98   97 × 96   89 × 89

7. Perform the following multiplications by the supplementary method:

    103 × 107   102 × 106   104 × 105   108 × 109   111 × 112

8. Multiply using only 2 as a multiplier:

234	678	1123	5640
× 842	× 428	× 284	× 248

9. Multiply using only 3 as a multiplier:

574	326	4111	12120	40107
× 93	× 93	× 39	× 9393	× 2793

10. Determine the number of digits in the following products:

    13 × 36 ____   12 × 143 ____   234 × 234 ____
    42 × 91 ____   76 × 421 ____   608 × 709 ____
    76 × 48 ____   31 × 168 ____   213 × 615 ____

    Also estimate the products by rounding each number off to one non-zero digit.

11. What happens to the product if
    (a) both the multiplier and multiplicand are multiplied by 4?
    (b) both the multiplier and multiplicand are multiplied by 5?
    (c) the multiplicand is increased by 100?
    (d) the multiplier is increased by 100?
    (e) the multiplier is increased by 1?
    (f) the multiplicand is doubled and the multiplier is halved?
    (g) the multiplier is decreased by itself?

12. Write out a story problem (a real one) in which there is a one-digit multiplicand and a three-digit multiplier.   Solve the problem.

13. Check all the examples in exercise No. 8 by the excess-of-nines check.

14. Check all the examples in exercise No. 9 by the excess-of-elevens check.

15. Discuss the use of the complementary method in 81 × 84, 76 × 83, and the use of the supplementary method in 117 × 118 and 123 × 126.

3.7 Multiplication in Other Bases

The principles of multiplication which have just been described for use in the decimal scale are equally applicable for multiplications which are performed in any scale. If a student understands the synthesis process and the multiplication operation concomitant with it then he ought to have little difficulty in performing multiplications of numbers in bases different from ten. Since multiplication is another form of addition, it, too, can be represented linearly. When one is asked to find the sum of 4 threes he can lay off these 4 threes along a number line which has been scaled to a base of ten. Then he would arrive at the number 12 marked on the horizontal scale and would conclude that 4 threes are the same as 12. Likewise, should one wish to find the product of 4 threes when the base is different from ten, say six, then he would lay off a distance of 3 ones four times along a scale whose base is six. Then he would arrive at the number delineated thereon as 20 and would conclude that 4 threes are the same as 2 sixes.

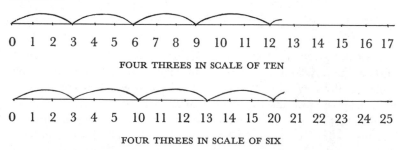

0 1 2 3 4 5 6 7 8 9 10 11 12 13 14 15 16 17

FOUR THREES IN SCALE OF TEN

0 1 2 3 4 5 10 11 12 13 14 15 20 21 22 23 24 25

FOUR THREES IN SCALE OF SIX

The use of the latter line diagram will enable us to ascertain all of the threes facts (primary combinations, that is) in the scale of six. We see that:

$$0 \times 3 = 0 \qquad 1 \times 3 = 3 \qquad 2 \times 3 = 10$$
$$3 \times 3 = 13 \qquad 4 \times 3 = 20 \qquad 5 \times 3 = 23$$

Since we are interested only in the primary combinations—the products of single-digit numbers—we have exhausted all the possibilities of single-digit multiples of 3 in the base six. What is six times 3 in the base six?

If one were working for any length of time in a particular base it would be desirable to learn the primary multiplication facts associated with that base. For instance, if one were to perform multiplications in the base seven he would have to become very well acquainted with the following facts, or at least have the table available for ready reference.

×	0	1	2	3	4	5	6
0	0	0	0	0	0	0	0
1	0	1	2	3	4	5	6
2	0	2	4	6	11	13	15
3	0	3	6	12	15	21	24
4	0	4	11	15	22	26	33
5	0	5	13	21	26	34	42
6	0	6	15	24	33	42	51

PRIMARY MULTIPLICATION AND DIVISION
FACTS IN BASE SEVEN

If we are given two factors (multipliers) in base seven we find one of them in a row and the other one in a column. Then we enter the table via the row and the column to the cell which is common to both the given row and the given column. Thus if we want to know the product of 4×3 we enter the row containing the number 4 and the column headed by the number 3. The cell common to both the row and column contains the numeral 15. Thus $4 \times 3 = 15$ (seven). From the table does $5 \times 2 = 2 \times 5$? Does $5 \times 6 = 6 \times 5$? Compare 3×4 with 6×2. How many sets of factors have a product of 22? What is the square of 6 in base seven?

Let us apply the multiplication facts, base seven, in more difficult situations. Let us multiply a three-digit number by a single digit. The example: 5×342
The algorism:

Base²	Base	Ones
$(7)^2$	(7)	(1)
3	4	2
		$\times 5$

5 × 2 = 13: write 3, carry 1 seven
5 × 4 = 26: add in 1. This makes 30. Write 0, carry 3
    (the 3 means 3 seven-sevens).
5 × 3 = 21: add in 3. This makes 24. Write 4, carry 2
    (the 2 means $2 - 7^3$).

The completed solution will look like this:

$$\begin{array}{r} 3\ 4\ 2 \\ \times\ 5 \\ \hline 2\ 4\ 0\ 3 \end{array}$$

Let us show another version or thought pattern of a similiar example. We will do all the multiplications first and then the necessary regrouping. Multiply 3325 by 6 in the base seven.

7^3	7^2	7	1	Place values
3	3	2	5	Multiplicand
			× 6	
24	24	15	42	Partial products

2	2	4		
24	24	15	42	Regrouping
26	26	22	42	

| 2 | 6 | 6 | 2 | 2 | Product |

If the student has mastered the principles and the operations involved in doing the preceding multiplication examples he should encounter little or no difficulty in doing more difficult examples. Let us multiply 1435 by 23 in the base seven.

1 4 3 5	3 5's are 21. Write 1, carry 2.
	3 3's are 12, add 2 and obtain 14. Write 4, carry 1.
× 2 3	3 4's are 15, add 1 and obtain 16. Write 6, carry 1.
4 6 4 1	3 1's are 3, add 1 and obtain 4. Write 4.
3 2 0 3	2 5's are 13. Write 3, carry 1.
	2 3's are 6, add 1 and obtain 10. Write 0, carry 1.
	2 4's are 11, add 1 and obtain 12. Write 2, carry 1.
	2 1's are 2, add 1 and obtain 3. Write 3.
4 0 0 0 1	Now show that the addition of the partial products gives 40001.

The check which is most frequently used for proving multiplications done in non-decimal scales is the reversal of the factors; we interchange both the multiplier and the multiplicand and perform the operation again.   If we obtain the same product we will assume that the original answer is correct.   Another desirable method for checking multiplication examples is the one-number check or the "base less one" check.   This rule is comparable to the rule of casting out nines when the base is ten.   Thus in the preceding example we could prove our work by casting out sixes.   If we do this we will be able to cast out the 1 and the 5 in the multiplicand, add the 4 and 3, and find an excess of 1 in the multiplicand.   If we add the digits in the multiplier we obtain 5 which is the excess of sixes in the multiplier.   The product of these two excesses is 5 × 1 or 5.   Now we find the excess of sixes, 4 + 1, in the product and since this is also 5 we shall assume that the original product is correct.

We used another check for proving multiplications in base ten known as the "base plus one" check.   When the examples were done in base 10 we found the excess of elevens.   Now when the base is seven we can use the same rules or procedure for finding the excess of eights.   This method involves finding the sum of the digits in the odd-numbered places and subtracting the sum of the digits in the even-numbered places.   We will use this rule for finding the excess of eights in the terms of the example above.   The excess of eights in the multiplicand is $(4 + 5) - (1 + 3)$ which equals 5.   The excess of eights in the multiplier is $(3 - 2)$ or 1.   Then 1×5 is 5.   Now we examine the product and ascertain the excess of eights in it.   We find this to be 5 also, for $1 + 0 + 4 = 5$ and $0 + 0$ is 0 and so $5 - 0$ is 5.   Therefore we assume that the original product is correct.

It is also possible to check multiplication examples by division. Since the multiplication of two numbers yields a product, then the product divided by either one of them should yield the other.   The use of this procedure for checking will be reserved until we have discussed the division operation.

Examples:

42	435	623
× 5 (seven)	× 5 (eight)	× 8 (nine)

426	2342	2233
× 7 (eight)	× 6 (seven)	× 4 (six)

3.8 Short Cuts in Multiplication

Occasionally it is possible and convenient to employ a short method of operation or short cut to obtain the product in a multiplication example thereby eliminating the laborious computation.   Some of the more common ones are given here.

1. *To multiply a number by* 10, *a power of* 10, *or a multiple of* 10. Multiply the given number by the non-zero part of the multiplier (the numeral exclusive of the terminal zeros) and annex as many zeros to the product as there are in the multiplier.   In other words, when we multiply by 10 or a power of 10 the digits take places farther to the left.   We often hear it said, quite erroneously, "Move the decimal point" in connection with this type of example.   The decimal point does not move; it is always located directly behind the ones digit; it's the digits which move when one multiplies by 10, 100, 300, or 3000.

Illustrations: $10 \times 34 = 340$ $2010 \times 18 = 36180$
$100 \times 27 = 2700$ $1100 \times 13 = 14300$
$300 \times 13 = 3900$ $201000 \times 245 = 49245000$

In other words we multiply by the number represented by all the digits except the terminal zeros, then we annex zeros to the product equal in number to the number of terminal zeros in the multiplier.   In 2305000×1732 we multiply 1732 by 2305 and then annex three zeros to the product.   Sometimes both the multiplicand and multiplier are multiples of 10, in which case we also multiply the non-zero parts and annex as many zeros as there are (terminal zeros, that is) in the two factors combined.   In 1200×1300 we multiply 12 times 13 for 156 and then annex 4 zeros.   The product is 1,560,000.

2. *To multiply a number by* 5, 50, 500 *or* 5×10^n.   Since 5 is one-half of 10, we multiply the given number by 10 and then take one-half of it.   Since 50 is $\dfrac{100}{2}$ we can multiply the given number by $\dfrac{100}{2}$ instead of by 50.   Since 500 is half of 1000 we can multiply by $\dfrac{1000}{2}$ when multiplying by 500.

Illustrations: $5 \times 76 = \frac{1}{2} \times 10 \times 76$ $= 380$
$50 \times 88 = \frac{1}{2} \times 100 \times 88$ $= 4400$
$500 \times 84 = \frac{1}{2} \times 1000 \times 84$ $= 42,000$
$5000 \times 23 = \frac{1}{2} \times 10,000 \times 23 = 115,000$

3. *To multiply a number by* 25, 250, 2500, *or* 25 × 10^n. Since 25 is one-fourth of 100, we multiply the given number by 100 and then take one-fourth of it. Since $250 = \dfrac{1000}{4}$ we can multiply the given number by $\dfrac{1000}{4}$ instead of by 250. Since 2500 is one-fourth of 10,000 we can multiply by $\dfrac{10,000}{4}$ when multiplying by 2500.

Illustrations:
$$25 \times 44 = \tfrac{1}{4} \times 100 \times 44 = 1100$$
$$250 \times 812 = \tfrac{1}{4} \times 1000 \times 812 = 203,000$$
$$2500 \times 1648 = \tfrac{1}{4} \times 10,000 \times 1648 = 4,120,000$$

The student should observe that the use of the commutative law suggests that the fractional part of the multiplicand should be found first and then this product multiplied by the power of 10.   In the most condensed form we can say for problems of this type, "Take a fractional part of the multiplicand and then annex the necessary number of zeros."

4. *To multiply a number by* 75, 750, 7500, *or* 75 × 10^n. Since 75 is three-fourths of 100, we multiply the given number by 100 and then take three-fourths of it. Since 750 is $\dfrac{3 \times 1000}{4}$ we can multiply the given number by $\dfrac{3 \times 1000}{4}$ instead of by 750. Since 7500 is three-fourths of 10,000 we can multiply by $\dfrac{3 \times 10,000}{4}$ when multiplying by 7500.

Illustrations:
$$75 \times 12 = \tfrac{3}{4} \times 100 \times 12 = 900$$
$$750 \times 416 = \tfrac{3}{4} \times 1000 \times 416 = 312,000$$
$$7500 \times 484 = \tfrac{3}{4} \times 10,000 \times 484 = 3,630,000$$

5. *To multiply by* 125, 1250, 12500, *or* 125 × 10^n. Since 125 is five-fourths of 100, we multiply the given number by 100 and then take five-fourths of it. Since 1250 is $\dfrac{5 \times 1000}{4}$ we can multiply the given number by $\dfrac{5 \times 1000}{4}$ instead of by 1250. Since 12,500 is five-fourths of 10,000 we can multiply by $\dfrac{5 \times 10,000}{4}$ when multiplying by 12,500.

Illustrations:
$$125 \times 604 = \tfrac{5}{4} \times 100 \times 604 = 75,500$$
$$1250 \times 1216 = \tfrac{5}{4} \times 1000 \times 1216 = 1,520,000$$
$$12,500 \times 564 = \tfrac{5}{4} \times 10,000 \times 564 = 7,050,000$$

In the latter example we find five-fourths of 564 and annex four zeros.

6. *To multiply a number by* 9, 49, 99, 499, *etc.* Since 9 is equal to one less than 10 we multiply the given number by $10 - 1$. This is equivalent to saying that we subtract the given number from ten times the number. To multiply a number by 49 we multiply first by 50 and then subtract the given number, for we know that 49 is equal to $50 - 1$. To multiply by 99 we subtract the given number from 100 times the number. When we multiply a number by 499 we multiply first by 500 (by the short form explained above) and then subtract the number from this product. There are many other examples which can be solved in similar fashion.

Illustrations: $9 \times 19 = (10 - 1) \times 19 = 190 - 19 = 171$
$49 \times 38 = (50 - 1) \times 38 = 1900 - 38 = 1862$
$99 \times 603 = (100 - 1) \times 603 = 6030 - 603 = 5697$

7. *To multiply two teen numbers together.* The algebraic interpretation of this type of problem suggests that "the product of two binomials having a common term is equal to the square of the common term increased by the sum of the other terms multiplied by the common term plus the product of the other terms." In other words: $(a + r)(a + s) = a^2 + (r + s) \times a + r \times s$. If the numbers are both teen numbers they can both be expressed as 10 plus a single-digit number. To find their product first find the sum of the ones digits and multiply that sum by 10. Add this number to 100 and then add in the product of the digits in the ones places. To multiply 17 by 18 we first add 7 and 8 and multiply their sum by 10. This gives us 150, which we add to 100. Now we add in 56, which is the product of 7 and 8. Our final answer, 306 [150 + 100 + 56], is the product of 17×18.

Illustrations:

	16		13
	× 19		× 18
$(6 + 9) \times 10$	150	$(8 + 3) \times 10$	110
add in 100 (10×10)	100	10×10	100
9×6	54	8×3	24
	304		234

Naturally if these multiplications are written out as they are above there would be no short cut to the operation. It is assumed that these operations should be done without paper and pencil and that only the product is written.

8. *To multiply by a composite number.*   If a number can be broken up into the product of sets of multipliers then the desired product can be obtained by multiplying the multiplicand by these single-digit numbers in any order.   Thus to multiply by 15 we might first multiply by 3 and then that product by 5.   To multiply by 28 we might first multiply by 4 and then by 7.   To multiply by 12 we might first multiply by 6 and then double that product.   There are innumerable examples of this type.

Illustrations: $35 \times 223 = 5 \times 7 \times 233 = 5 \times 1631 =$ 8155
$48 \times 123 = 6 \times 8 \times 123 = 6 \times \ 984 =$ 5904
$45 \times 234 = 5 \times 9 \times 234 = 5 \times 2106 = 10{,}530$

9. *To multiply 2 two-digit numbers ending in* 5.   The principles outlined here will be an extension of those given in short cut No. 7. Now we have a special case in which both the digits in the ones places are 5.   Thus each of the digits in the tens places will be multiplied by 5.   This is equivalent to saying that we must find the sum of the digits in the tens places and then multiply by 5.   (To multiply by 5 we take half of the multiplicand and express that number as tens.) Now we multiply this product by 10.   Multiply the digits in the tens places and express this number as hundreds.   Now 5×5 is 15. We add three terms: the cross products, the product of the tens digits, and the 25.   The rule can now be restated in simpler terms; namely, take half the sum of the tens digits and express this amount as hundreds, then add the product of the tens digits also expressed in hundreds, and then add 25.   It will be noted that if half the sum of the tens digits is integral the required product will end in 25 and if non-integral the product will end in 75.

Illustrations:

	45		85		85
	× 35		× 65		× 25
$\frac{1}{2}(4+3)$ in 100's	350	$\frac{1}{2}(6+8)$ in 100's	700	$\frac{1}{2}(2+8)$ in 100's	500
3×4 in 100's	1200	6×8 in 100's	4800	2×8 in 100's	1600
5×5	25	5×5	25	5×5	25
	1575		5525		2125

10.   *To multiply a two-digit number by* 11.   To multiply by 11 is equivalent to multiplying by 10 and by 1 and adding the results. When this is done the only addition performed with the partial products is the addition of the two given digits.   This new sum becomes the digit in the tens place and the digit originally in the

tens place is now in the hundreds place. In other words, add the two digits together and insert their sum between the two given digits. If the sum is more than 9 write only the ones digit between them and increase the original tens digit by one (carrying) for the new number in the hundreds place.

Illustrations:

$$34 \times 11$$
$$3 + 4 = 7 \quad \overline{3(7)4}$$

Insert 7 between 3 and 4.
$$11 \times 34 = 374$$

$$72 \times 11$$
$$7 + 2 = 9 \quad \overline{7(9)2}$$

Insert 9 between 7 and 2.
$$11 \times 72 = 792$$

$$59 \times 11$$
$$5 + 9 = 14 \quad \overline{5(14)9} = 649$$

Insert 14. Write 4, carry 1.
$$11 \times 59 = 649$$

11. *To multiply a large number by* 11. Since multiplying a number by 11 gives one the original digits in combinations or sums all we need to do is to add some of the digits in some order and write them in some order. This order is as follows: To the given number prefix a zero to the left and annex a zero to the right. Now add the digits in pairs beginning at the far right and proceeding to the left. The new alignment of digits will represent 11 times the original number.

Illustrations:

$$4236 \times 11$$

0 4 2 3 6 0
4 6 5 9 6

$$28754 \times 11$$

0 2 8 7 5 4 0
3 1 6 2 9 4

12. *To multiply two numbers which are both slightly less than or more than some power of* 10. In section 3.4 the reader will find reference to the "complement" method and the "supplement" method of multiplication. Use the complement method for finding the product of 97 by 96 and the supplement method for finding products of numbers like 107 × 105.

Illustrations:

$$97 \quad \text{complement is 3}$$
$$\times\ 96 \quad \text{complement is 4}$$
$$(96 - 3 = 93); \ (4 \times 3 = 12)$$
Product is 9312

$$105 \quad \text{supplement is 5}$$
$$\times\ 107 \quad \text{supplement is 7}$$
$$(107 + 5 = 112); \ (7 \times 5 = 35)$$
Product is 11235

13. *To multiply two numbers together, one of which is a decimal fraction, when it is convenient to make a transformation.* Though the topic

of decimal fractions has not been discussed, one or two suggestions relating to operations with them are given here.   We have established elsewhere that $a \times b = b \times a$.   Now it should be easy for the student to show that the cost of 2 three-cent stamps will be the same as the cost of 3 two-cent stamps.   In other words, if $a \times \dfrac{b}{100} = b \times \dfrac{a}{100}$, then $\dfrac{a \times b}{100} = \dfrac{b \times a}{100}$.   If this is so, then arithmetically .25 × 88 is the same as 25 × .88, and this principle will be useful on numerous occasions.   Thus the cost of 25 pounds of coffee at 88 cents per pound will be the same as the cost of 88 pounds of coffee at 25 cents per pound. The algorism for the latter problem will be 88 × $\$\frac{1}{4}$.   Then the cost of 25 pounds of coffee at 88 cents per pound will be $22.   The suggested algorism is more convenient to use than the standard one of 25 × $.88.

Illustrations: 75 × $4.80 =   125 × $ .72 =

480 × $ .75 =   72 × $1.25 =

480 × $$\frac{3}{4}$ = $360.   72 × $$\frac{5}{4}$ = $90.

14.   *To find a given per cent of a number when the per cent can be expressed more conveniently as a simple common fraction.*   The subject of percentage will be treated later in the text but it is desirable to say a few words here about short cuts which can be used in finding a per cent of a number. Should one wish to find 50 per cent of a number he should take half of the number, for $50\% = .50 = \dfrac{50}{100}$ which is equivalent to $\frac{1}{2}$. If the per cent is 25, then one should take $\frac{1}{4}$ of the number; for 75% use $\frac{3}{4}$ as the multiplier, etc.   If the per cent is 10%, 20%, 30%, etc., one should use respectively $\frac{1}{10}$, $\frac{2}{10}$ or $\frac{1}{5}$, $\frac{3}{10}$ etc.   If the multiplier is $33\frac{1}{3}\%$ it is more convenient to find $\frac{1}{3}$ of the number than it is to multiply by .$33\frac{1}{3}$.   For $12\frac{1}{2}\%$ we use $\frac{1}{8}$, for $37\frac{1}{2}\%$ we use $\frac{3}{8}$, for $62\frac{1}{2}\%$ we use $\frac{5}{8}$, etc.   In the study of per cent and percentage the student will learn common fraction equivalents of many decimal fractions or per cents.

EXERCISES

SET 13

1. Show 4 × 3 in base seven on a line diagram.
2. Show 5 × 4 in base eight on a line diagram.
3. Show on the above lines that 3 × 4 is the same as 4 × 3 and that 4 × 5 = 5 × 4.
4. Write out in table form the primary multiplication facts in scale eight and also in scale twelve.
5. Multiply in the scale of eight:

4216	3745	6027	3112
× 32	× 43	× 67	× 34

6. Multiply in the scale of twelve:

42T6	3745	607E	TETE
× 32	× 2E	× T4	× 1E

7. Check the examples in question No. 5 by casting out sevens and by finding the excess of nines.
8. Check the examples in question No. 6 by casting out elevens and by finding excess of thirteens.

In items 9 through 14 write only the products—do not copy the examples.

9. 20 × 62   500 × 231   700 × 514   9000 × 9000
       300 × 24   7000 × 4028   1100 × 800   17,000 × 200
10. 50 × 428   25 × 628   75 × 4420   125 × 6400
        500 × 912   75 × 448   25 × 2656   250 × 2400
11. 9 × 71   9 × 3200   99 × 816   49 × 248,000
        49 × 72   49 × 7300   199 × 612   999 × 666,000
12. 18 × 17   12 × 19   45 × 15   35 × 35
        14 × 16   13 × 17   75 × 95   65 × 65
13. 11 × 25   11 × 90   11 × 236   11 × 6254
        11 × 98   11 × 67   11 × 3013   11 × 8898
14. 25 × \$.56   125 × \$.32   25 × \$48.24   25 × .1604
        75 × \$.84   250 × \$.12   75 × \$16.16   75 × 8.08

15. Develop rules for multiplying by (a) 51, (b) 98, and (c) 101.
16. Complete and illustrate the following rule: To square a number ending in 5...
17. In what scale does 7 × 6 = 39?   6 × 8 = 39?   9 × 6 = 39?
                   7 × 9 = 11?   4 × 3 = 11?
18. Are the following products possible?   If so, in what scale or scales?
    3 × 7 = 31   4 × 9 = 24   6 × 7 = 53   8 × 9 = 62
19. Determine the scale used in each example and complete the multiplication:

2234	5618	6703	22365
× 4	× 6	× 9	× 4
02	T4	21	82

20. Multiply 11001101 by 11011 in base two and prove your answer by expressing these numbers in base ten and then multiplying.

CHAPTER 4

DIVISION WITH WHOLE NUMBERS

4.1 Introduction

The second of the two operations associated with the analysis process is called division. Division is related to subtraction as multiplication is to addition, and division is related to multiplication as subtraction is to addition. In the former relationship we find likeness or sameness of process, while in the latter we find opposite processes at work. Just as subtraction is the inverse of addition, division is the inverse of multiplication. In multiplication we are given two factors and we are asked to find their product; in division we are given the product and one of the factors and we are asked to find the other factor. In a real sense, in a division problem, we know the product and are asked to find either the multiplier or the multiplicand when the other is known. In multiplication we know a and b and must find c (the product): $a \times b = (?)$. In division we know c and either a or b and must find the other factor: $a \times (?) = c$ or $(?) \times b = c$. The number in division which corresponds to the product in multiplication is called the *dividend* and the known factor of the operation is called the *divisor*. The dividend always represents the amount which is to be redistributed into smaller groups, and the divisor either tells us the size of the groups or the number of those groups. The answer obtained in a division example is called the *quotient*.

Division, being an operation of analysis, can be thought of as a subtraction operation repeated until the quantities represented by the dividend have become exhausted. Thus division is often defined as repeated subtraction. If we wanted to know how many yards of material there are in 39 feet, we would lay off the measure of 3 feet as often as possible. If this were material from which we were to cut strips each 3 feet long, then we would cut off pieces of that length until the 39 feet were exhausted. We would find that we could do this 13 times.

The pictorial representation of this solution would look like this:

The same problem illustrated as a subtraction operation would reveal that we subtract 3 feet from the 39 feet 13 times.

39 feet			5 times	12 feet	
− 3 feet	1 time			− 3 feet	10 times
36 feet			6 times	9 feet	
− 3 feet	2 times			− 3 feet	11 times
33 feet			7 times	6 feet	
− 3 feet	3 times			− 3 feet	12 times
30 feet			8 times	3 feet	
− 3 feet	4 times			− 3 feet	13 times
27 feet			9 times	0	

4.2   The Two Concepts of Division

There are two different and distinct interpretations of division. One asks us to find the number of groups of a given size which can be formed from a given quantity and the other asks us to find the number of items in each group if we know the number of groups. The former concept is referred to as *measurement division* and the latter is part-taking or *partitioning division*. In the first type one is asked to find the multiplier (the number of groups) and in the second type one is asked to find the multiplicand (the size of the groups). The measurement idea asks one to find the number of sub-groups when the size of the groups is known. Example: How many $2 ties can I buy with $8?

$$\underline{\quad?\quad} \times \$2.00 = \$8.00$$

The partitioning idea asks one to find the size of the sub-groups when the number of groups is known. Example: Divide $40 among 8 people.

$$8 \times \underline{\quad?\quad} = \$40.00$$

Most teachers introduce division through the measurement concept even though it is assumed that children have had experience sharing some of their material possessions with playmates long before coming to school.   It seems that measurement division is simpler to objectify. Illustrations like the following are common in children's experiences:

1. How many nickels are there in a quarter of a dollar?
2. How many sandwiches can I make from 12 slices of bread?
3. How many weeks are there in a 30-day month?
4. How many groups of 3 are there in 9?

$$x\ x\ x\ x\ x\ x\ x\ x\ x$$
$$(x\ x\ x)\ (x\ x\ x)\ (x\ x\ x)$$

5. How many 7's are there in 25?

$$(x\ x\ x\ x\ x\ x\ x)\ (x\ x\ x\ x\ x\ x\ x)\ (x\ x\ x\ x\ x\ x\ x)\ x\ x\ x\ x$$

6. How many 23's are there in 76?

$$\begin{array}{r} 76 \\ -\ 23 \\ \hline 53 \end{array}$$ (1) there will be one 23 with 53 remaining $1 \times 23 = 23$

$$\begin{array}{r} -\ 23 \\ \hline 30 \end{array}$$ (2) there will be one more 23 with 30 remaining $2 \times 23 = 46$

$$\begin{array}{r} -\ 23 \\ \hline 7 \end{array}$$ (3) there will be one more 23 with 7 remaining $3 \times 23 = 69$

In summary, measurement division asks one to find the number of equal subgroups when the total number and the size of the sub-groups are known; we are to find the multiplier which represents the number of groups of equal size.

Since partitioning division is a form of part-taking or sharing operation it is akin to the "one-for-you" concept which children learn at an early age.   Illustrations like the following are very common in children's experiences:

1. Share 12 marbles with 2 other boys.
2. Regroup 8 rabbits into 4 pens with the same number in each.
3. Divide 15 cents among 3 people equally.
4. Divide 24 sandwiches among 4 boys.
5. Out of 8 players form 2 relay teams.
   Use the one-here and one-there idea until the 8 players have been used.

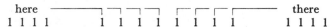

here ——————— ⌐ ⌐ ⌐   ⌐ ⌐ ⌐ ⌐——————— there
1 1 1 1   1 1 1 1 1 1 1 1   1 1 1 1

6. Divide 18 cookies equally among 3 boys, A, B, and C.

o o o   o o o   o o o   o o o   o o o   o o o
A B C   A B C   A B C   A B C   A B C   A B C

Each boy will receive 6 cookies.

7. Rearrange 12 rabbits so that there will be the same number of rabbits in each of three pens.

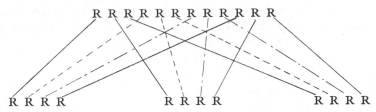

In summary, partition division asks one to find the number in each sub-group when the total number and the number of sub-groups are known; we are to find the multiplicand which represents the size of the group.

The student should study the following illustrations:

1. How many pieces 9 inches long can be cut from a stick 36 inches long?

2. If a stick 36 inches long is cut into 9 pieces of equal lengths, how long will each piece be?

1. |————+————+————+————| Measure off 9 inches as often as possible.   Answer: 4 times.

2. |————————+————————+————————| To divide into 9 equal parts we first divide into 3 equal parts.   Then we divide each of these parts into 3 equal parts.   Each part will be 4 inches

|—+—+—+—+—+—+—+—+—| long.

4.3   The Primary Division Facts

It has been pointed out that division is the inverse of multiplication and that therefore all of the division facts should be learned in connection with the learning of the multiplication facts.   Since 4 sevens are 28 ($4 \times 7 = 28$) then if we divide 28 by 7 we are asking either of these two questions: (*a*) How many groups of 7 can be formed from a group of 28? (*b*) If 28 is divided into 7 equal parts, how many will there be in each part?   In the abstract $28 \div 7 = 4$.   When the student learns that $6 \times 9 = 54$ he should also learn that when 54 is divided by either of the two factors he should obtain the other.   Thus $54 \div 6 = 9$ and $54 \div 9 = 6$.   In either case we read the example as, "54 divided *by* something." This something can never do the dividing; that work or operation must be performed by the operator. We really are finding the number of sub-groups which would be equivalent to 54 or we are finding the size of each group when we know the number of sub-groups.

The table of primary multiplication facts is given in Chapter 3 on page 94. We use this table to find the product when we know two factors. Now if we know the product of two numbers we find that number in the table and find the two numbers which head that row and that column containing the given number. Thus if our dividend is 48 we find from our table that 6 × 8 is 48, thus 48 ÷ 6 = 8 and 48 ÷ 8 = 6. Students usually organize their multiplication facts in table form but seldom write the division facts in such form. The latter should be plucked quite easily from the former. When one learns a set of multiplication facts he should learn a set of concomitant facts at the same time but we are not so sure that students do. It must be pointed out that if one learns the multiplication table of sixes then he should have learned the accompanying division facts: Thus

$$1 \times 6 = 6 \quad \text{so } 6 \div 1 = 6 \text{ and } 6 \div 6 = 1$$
$$2 \times 6 = 12 \quad \text{so } 12 \div 2 = 6 \text{ and } 12 \div 6 = 2$$
$$3 \times 6 = 18 \quad \text{so } 18 \div 3 = 6 \text{ and } 18 \div 6 = 3$$
$$4 \times 6 = 24 \quad \text{so } 24 \div 4 = 6 \text{ and } 24 \div 6 = 4, \text{ etc.}$$

Only a small per cent of all division examples will come out even, that is, with no remainders. If the divisor is 2, half of all possible examples with integral dividends will have integral quotients. If the divisor is 3, one out of every three examples will have no remainder, if the divisor is 5, one out of 5, or 20 per cent, of all division examples with integral dividends will be exact—will have no remainder.

From the above we can see that a large per cent of all division examples will be uneven, necessitating some proper disposal of the remainders. There are three types of problems with remainders; in other words, the remainder can be handled in any one of three different ways depending upon the interpretation of the problem. There are these three treatments: (1) To increase the integral quotient by 1. (2) To use the remainder as a part of the quotient, a fractional part. (3) To disregard the remainder completely, to throw it away. Let us illustrate these three treatments with real problem situations.

1. To increase the integral part of the quotient: "How many school buses will be needed to transport 480 pupils if each bus can accommodate 50 pupils?"

Answer: 10 buses.

2. To use the remainder and form a fractional part in the quotient: "How much money will each boy receive if $18 is divided equally among four of them?"

Answer: 4\frac{1}{2}$.

3. To disregard the remainder entirely: "How many intra-mural basketball teams of 5 players each can be formed from a squad of 36 players?"

Answer: Seven teams with one player remaining.

Students usually meet this form first for they practice division examples with abstract terms. They write: $28 \div 3 = 9 R 1$; $39 \div 5 = 7 R 4$, etc. The remainder is always a part of the dividend.

The student of arithmetic should be encouraged to appraise the given problem situation correctly in order to make proper disposal of the remainder.

4.4 Principles Underlying the Division Operation

Like the other operations, there are a few basic principles governing the division operation.

Principle 1. If the divisor is 1, the quotient is the same as the dividend. In other words, if a quantity is to be divided into one part, there will be the given number in that part, and if we want to find the number of groups of size 1 in the given number, there will be that number for it is made up of that many ones. Hence $N \div 1 = N$.

Principle 2. Division by zero is impossible. In other words it is impossible to divide a given quantity into zero parts and it is equally impossible to find the number of groups of size 0 which can be formed from a given quantity. Hence $N \div 0$ has no solution.

Principle 3.   The dividend can be treated as a single quantity made up of ones or it can be considered as the sum of its parts.   In other words, 46 ÷ 2 can be treated as the single amount 46 ÷ 2, for 23, or as 4 tens and 6 ones divided by 2, for a quotient of 2 tens and 3 ones, which in turn is equal to 23.

Principle 4.   If both the dividend and divisor are multiplied or divided by the same non-zero number, the quotient is unaffected.   This principle is especially useful in working with fractions and will be discussed in more detail in a later chapter.   The rule is often referred to as the Golden Rule of fractions and suggests that the operation which one performs to one term of the fraction can also be done to the other without any mathematical disturbance.   However, only the multiplication and division operations are applicable; the rule does not hold for addition and subtraction.   If one should double the amount in the dividend and also double the size of the divisor there will be no change in the original quotient.

$$a \div b = 2a \div 2b = 7a \div 7b = \tfrac{1}{2}a \div \tfrac{1}{2}b = Na \div Nb \text{ if } N \neq 0$$

Principle 5.   If one of two numbers is divisible by a third number, their product is also divisible by the third number.   In other words, if 33 is divisible by 11 then 7 × 33 is also divisible by 11.   Since 15 is divisible by 3 and 5 and 28 is divisible by 4 and 7, then the product of 15 times 28, or 420, is divisible by 3, 5, 4, and 7.

4.5   The Division Algorism

Since division is an operation of analysis it must be analogous to the operation of subtraction.   Thus to find how many groups of 2 there are in a larger group of 14 we proceed as if we are actually packaging items in groups of 2 until they are all used up; we want to know how many groups of 2 can be formed from the group of 14. We remove one group of 2 and have 12 left.   Then we remove another group of 2 and have 10 left.   We continue doing this until we have formed 7 groups of size 2 and have used up all of the original group of 14.   Now if we want instead to divide the 14 into 2 groups, we put one in each of the 2 groups and will have 12 left to distribute. Then we remove 2 more—one for each group—and have 10 left. We continue doing this until we have used up the entire group of 14. In the former case we will obtain 7 groups of 2 in each group (measurement division) while in the latter case we will have 7 in each of the 2 groups (partitioning division).

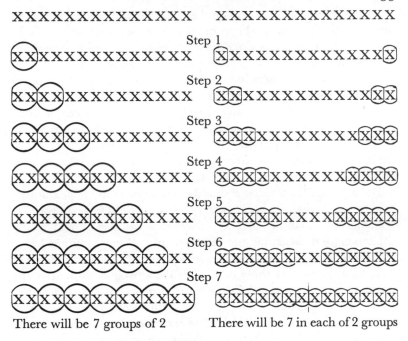

XXXXXXXXXXXXXX   XXXXXXXXXXXXXX

Step 1

Step 2

Step 3

Step 4

Step 5

Step 6

Step 7

There will be 7 groups of 2   There will be 7 in each of 2 groups

The two questions asked above can be expressed symbolically as:

14 (stars) ÷ 2 (stars) = _____   14 (stars) ÷ 2 = _____

If the problems above were to be solved as subtraction algorisms they would look like this:

(a)   14 stars   (b)   14 stars
    − 2 stars   1 group of 2   − 2 stars   1 in each group {one for you / one for me}
     12 stars   12 stars
    − 2 stars   2 groups of 2   − 2 stars   2 in each group {one for you / one for me}
     10 stars   10 stars
    − 2 stars   3 groups of 2   − 2 stars   3 in each group {one for you / one for me}
      8 stars   8 stars
    − 2 stars   4 groups of 2   − 2 stars   4 in each group {one for you / one for me}
      6 stars   6 stars
    − 2 stars   5 groups of 2   − 2 stars   5 in each group {one for you / one for me}
      4 stars   4 stars
    − 2 stars   6 groups of 2   − 2 stars   6 in each group {one for you / one for me}
      2 stars   2 stars
    − 2 stars   7 groups of 2   − 2 stars   7 in each group {one for you / one for me}
      0   0

From the foregoing illustration the reader should observe that both measurement and part-taking division can be illustrated by subtraction. One continues to subtract from the original amount (the dividend) until that amount has become exhausted.

After many experiences like the above the student should begin to develop an insight into the mechanics of the operation and should seek ways and means of shortening the algorism. If one were to think through a series of examples like the following he ought to arrive at a shortened algorism with a high degree of understanding of the mechanical process. In other words, the student should be able to rationalize the process of division.

The algorism for division should be introduced only after students have learned that division is another way of doing subtraction examples and that the first approach to a solution should be by estimation (or the scientific guessing method). When confronted with a division example like 15 + 3 one asks himself this question: Will there be as many as 1 three in 15? If the answer is affirmative the second question is posed: Will there be as many as 10 threes in 15? If the answer is negative, and it is, we return to find out how many ones of threes there are in 15. If the example is interpreted as part-taking division (15 ÷ 3), we ask, "Will there be as many as 1 in each group?" Then, "Will there be as many as 10 in each group?" Here again the answer is negative so we return to find how many ones there will be in each group. The written algorism can take one of many forms with the latter being the most generally accepted:

$$15 \div 3 = \quad 3 \,\underline{)\ 15} \qquad 3 \,)\, 15 \,(\qquad 3 \,\overline{)\ 15}$$

and after the study of fractions in the form of $\frac{15}{3}$.

Let's rationalize one or two division examples. Suppose we want to divide 72 by 4. 4) 72. First let us ask ourselves if there will be as many as 10 fours in 72. Will there be as many as 20 fours in 72? We determine that the answer will be a teen number, more than ten but less than 20. Now 10 fours are 40 so if we subtract 40 from 72 there will be 32 remaining. We should know that there are 8 fours in 32 so altogether there will be 18 fours in 72.

```
                 10            8 ⎫
  4 ) 72       4 ) 72         10 ⎬ 18
  − 40  10 fours   40       4 ) 72
  ────          ────          40
   32            32          ────
  − 32   8 fours               32
  ──────────                 ────
      18 fours                32
                            ────
                               0
```

For a second example let us divide 348 by 12. The first question is, "Will there be at least 1 twelve in 348?" Obviously yes. Then, will there be as many as 10 twelves in 348? Yes, because 10 twelves = 120.

Will there be as many as 20 twelves in 348? $20 \times 12 = 240$. Yes. Will there be as many as 30 twelves in 348? $30 \times 12 = 360$. No.

We know that the quotient is somewhere between 20 and 30 because $20 \times 12 = 240$ and $30 \times 12 = 360$ and our number 348 (the dividend) is between 240 and 360. If we remove the 20 groups of 12 from 348 we will have 108 left. Now 108 contains 9 groups of 12 so in 348 we have 29 groups of 12. $348 \div 12 = 29$.

```
                      20                          9 ⎫
                 12 ) 348                        20 ⎬ 29
  20 × 12 =          240              12 ) 348
                    ────              − 240
                                     ────
                                      108
                        9 × 12 =      108
                                     ────
```

The algorism can be streamlined to a more compact and perhaps more mature arrangement of symbols. When one keeps place value uppermost in mind and writes numbers in their proper columns the algorism step by step would look like this:

	2	2	2	2	29	29
12) 348	12) 348	12) 348	12) 348	12) 348	12) 348	12) 348
		24	24	24	24	24
			10	108	108	108
						108

The quotient is 29 and the completed algorism in its simplest form is given in the last box.

For a more difficult example let us find the quotient when 889 is divided by 27. We can interpret this example to mean either (*a*) How many groups of size 27 can be formed from 889? or (*b*) How many will there be in each group if 889 is divided into 27 groups of the same size? Either of these interpretations will produce the same algorism.

We begin by asking either (*a*) Will there be as many as 10, 20, 30, 40...in each group? or (*b*) Will there be as many as 10, 20, 30, 40, ... groups? We determine that the quotient will be more than 30 but less than 40: $30 \times 27 = 810$. If we remove 810 from the larger quantity 889 there will be 79 remaining to be divided. From this amount we can take only 2 groups of 27 (54) and there will be 25 items remaining. Thus $889 \div 27 = 32$, remainder of 25.

$\begin{array}{r} 889 \\ 30 \times 27 = 810 \\ \hline 79 \\ 2 \times 27 = 54 \\ \hline 25 \end{array}$	$\begin{array}{r} 27\,)\ 889 \\ 810\ \|\ 30 \\ \hline 79 \\ 54\ \|\ 2 \\ \hline 25\ \|\ 32 \end{array}$	$\begin{array}{r} 2\} \\ 30\} \ 32 \\ 26\,)\ 889 \\ 810 \\ \hline 79 \\ 54 \\ \hline 25 \end{array}$	$\begin{array}{r} 32 \\ 27\,)\ 889 \\ 81 \\ \hline 79 \\ 54 \\ \hline 25 \end{array}$

4.6   Finding the First Quotient Figure

Perhaps the biggest difficulty encountered in doing division examples comes at the very outset when one tries to find the first figure of the quotient. Because he often tries different numbers before obtaining the correct figure these numbers used are often referred to as "trial quotients." If one follows the approach just outlined, he has gained enough insight into the process and the example to determine the size of the quotient. He should be able to tell rather quickly whether the answer is in ones, tens, hundreds, etc. Having made this decision he next is confronted with the task of finding how many of these units (ones, tens, hundreds, etc.) will be the correct quotient figure. In the preceding example, $889 \div 27$, we determined that the quotient would be in tens, either 1 ten, 2 tens, 3 tens, etc. How many tens of 27's then are there in 889? Now there will be just as many tens of 27's in 889 as there are 27's in 88. (We are seeking the unknown: (*how many*) tens of 27 will equal 88 tens). Since there are three 27's in 88 there will be 3 tens of 27's in 889. To the elementary school pupil this approach presents numerous difficulties and very awkward verbalization, but psychologically is a very sound approach.

Now we will present the two major methods recommended to help the learner estimate or guess this first quotient figure. These are discussed in later elementary arithmetic texts as the *Apparent method* ("one" rule) and the *Increase-by-one method* ("two" rule) and will be explained here.

(*a*) *The Apparent Method.* This method involves rounding down to the given integral value of the largest unit of the divisor. If the divisor is 23, 39, 45, 58, 63, 77, or 88 we round down to 20, 30, 40, 50, 60, 70, and 80. If the divisor is 123, 246, 372, 456, 582, 673, or 897 we round down to 100, 200, 300, 400, 500, 600, and 900 respectively. This method is suggested as feasible when the fractional part of the largest unit is less than half the unit. If the divisor is 734 we use 700 as our trial divisor, for the fractional part of the unit (34/100) is less than half of the unit one hundred. Thus to divide 6152 by 734 we ascertain how many 7 hundreds there are in 61 hundreds. Our first trial quotient figure is 8.

(*b*) *The Increase-by-One Method.* This method involves rounding to the next integral value of the largest unit of the divisor. If the divisor is 23, 39, 45, 58, 62, 77, or 88 we round up to 30, 40, 50, 60, 80, and 90. If the divisor is 123, 246, 372, 456, 582, 673, or 897 we round up to 200, 300, 400, 500, 600, 700, and 900 respectively. This method is suggested as feasible when the fractional part of the largest unit is equal to or more than half of the unit. If the divisor is 673 we round up to 700, for our trial divisor since the fractional part of the unit (73/100) is more than half of the unit, one hundred. Thus to divide 3143 by 673 we ascertain how many 7 hundreds there are in 31 hundreds.

An alternative method referred to as "the use of helping tables" has gained some degree of popularity in recent years. The student is required to list all the integral multiples (in table form) of the given divisor and use them as "ready references" when doing division examples. Thus if one were to divide 97 by 17 he would make a table of seventeens thus:

$1 \times 17 = 17$	$4 \times 17 = 68$	$7 \times 17 = 119$
$2 \times 17 = 34$	$5 \times 17 = 85$	$8 \times 17 = 136$
$3 \times 17 = 51$	$6 \times 17 = 102$	$9 \times 17 = 153$

From the table of seventeens we discover that there are only 5 seventeens in 97 (6 × 17 is 102 and hence is too large) so 97 ÷ 17 = 5 with a remainder.   Since 5 × 17 is 85 there will be a remainder of 12. Thus

$$
\begin{array}{r}
5 \\
17\overline{)\;97} \\
85 \\
\hline
12 \text{ remainder}
\end{array}
$$

Should the example be 1209 ÷ 23 we would make a table of twenty-threes for reference:

1 × 23 = 23	5 × 23 = 115	5	52
2 × 23 = 46	6 × 23 = 138	23) 1209	23) 1209
3 × 23 = 69	7 × 23 = 161	115	115
4 × 23 = 92	8 × 23 = 184		59
	9 × 23 = 207		46
			13

Since 115 is the multiple of 23 which is smaller yet near to 120, the first quotient figure is 5 (and is placed in the tens place).   When the division is continued we must divide 59 by 23 and from inspection we find the quotient figure to be 2.   When the division is completed the integral part of the quotient is 52 and the remainder is 13.

Thus we find three distinct approaches to finding the quotient figures: the apparent method, the increase-by-one method, and the helping-tables method.

Another form of algorism can be shown by use of the decomposition or regrouping technique.   Thus if one were to divide 1000 by 5 he would not obtain an integral number of thousands; instead he would regroup the 1 thousand into 10 hundreds and then divide by 5.   The quotient then would be 2 hundred.

$$
5\underline{)\;1\text{ thousand}} = 5\underline{)\;10\text{ hundreds}}
$$
$$
2\text{ hundreds}
$$

The example can be solved by another algorism in the form of place value representations.   Thus

Thousands	Hundreds	Tens	Ones
5) 1			

must be rewritten as

	Thousands	Hundreds	Tens	Ones
5)		10		
		2		

before the operation can be done.

Witness the regrouping necessary for the solution of the example: 1725 ÷ 5. Normally the dividend is composed of 1 thousand + 7 hundreds + 2 tens + 5 ones. When this number is divided by 5 we see that there will not be as many as 1 thousand fives in the quotient so it will be necessary to convert the 1 thousand of the dividend to 10 hundred and combine with the 7 hundred. Then the dividend takes on this form: 17 hundreds + 2 tens + 5 ones. Now we are sure that there will be a definite number of hundreds in the quotient, namely 3. When 3 hundred 5's have been removed from the 17 hundreds there will be 2 hundreds remaining. These are expressed as 20 tens and are combined with the 2 tens to make 22 tens. Now when we divide by 5 we obtain 4 tens of 5's in 22 tens with 2 tens left over. These 2 tens are combined with the 5 ones to make 25 ones. Now the 25 is divided by 5 for a quotient of 5. Thus the completed quotient is 3 hundreds + 4 tens + 5 ones or 345.

```
5 ) 17 hundreds   2 tens   5 ones
    3 hundreds   (2 hundreds remaining are regrouped as tens)
            5 ) 22 tens   5 ones
                4 tens   (2 tens remaining are regrouped as ones)
                    5 ) 25 ones
                        5 ones     Quotient of 1725 ÷ 5 is 345.
```

In summary let us solve the following problem: Mr. Jones sold 12 young steers whose combined weights totaled 10,272 pounds. What was the average weight per steer? The problem suggests redistributing the total weight into 12 equal parts which can be done by repeated subtraction or formal division. The latter will be more expedient. We will begin by asking if the steers will weigh as much as 1 pound each. Yes. Will they weigh as much as 10 pounds each? Yes. Will they weigh as much as 100 pounds each? Yes. Will they weigh as much as 1000 pounds each? No. Then we have determined that the first quotient figure will represent hundreds—all other places to the left in the quotient will be vacant (or will be filled with imaginary zeros).

$$
\begin{array}{r}
* \\
12\overline{)\,1\ 0\ 2\ 7\ 2}
\end{array}
\qquad
\begin{array}{r}
8 \\
12\overline{)\,1\ 0\ 2\ 7\ 2}
\end{array}
$$

There will be as many hundreds of twelves in the dividend as there are twelves in 102 (hundreds). There are 8 twelves in 102, therefore there will be 800 twelves in 10,272. Eight (hundred) twelves will be 96 (hundred). Subtract 96 (hundred) from 102 (hundred) leaving a remainder of 6 (hundred).

$$
\begin{array}{r}
8 \\
12\overline{)\,1\ 0\ 2\ 7\ 2} \\
9\ 6 \\
\hline
6
\end{array}
$$

Now we combine the 6 hundred with the 7 tens for a total of 67 tens. How many tens of twelves will there be in 67 tens? Just as many as there are twelves in 67. There will be 5. Therefore 5 tens of twelves will be 60 tens and when subtracted from 67 tens will leave 7 tens.

$$
\begin{array}{r}
8\ 5 \\
12\overline{)\,1\ 0\ 2\ 7\ 2} \\
9\ 6 \\
\hline
6\ 7 \\
6\ 0 \\
\hline
7\ 2
\end{array}
$$

Now we combine the 7 tens with the 2 ones for a total of 72 ones. How many twelves will there be in 72 ones? There will be 6, for 6 twelves are 72.

When we subtract there will be no remainder; the division is exact.

$$
\begin{array}{r}
8\ 5\ 6 \\
12\overline{)\,1\ 0\ 2\ 7\ 2} \\
9\ 6 \\
\hline
6\ 7 \\
6\ 0 \\
\hline
7\ 2 \\
7\ 2 \\
\hline
\end{array}
$$

The average weight per steer is 856 pounds.

Though the above problem was approached verbally through the measurement concept of division the two algorisms are identical. Instead of saying that there will be 800 twelves in 10,272 we say that each of the steers will weigh at least 800 pounds. Then we say later that each will weigh an additional 50 pounds and finally 6 pounds more. When we redistribute the 10,272 pounds of weight among 12 cattle there will be 856 pounds assigned to each one.

EXERCISES

SET 14

1. If $a \div b = c$, evaluate $4a \div 4b$, $12a \div 12b$, $na \div nb$.
2. Show $564 \div 4$ in 4 different algorisms.
3. Show $15 \div 3$ as measurement (in pictorial form).
4. Show $12 \div 3$ as partitioning (in pictorial form).
5. Show $149 \div 23$ as repeated subtraction.
6. Show $28 \div 4$ geometrically (by use of a line diagram).
7. Write out two problems in essay form illustrating measurement and two illustrating the partitioning interpretation of division.
8. Show that one-third of all the division examples with integral dividends from 1 to 21 inclusive, with divisor 3, will have no remainders.
9. When the problem refers to part-taking division, what does the following mean: $169 \div 17$?
10. Find the values of the following and state any general principles you can prove: $N \div N$ ($N \neq 0$), $N \div 1$, $0 \div N$ ($N \neq 0$), $N \div 0$.
11. Write out two inexact division problems in essay form in which the remainder is used as a fractional part in the quotient and two in which the remainder is discarded completely.

4.7 Other Division Algorisms

The algorism explained in the previous paragraphs is the one used most commonly today. However, the present form of algorism has had a long and varied evolution. Some of these forms are presented here for the enlightenment of the curious student and for the interest of others. A look at other forms should deepen one's understanding of division as a process.

A method very common in olden times was known as the "galley" method, so named because the solution, in its final form, was said to resemble a ship. A brief explanation of the algorism follows: Let us divide 79 by 13.

Step 1. Write the divisor immediately below the dividend aligning the left-hand digits.

$$79$$
$$13$$

Step 2. Write the quotient figure to the right of the solution:

$$79 \ (\ 6$$
$$13$$

Step 3. Multiply the divisor by the quotient, moving from left to right, and then perform the subtractions. Each time a number is used the figure is crossed out.

	$6 \times 1 = 6$
	Cross out the 1.
79 (6	Subtract 6 from 7.
13	Cross out the 7.
	Write 1 above the 7 $(7 - 6$ is 1$)$.
	$6 \times 3 = 18$
	Cross out the 3.
	Subtract 18 from 19.
	Cross out the 19 and write 1.

The solution of the division example will take the following form:

$$
\begin{array}{ccccc}
 & & 1 & 1 & 11 \\
79\ (\ 6 & 79\ (\ 6 & 79\ (\ 6 & 79\ (\ 6 & 79\ (\ 6 \\
13 & 13 & 13 & 13 & 13
\end{array}
$$

Quotient is 6, the remainder is 1.

The student should rework the following example according to the directions given if he desires a working knowledge of the galley method.

Divide 4896 by 27.

4 8 9 6 (1
2 7

Write the divisor under the dividend at far left. Determine the first quotient figure 1.
Write it to the right of the dividend.

2 1
4 8 9 6 (1
2 7

Multiply $1 \times 2 = 2$, cross out 2 of the 27, subtract 2 from 4, write 2 above the 4 and cross out the 4.
Multiply $1 \times 7 = 7$, cross out the 7 of the 27, subtract 7 from 8, write 1 above the 8 and cross out the 8.

5		
2 1	2 1	Rewrite the divisor one place to the
4 8 9 6 (1 8	4 8 9 6 (1 8	right. The next quotient figure will
2 7	2 7 7	be 8. 8 × 2 = 16, cross out 2 of the
2 7	2	27, subtract 16 from 21, write 5 and

cross out 21.

(Note how and where the divisor is written)

5	5	
2 1 3	2 1 3	Multiply 8 × 7 = 56, cross out 7 of
4 8 9 6 (1 8	4 8 9 6 (1 8 1	the 27, subtract 56 from 59, write 3,
2 7 7	2 7 7 7	and cross out 59.
2	2 2	

5 1	5 1	
2 1 3	2 1 3 9	Rewrite the divisor one place to the
4 8 9 6 (1 8 1	4 8 9 6 (1 8 1	right. The next quotient figure is 1.
2 7 7 7	2 7 7 7	1 × 2 = 2, cross out 2 of the 27,
2 2	2 2	subtract 2 from 3, write 1, and cross

out 3.

Multiply 1 × 7, cross out 7 of the 27, subtract 7 from 16, write 9, and cross out 16.

The quotient is 181 with a remainder of 9.

If the divisor of a given division example is a single-digit number or a simple two-digit number or even a larger number which permits ease of handling, the entire division operation can be performed (mentally) without the use of paper and pencil and only the quotient recorded. Thus if one wished to know the quotient of 726 divided by 3 he would determine first that the answer would be in hundreds and then he would proceed to divide. His thinking might follow this pattern: There are 2 threes in 7, write 2 carry 1. There are 4 threes in 12, write 4. There are 2 threes in 6, write 2. The quotient is 242.

If the divisor is a single-digit number of a "teen" number we can easily perform division examples by this *short division* method (so-called because of its shortened form). Let us divide 900 by 12. We determine first that the quotient will be a two-digit number; the answer will be less than 1 hundred. There are 7 twelves in 90. 7 × 12 = 84. Subtract 84 from 90, write 7 in the quotient, carry 6.

How many twelves in 60? There are 5 so we write 5 in the ones place in the quotient for a complete quotient of 75.

If the divisor is something like 40, 50, 60, etc., or 200, 300, 400, etc., or 3000 or 4000, etc., we can also perform the division in this shortened form.

4.8 Division in Other Bases

Once the division algorisms are thoroughly understood when applied to numbers in the decimal scale (base ten) the same principles and generalizations can be applied to division examples when the base is different from ten. Should one encounter the example 15 ÷ 6 in the base seven he can interpret the example either of two ways: (a) How many groups of size 6 are there in 1 group of seven plus 5? or (b) How many would there be in each group if we rearrange the 1 seven plus 5 into 6 equal groups?

Since one is not too familiar with the multiplication facts in different bases it might be feasible to construct helping tables for ready reference. Thus in the base seven

$$1 \times 6 = 6$$
$$2 \times 6 = 15$$
$$3 \times 6 = 24, \text{ etc.}\quad \text{Then } 15 \div 6 \text{ (seven) is 2.}$$

Divide 43 by 7 in the base nine. If one has memorized the sevens table in base nine he could refer to these known facts. If not, here again a list of multiplication facts should prove helpful.

$$
\begin{array}{ll}
1 \times 7 = 7 & 5 \times 7 = 38 \\
2 \times 7 = 15 & 6 \times 7 = 46 \\
3 \times 7 = 23 & 7 \times 7 = 54 \\
4 \times 7 = 31 & 8 \times 7 = 62 \\
\end{array}
$$

Therefore, in the base nine, there are 5 sevens in 43 with a remainder of 4.

$$
\begin{array}{ccc}
7\,)\,4\ 3\ (& \quad 7\,)\,4\ 3\ (\ 5 & \quad 7\,)\,\overset{3}{\cancel{4}}{}'3\ (\ 5 \\
 & \underline{3\ 8} & \underline{3\ 8} \\
 & & 4
\end{array}
$$

Recall that 5 × 7 is the same as 3 groups of nine plus 8. Eight from one nine and 3 is 4. The remainder is 4.

Let's try another longer division example, this time in base six.

$$15 \overline{)\, 5\ 2\ 2\ 2\,}$$

$$
\begin{array}{r}
2 \\
15 \overline{)\, 5\ 2\ 2\ 2\,} \\
3\ 4 \\
\hline
1\ 4
\end{array}
$$

Let the first trial quotient be 3.
This is too large, for 3 × 15 (base six) is 53.
Therefore the first quotient figure is 2.
2 × 15 (six) is 34 (six).

$$
\begin{array}{r}
2\ 5 \\
15 \overline{)\, 5\ 2\ 2\ 2\,} \\
3\ 4 \\
\hline
1\ 4\ 2 \\
1\ 3\ 1 \\
\hline
1\ 1\ 2
\end{array}
$$

4 from 1 six plus 2 is 4.   3 from 4 is 1.

The second quotient figure is 5.
5 × 15 is 131 (six).
131 from 142 leaves 11 (six).   Bring down 2.

$$
\begin{array}{r}
2\ 5\ 4 \\
15 \overline{)\, 5\ 2\ 2\ 2\,} \\
3\ 4 \\
\hline
1\ 4\ 2 \\
1\ 3\ 1 \\
\hline
1\ 1\ 2 \\
1\ 1\ 2
\end{array}
$$

The next quotient figure is 4.   4 × 15 (six) is 112.   Subtracting 112 from 112 gives a remainder of 0 and the division is exact.

The quotient is 254.

The student should see the parallelism between division in any base with the known principles of division in base ten.   Some practice with division in non-decimal bases would soon develop proficiency in this area.

4.9   Checks in Division

Since division is the inverse of multiplication we ought to be able to prove our work by the use of multiplication.   In division we are really trying to find a missing factor (in the abstract), so after we have found it we ought to be able to check our work by multiplication. The two factors ought to produce the given dividend.   In the example, 42 ÷ 7, we are really finding the missing term in this multiplication example: ?   × 7 = 42, and when we find it we try our success by testing it.   We want to know if 6, the number obtained as our quotient, times 7 is 42.   If it is, then we have obtained the correct quotient.   In the example, $125 ÷ $25, we want to know how many jackets costing $25 each can be bought with $125. When we find an answer, in this case 5, we test it to see if 5 coats at $25 each will cost $125. (5 × $25 = $125). Thus we can check our examples by multiplying the complete quotient by the divisor; if we obtain the dividend, then the division example has been solved correctly (we say that it checks). Then *Complete Quotient times the Divisor equals the Dividend* or *Divisor × Complete Quotient = Dividend.*

If the division is not exact and there is a remainder, then the partial quotient and divisor are multiplied and the remainder is added to this product to produce the given dividend.

divisor × partial quotient + remainder = dividend

Example:

$$4\,\overline{)\,26} \qquad 4\,\overline{)\,26}^{\,6\frac{1}{2}} \quad \text{If } 6\frac{1}{2} \times 4 \text{ is } 26, \text{ the solution is correct.}$$

$$4\,\overline{)\,26} = 6,\,\text{R } 2 \qquad \text{If } 6 \times 4 + 2 \text{ is } 26, \text{ the solution is correct.}$$

The multiplication method is the most common form for checking division examples and very often by this method the checking can be performed without the use of pencil and paper, even by children in the fifth grade, who incidentally should be encouraged to check all examples.

We have proved the basic principle known as the commutative law with respect to multiplication, namely, $a \times b = b \times a$. Then if 4×7 is the same as 7×4 in the abstract we can safely conclude that 28 divided by either of these two factors will produce the other. If $28 \div 4 = 7$, then when we divide 28 by 7 we ought to get 4. If we do, we assume a correct solution.

Let us divide 2448 by 72 and prove that our solution is correct.

Solution: 34   The quotient is 34.   72   Check.

$$72\,\overline{)\,2448}$$
$$216$$
$$\overline{288}$$
$$288$$

$$34\,\overline{)\,2448}$$
$$238$$
$$\overline{68}$$
$$68$$

If when the quotient is made the divisor, the original divisor becomes the new quotient, then we assume a correct solution. In short, if the divisor and quotient can be interchanged without any mathematical disturbance, then the work is correct.

If $x\,\overline{)\,y}^{\,z},$ then $z\,\overline{)\,y}^{\,x}.$

One of the most interesting checks for division examples is the excess-of-nines check. Some of the principles of the excess-of-nines check were discussed in the chapter on multiplication. It is sufficient here to state the basic theorem:

> The excess of nines (or elevens) in the divisor multiplied by the excess of nines (or elevens) in the partial quotient increased by the excess of nines (or elevens) in the remainder is equal to the excess of nines (or elevens) in the dividend.

In other words this is the same rule illustrated in the early part of this section but here we use the excesses instead of the numbers themselves.

EXERCISES

SET 15

1. Solve the following division examples:

57,095 ÷ 79	72,072 ÷ 36	17,962 ÷ 384
72,618 ÷ 29	99,090 ÷ 30	202,202 ÷ 101
2040 ÷ 340	42,270 ÷ 68	78,962 ÷ 361

2. Check the examples in the first column of exercise No. 1 by the use of multiplication.
   Check those in the second column by the excess-of-nines check.
   Check those in the last column by the excess-of-elevens check.
3. When 42,816 is divided by 59 the answer will be in (thousands, hundreds, tens, or ones)? About how many of those units?
4. Copy and complete this form:

Example	Quotient will be in hundreds, tens, or ones	Quotient will be about
7428 ÷ 21		
1564 ÷ 381		
7881 ÷ 56		
429 ÷ 16		
87405 ÷ 109		

5. How many dozen eggs in 900 eggs?
   How many pounds of coffee in 8100 ounces?
   How many tons of coal in 15,000 pounds?
   How many yards of ribbon in 10,000 inches?
   How many square yards of canvas in 8100 square feet of canvas?
   How many sextets can be formed from 100 musicians?
6. Write out and solve six more problems similar to the above but using different units of measurement.

7. Divide 2 million by 2 thousand.
   Divide $7\frac{1}{2}$ thousand by 35 tens.
   Divide 35 hundred by $\frac{1}{2}$ of 8 tens.
   Divide one quarter million by $2\frac{1}{2}$ hundred.
   Divide 10 thousand by the product of 2 tens and 3 tens.
   Divide 300 thousand by $\frac{1}{2}$ the product of 10 and 5 hundred.

8. Change the following to Hindu-Arabic numbers and then divide:

   MCLXI ÷ XLII $\overline{\text{DC}}$ ÷ $\overline{\text{VI}}$

   $\overline{\text{LDV}}$ ÷ V

SET 16

1. Perform the following divisions by the galley method:
   $4268 \div 14$ $9898 \div 32$ $97,619 \div 233$ $50,209 \div 876$

2. Perform the following divisions and check by using division.
   $47\,\overline{)9874}$ $78\,\overline{)4295}$ $173\,\overline{)20709}$ $594\,\overline{)60034}$

3. Check examples in question No. 1 by casting out nines.

4. Check examples in question No. 2 by the excess-of-elevens check.

5. Show in picture form:
   (a) $12 \div 3$ as partitioning
   (b) $15 \div 3$ as measurement
   (c) $9 \div 2$ on a line diagram (as measurement)
   (d) $11 \div 3$ on a line diagram (as partitioning)

6. Divide 456 by 39 by repeated subtraction.

7. Divide 4089 by 47, writing no digit larger than 5 in the quotient.

8. Divide in the designated base:
   (a) $17 \div 3$ base nine   (c) $111 \div 7$ base eight
   (b) $23 \div 4$ base five   (d) $2424 \div 5$ base six

9. How many groups of size 125 are there in 10 million?
   How many groups of 750 are there in 3000 tens?
   If the dividend is 10,428 and the quotient is 237, find the divisor.
   If the divisor is 478 and the quotient is 98, what is the dividend?

10. Write out a division problem in essay form (if possible), illustrating measurement division having a quotient of $7\frac{1}{2}$ cents.

11. When 77 is divided by 8 the remainder is 5 and when 77 is divided by 9 the remainder is also 5. Can you explain this?

12. On a number line show how to divide 24 by 6.

13. Do not copy these examples. Using the short-division algorism write quotients for the following:
    $4\overline{)23468}$ $3\overline{)630129}$ $5\overline{)110605}$ $6\overline{)121248}$ $12\overline{)864024}$

    $7\overline{)35056}$ $2\overline{)113678}$ $8\overline{)801608}$ $9\overline{)324423}$ $12\overline{)891252}$

14. Write definitions of the following terms: quotient, division, dividend, partitioning, excess of elevens, algorism.

15. Discuss the following as being either true or false.

(*a*) If both the dividend and divisor are increased, the quotient is increased.

(*b*) If both the divisor and dividend are decreased, the quotient is decreased.

(*c*) If both the dividend and divisor are increased the same amount, the quotient remains unchanged.

(*d*) If both the dividend and divisor are decreased the same amount, the quotient remains unchanged.

(*e*) If a number is divisible by both 2 and 4, then it is divisible by 8 and the converse is also true.

4.10   Short Cuts in Division

Occasionally it is possible to obtain the answer to a division example with little or no paper and pencil work. There are some division examples which permit short cuts to the solution though to the student uninitiated to work of this kind these shortened forms may appear to be more painstaking than the regular long division method. A few short cuts in performing division examples are given here to encourage students to strive for efficient methods of performance.

1. To divide a number by 10. Rewrite the digits of the number in the same sequence, moving all of them one place to the right. Thus $45 \div 10 = 4.5, 7 \div 10 = .7, 901 \div 10 = 90.1$, etc. (The common expression, though erroneous, is to say, "Move the decimal point one place to the left." The decimal point never moves, it always remains just after the ones place between the ones digit and the tenths digit.) Rules for dividing a number by 100, 1000, etc., can be derived from the one above.

2. To divide a number by 5. First divide the number by 10 and then double the result. Since dividing by 5 is the same as taking $\frac{1}{5}$ of the number, and since $\frac{1}{5}$ is equivalent to $\frac{2}{10}$, we multiply the given number by $\frac{2}{10}$ when we wish to divide it by 5. We know that $45 \div 5 = 9$. Also if 45 is divided by 10 we obtain 4.5 which when doubled also produces 9. Divide 722 by 5. First divide 722 by 10 which gives 72.2. Now this result is multiplied by 2 for 144.4. Thus $722 \div 5 = 144.4$. Rules for dividing a number by 50, 500 etc., can be derived from the one above.

3. To divide a number by 25. Divide the number by 100 and then multiply the result by 4. Dividing by 25 is the same as taking $\frac{1}{25}$ of the number, and $\frac{1}{25}$ is equivalent to $\frac{4}{100}$. $284 \div 25 = 284 \times \frac{1}{25}$ $= 284 \times \frac{4}{100} = \frac{284}{100} \times 4 = 2.84 \times 4 = 4 \times 2.84 = 11.36$. In like

manner 6400 ÷ 25 must equal 4 × 64, or 256.   Rules for dividing
by 250, 2500, etc., can be derived from the one above.

4. To divide a number by a composite number.   Divide the number by
one of the factors of the divisor.   Then divide the quotient by another
factor of the divisor.   Then divide this quotient by another factor of
the divisor until all the factors have been used successively as divisors.
To divide 1728 by 12 we could first divide by 2, then by 3, and then
by 2 again, for 2 × 3 × 2 is the same as 12.

$$1728 \div 2 = 864 \qquad 864 \div 3 = 288 \qquad 288 \div 2 = 144$$

$$\text{Then } 1728 \div 12 = 144$$

To divide a number by 56, use the divisors 7 and 8; to divide a
number by 125, divide successively by 5, 5, and 5 again.

$$7336 \div 56 = 7\,)\,\overline{7336} \qquad\qquad 62550 \div 125 = 5\,)\,\overline{62550}$$
$$8\,)\,\overline{1048} \qquad\qquad\qquad\qquad 5\,)\,\overline{12510}$$
$$\overline{131} \qquad\qquad\qquad\qquad\qquad 5\,)\,\overline{2502}$$
$$7336 \div 56 = 131 \qquad\qquad 62550 \div 125 = 500\tfrac{2}{5} \qquad 500\,\tfrac{2}{5}$$

4.11   Prime Numbers and Composite Numbers

Every integer can be written as a product of two integers.   The
given integer is called the product and the numbers which produce
that product are called the *factors*.   A factor of a number is an exact
divisor of the number.   Thus the number 5 has the factors 1 and 5,
the number 6 has two sets of factors, namely, 2 × 3 and 1 × 6.   The
number 7 has only one set of factors; the number 8 has more than one
set of factors; 9, 10, and 12 have at least two sets of factors.   Numbers
which have only one set of unique factors are called *prime* numbers.
Prime numbers can be divided exactly only by themselves and unity.
Numbers which have more than one set of factors are called *composite*
numbers.   (Zero and 1 are neither prime nor composite by definition
or agreement.)

It is quite an easy matter to determine the prime numbers less than
100, and if the student is familiar with the multiplication facts, by the
process of elimination he ought to become equally familiar with the
prime numbers less than 100.   The prime numbers between 1 and

100 are 2, 3, 5, 7, 11, 13, 17, 19, 23, 29, 31, 37, 41, 43, 47, 53, 59, 61, 67, 71, 73, 79, 83, 89, and 97. Determining the prime numbers greater than 100 is quite a different matter. Eratosthenes, who lived about 250 B.C. performed the following experiment. He wrote in succession a series of numbers on a piece of parchment paper. He knew that 2 was the only even prime number so it was necessary to consider only the odd numbers. Knowing that 3 is a prime number, he knew that every third number in the series would be divisible by 3, so he punched out every third odd number. The next odd number after 3 is 5, which is prime, and every fifth number thereafter is a multiple of 5 so it must be punched out; 11 is prime and every eleventh odd number is composite, and so on. When he had concluded his experiment all the composite numbers had been punched out leaving holes in the parchment with only the prime numbers remaining. Hence this procedure for finding the prime numbers is very appropriately called the *sieve of Eratosthenes*.

2 3 5 7 9 11 13 15 17 19 21 23 25 27 29 31 33 35 37 39 41 43 45 47 49 51 53

2 3 5 7 9 11 13 15 17 19 21 23 25 27 29 31 33 35 37 39 41 43 45 47 49 51 53

2 3 5 7 9 11 13 15 17 19 21 23 25 27 29 31 33 35 37 39 41 43 45 47 49 51 53

2 3 5 7 9 11 13 15 17 19 21 23 25 27 29 31 33 35 37 39 41 43 45 47 49 51 53

Though the sieve of Eratosthenes is interesting it is not very practical for determining whether or not large numbers such as 237, 279, and 111,113 are prime numbers. To test for primeness we make use of the following theorem based on the square root of a number. Theorem: Every number has a square root equal to an integer and a fraction. (Either the integer or the fraction can be zero.) If the number does not have a prime divisor equal to or less than the integer, then the number is prime.

$$\sqrt{N} = I \quad \text{plus a fraction}$$

If the value of the fraction is zero, then N is a perfect square and hence N is composite.

Given a number N, it is either composite or prime. In either case $\sqrt{N} = I$ plus a fraction. If N is a composite number both of its factors cannot be greater than the integer I. If N = 404 both of its factors cannot be greater than 20, for $\sqrt{404} = 20$ plus a fraction. If N is 631 both of its factors cannot be greater than 25, for $\sqrt{631} = 25$ plus a fraction.   If N is a prime number we need to test for factors only those prime numbers less than or equal to the integral part of its square root.   If N = 97 we test for factors only prime numbers less than 9, for $\sqrt{97} = 9$ plus a fraction.   If we think there is a factor larger than 9 we would have found its companion factor as we tried divisors less than 9.   To determine if 97 is a prime number we try the following divisors:

$$97 \div 2 = 48+$$
$$97 \div 3 = 32+$$
$$97 \div 5 = 19+$$
$$97 \div 7 = 13+$$

There are no factors of 97, different from 1×97, hence it is a prime number.

The application of this theorem presumes on the part of the learner some knowledge of square root; he must be able to find the square root of a number.   The student might be able to use the "square root method," logarithms, slide rule, tables of square roots, or any approved square root method.   A very practical and popular method (sometimes called the Newton method) which gives one a close approximation to the true square root of a number is given here.

To find the square root of a number:

1. Estimate the square root (any guess will do).
2. Divide the number by your estimate.
3. Find the average of your divisor and your quotient.
4. The average will be very close to the true square root of the given number.
5. For a closer value divide the number by the average and then again average the quotient and the divisor.

Example: Find $\sqrt{97}$

1. Estimate the square root as 9.   Divide $9\overline{)\,97}$ with $10.6 +$
   (The true square root is between 9 and 10.6)
2. Find the average of 9 and 10.6.   This is 9.8
   (9.8 is very close to the true square root of 97)
3. The process can be continued if necessary.

Example: Find $\sqrt{3893}$

1. Estimate the square root as 60.   Divide $60 \overline{) 3893}^{\ 64\ +}$
   (The true square root is between 60 and 64)
2. Average the quotient and the divisor: $\frac{1}{2}(64 + 60) = 62$
   (62 is very close to the true square root of 3893)

Test the number 3893 to determine whether it is prime or composite. To determine if it is composite we try all the prime numbers less than 62 as possible factors.   We try, in order, 2, 3, 5, 7, 11, 13, 17, 19, 23, 29, 31, 37, 41, 43, 47, 53, 59, and 61.   The problem looks more difficult than it really is, for when we try 17 as a divisor we obtain an integral quotient of 229.   Therefore the number 3893 is composite, for it contains at least two sets of factors, namely, 1 × 3893 and 17 × 229.

It is often necessary in arithmetic to know all the prime factors of a given composite number.   Often these can be found by inspection but it is more convenient to find them by a method we call successive division.   The method is illustrated here: Find all the prime factors of 210.

$$210 = 2 \overline{)\ 210}$$
$$3 \overline{)\ 105}$$
$$5 \overline{)\ 35}$$
$$7$$

Thus $210 = 2 \times 3 \times 5 \times 7$

The prime factors of 210 are 2, 3, 5, and 7.

Write 1980 in (prime) factored form.

$$1980 = 2 \overline{)\ 1980}$$
$$2 \overline{)\ 990}$$
$$3 \overline{)\ 495}$$
$$3 \overline{)\ 165}$$
$$5 \overline{)\ 55}$$
$$11$$

Thus $1980 = 2 \times 2 \times 3 \times 3 \times 5 \times 11$
or in exponential form
$1980 = 2^2 \times 3^2 \times 5 \times 11$

The largest known prime number was determined by Professor Robinson of the University of California in 1952.   In exponential form it is written as $2^{2281} - 1$ and is said to contain 687 digits.

4.12   The Greatest Common Divisor

Occasionally one is interested in finding the largest possible number which is a divisor of every number in a group of numbers.   In a set of numbers such as 2, 4, and 8, certainly one can perceive that the largest divisor common to all is 2; in the set of 9, 18, and 36, one should see that the largest divisor common to all is 9. The largest divisor for each of a given set of numbers is called the *greatest common divisor* (G.C.D.). Though the G.C.D. of a set of numbers can often be determined by inspection it can also be found by making use of the prime factors of all the numbers given. Find the G.C.D. of 54 and 72.

$$54 = 2 \overline{)\ 54} \quad 54 = 2 \times 3 \times 3 \times 3 \quad 72 = 2 \overline{)\ 72} \quad 72 = 2 \times 2 \times 2 \times 3 \times 3$$
$$3 \overline{)\ 27} \quad 54 = 2 \times 3^3 \qquad\qquad\quad 2 \overline{)\ 36} \quad 72 = 2^3 \times 3^2$$
$$3 \overline{)\ 9} \qquad\qquad\qquad\qquad\qquad\quad 2 \overline{)\ 18}$$
$$3 \qquad\qquad\qquad\qquad\qquad\qquad\quad 3 \overline{)\ 9}$$
$$\qquad\qquad\qquad\qquad\qquad\qquad\qquad\qquad 3$$

It is apparent from the solution above that both the numbers 54 and 72 contain a 2 and both contain a 3 × 3. Hence the greatest common divisor is 2 × 3 × 3 or 18. If we use the factored form of the numbers we select the factors common to both numbers using the lowest power of the factors which appear in both. We select the first power of 2 and the second power of 3.

If two numbers A and B can be factored as follows:

$$A = 2^3 \times 5^3 \times 7^2 \quad \text{and} \quad B = 2^4 \times 5^2 \times 11,$$

then the G.C.D. of both will be the third power of 2 times the second power of 5. G.C.D. = $2^3 \times 5^2 = 200$.

The short-division method of factoring illustrated above can be applied to all the numbers at once, dividing by any number which is a common divisor of all. Division is continued by dividing the quotients by a common divisor until the remaining quotients have no common divisor. The product of all the common divisors is the greatest common divisor.

$$2 \overline{)\ 54 - 72}$$
$$3 \overline{)\ 27 - 36}$$
$$3 \overline{)\ 9 - 12}$$
$$3 - 4$$

There are no more common divisors; therefore the G.C.D. is the

product of 2 × 3 × 3 or 18.   Find the greatest common divisor of
135, 315, and 450 by the short-division method.

$$
\begin{array}{r}
3\,)\ 135 - 315 - 450 \\
\hline
3\,)\ \ 45 - 105 - 150 \\
\hline
5\,)\ \ 15 - \ \ 35 - \ \ 50 \\
\hline
3 - \ \ \ 7 - \ \ 10
\end{array}
$$

There are no more common divisors; therefore the G.C.D. is
3 × 3 × 5 or 45.

The greatest common divisor is of use in arithmetic in changing
the form of a fraction.   Though the subject of fractions is not discussed until the next chapter the average reader will be acquainted
with the process known as "reducing a fraction to lower terms."
When one encounters the fraction $\frac{12}{15}$, he instinctively changes it to
simpler terms.   If the fraction is a more cumbersome one he must
search for the largest possible divisor of both the numerator and the
denominator.   Often the G.C.D. is simply the difference between the
two numbers or is a factor of the difference between them.   In the
fraction $\frac{12}{15}$ the difference between the two terms is 3 and hence 3 is
the G.C.D.   In changing the form of the fraction $\frac{34}{51}$ the difference
between the numbers is 17, hence the largest divisor of both 34 and 51
is 17 and the fraction can be changed to the simpler fraction of $\frac{2}{3}$.
The G.C.D. of 210 and 280 is their difference of 70; of 95 and 114
is their difference of 19; of 140 and 168 is their difference of 28.

When one is to find the G.C.D. of three or more numbers he should
find all the possible differences and then try the smaller difference
for the greatest common divisor.   The G.C.D. of 140, 168, and 182
is 14 (the difference between 182 and 168).   In the example above
whose G.C.D. is 45, the 45 is a factor of all the differences between
the numbers 135, 315, and 450.   The differences are 180, 135, and
315.

Many sets of numbers have no common divisor other than 1 and
are said to be *relatively prime* to each other.   Numbers such as 13 and
20; 21 and 29, 31 and 100, etc., are relatively prime because their
greatest common divisor is 1.

When there are only two numbers in the set we can find the G.C.D.
by a method known as the Euclidean algorism.   The rule makes use,
in part, of the difference idea just discussed and suggests that first you
divide the larger number by the smaller one.   Then divide the divisor
by the remainder.   Continue to divide the last divisor by the last

remainder until there is no remainder.   The last divisor thus used is the G.C.D.

Find the G.C.D. of 54 and 72 by the Euclidean algorism.

$$
\begin{array}{r}
1 \\
54\,\overline{)\,72} \\
54 \\
\hline
18
\end{array}
\quad
\begin{array}{r}
3 \\
\overline{)\,54} \\
54 \\
\hline
0
\end{array}
\quad \text{The last divisor 18 is the G.C.D.}
$$

Find the G.C.D. of 754 and 986 by the method of Euclid.

$$
\begin{array}{r}
1 \\
754\,\overline{)\,986} \\
754 \\
\hline
232
\end{array}
\quad
\begin{array}{r}
3 \\
\overline{)\,754} \\
696 \\
\hline
58
\end{array}
\quad
\begin{array}{r}
4 \\
\overline{)\,232} \\
232 \\
\hline
0
\end{array}
\quad \text{Therefore 58 is the G.C.D.}
$$

4.13   The Lowest Common Multiple

A multiple of a number is the product of that number and any other integer different from 0.   Thus the consecutive multiples of 7 are 7 [1 × 7], 14 [2 × 7], 21 [3 × 7], 28 [4 × 7], etc.   The multiples of 11 are 11, 22, 33, 44, etc.   In other words a number is a multiple of a given number if it is exactly divisible by the given number.   Hence 48 is a multiple of 2, 3, 4, 6, 8, 12, 16, 24, and 48 because it is exactly divisible by each of those numbers.   When we are given a group of numbers we often wish to find the lowest multiple which is a common multiple of all.   This number we call the *lowest common multiple* (L.C.M.); it is the smallest integer which is exactly divisible by all the given numbers.   Sometimes this common multiple can be found by inspection.   One can readily perceive that the common multiple of 4 and 5 is 20, the common multiple of 6 and 7 is 42, and that the common multiple of 9 and 12 is 36.   There are other multiples of these sets of numbers but we have listed here the *lowest* ones.   If these pairs of numbers are laid off on a number line an infinite number of times, the first point coincident to both would be the lowest common multiple. There would be other points of coincidence but the first one would be the *lowest* multiple.

0 1 2 3 4 5 6 7 8 9 10 11 12 13 14 15 16 17 18 19 |20| 21 22 23 24 25 26

We can write several multiples of the numbers and then select the number which is a multiple of all the given numbers. To find the L.C.M. of 8, 12, and 16 we write the multiples:

of 8 as 8, 16, 24, 32, 40, 48, 56, . . .
of 12 as 12, 24, 36, 48, 60, 72, . . .
of 16 as 16, 32, 48, 64, 80, . . .

We see that 48 is the lowest multiple common to all three numbers 8, 12, and 16.

If the lowest multiple cannot be found by inspection, we can make use of the factoring technique illustrated elsewhere. To find the L.C.M. of 18 and 24, we first write the numbers in their factored form.

$$18 = 2 \times 3^2$$
$$24 = 2^3 \times 3$$

Now since the multiple must be divisible by each of these numbers it must contain the highest powers of the several different factors represented in the two numbers. Since the different factors are 2 and 3 we must use the highest powers of these factors, namely, $2^3 \times 3^2$. Thus the L.C.M. for 18 and 24 is 8 × 9, or 72. Find the L.C.M. of 20, 30, and 56.

The factors of 20 are $2^2 \times 5$.
The factors of 30 are $2 \times 3 \times 5$.
The factors of 56 are $2^3 \times 7$.

The L.C.M. must contain the highest powers of all the different factors represented in the numbers. Therefore the L.C.M. of 20, 30, and 56 will be $2^3 \times 3 \times 5 \times 7$, or 840.

The utilitarian value of this concept finds its justification in enabling one to find the lowest common denominator when adding a series of fractions. The L.C.M. of the separate denominators becomes the lowest common denominator of all the given fractions.

The lowest common multiple of several numbers can be found by the use of successive division similar to that used in finding the G.C.D.

of several numbers. There is a slight difference in the divisions, however. In the former we divided by numbers which were common divisors of all the given numbers of the quotients remaining after one or more divisions. To find the L.C.M. we divide by prime numbers which are divisors of two or more of the given numbers. We write down the quotients and any numbers not divisible by the divisor. We continue to divide until no two numbers have common divisors. Then we multiply all the divisors and the quotients (on the last line) to obtain the L.C.M.

Let us illustrate by finding the L.C.M. of 140, 150, and 180.

2) 140 —	150 —	180	Every number is divisible by 2.
2) 70 —	75 —	90	75 is not divisible by 2 so it is written.
3) 35 —	75 —	45	35 is not divisible by 3 so it is written.
5) 35 —	25 —	15	Every number is divisible by 5.
7 —	5 —	3	

The L.C.M. $= 2 \times 2 \times 3 \times 5 \times 7 \times 5 \times 3 = 6300$.

No number divides two of the remaining quotients so the division is completed.

4.14   Principles of Factoring

Elsewhere in this chapter there is a discussion of principles underlying the division operation. The discussion is to be carried further here with a brief explanation of some principles underlying factoring.

1. A factor of a number is a factor of any of its multiples.

Since 5 is a factor of 15, it is a factor of 2×15, 3×15, etc. If $N \div a = b$ then $2N \div a = 2b$, $3N \div a = 3b$, etc. Since 2 is a factor of 28, it is also a factor of 56, 84, and any multiple of 28.

2. If a number is divisible by each of two numbers, relatively prime, it is divisible by their product.

Since 2 is a factor of 12 and 3 is also a factor of 12, then 2×3 or 6 is a factor of 12. (12 ÷ 6 is exact.) If $R \div a = n$ and $R \div b = m$, and a and b are relatively prime, then $R \div (a \times b) = \dfrac{m \times n}{R}$ which is exact. The number 240 is divisible by both 5 and 6, (relatively prime) therefore it is divisible by 30.

3. A factor of each of two numbers is a factor of their sum, their difference, and their product.

Since 9 is a factor of 18 and 63, it is a factor of 81, 45, and 1134. If a and b are both even numbers (divisible by 2), then $a + b$, $a - b$, and $a \times b$ are also even numbers.

4. If the product of two numbers is 1, then each number is, by definition, the reciprocal of the other.

In other words, the reciprocal of a number is equal to the quotient of 1 divided by the number. The reciprocal of N is $\frac{1}{N}$, of $\frac{2}{3}$ is $\frac{3}{2}$, of $\frac{1}{7}$ is 7. Since $\frac{4}{5} \times \frac{5}{4} = 1$, then each is the reciprocal of the other.

There are many other principles and relationships affecting the division operation and some of these the student will be asked to demonstrate as exercises later.

4.15   Tests for Divisibility

Occasionally it is desirable to know whether or not a given number is divisible (produces an integral quotient) by certain other numbers like 2, 3, 4, 5, 6, etc.   There are tests which one can apply to ascertain this information without performing the division.   However, in some cases, as with the divisor 7, it is simpler to perform the actual division than to apply any test.   We shall list here a few of the tests for divisibility.

Divisibility by 2.   A number is divisible by 2 if the ones digit is divisible by 2.

Examples: 34   536   33,338

Divisibility by 3.   A number is divisible by 3 if the sum of its digits is divisible by 3.

Examples: 111   123   630,117

Divisibility by 4.   A number is divisible by 4 if the number formed by the two right-hand digits is divisible by 4.

Examples: 124   348   211,808

Divisibility by 5.   A number is divisible by 5 if the ones digit is a zero or a 5.

Examples: 45   3370   567,395

Divisibility by 6. A number is divisible by 6 if it is an even number and is divisible by 3.

Examples: 24   648   323,112

Divisibility by 8. A number is divisible by 8 if the number formed by the last three right-hand digits is divisible by 8.

Examples: 88   1728   344,512

Divisibility by 9. A number is divisible by 9 if the sum of its digits is divisible by 9.

Examples: 117   4410   345,672

Divisibility by 10. A number is divisible by 10 if the ones digit is zero.

Examples: 30   780   567,040

Other tests for divisibility can be devised by the student but the ones given here are the most useful ones.

4.16   Square Root

The square root of a number is another number which when multiplied by itself will produce the original number. We are assuming that a number has already been squared, and we are to find the number which was used as a factor two times. Should we wish to find the square root of 36, we must find a number which when multiplied by itself will produce 36. Hence 6 is the square root of 36 for when squared it will produce 36. What number multiplied by itself will equal 121? In symbolic form we write the question this way: $\sqrt{121}$, and since we know that $11 \times 11 = 121$, then $\sqrt{121} = 11$. When finding the square root of a number, we are interested in its factors, for we want to separate all of its factors into two identically equal groups. For instance, if we want to find the square root of 225, we first factor 225 into $3 \times 3 \times 5 \times 5$ and then we rearrange these factors into two identical pairs, 3×5 and 3×5. One pair represents the square root of 225. If a given number is a perfect square the easiest method for finding its square root is by the factoring process. Let us find the square root of 324 by the factoring method.

$$
\begin{aligned}
324 &= 2 \times 162 \\
&= 2 \times 2 \times 81 \\
&= 2 \times 2 \times 3 \times 27 \\
&= 2 \times 2 \times 3 \times 3 \times 9 \\
&= 2 \times 2 \times 3 \times 3 \times 3 \times 3
\end{aligned}
$$

When these factors are arranged into two equal groups, we have 2 × 3 × 3 in each one of them. Therefore the product of 2, 3, and 3, or 18, represents the square root of 324.

The number 10,404 factors into 2 × 2 × 3 × 3 × 17 × 17, so its square root is equal to the product of 2 × 3 × 17, or 102.

A second method of finding the square root of a number which has already been discussed in section 4.12 is an approximation method, sometimes called Newton's method. This method makes use of dividing and averaging until a number approximating the true square root is obtained. Let us illustrate by finding the square root of 28. We first estimate the root as 5 and then divide 28 by 5. This results in a quotient of 5.6. The quotient and divisor are now averaged, $\frac{1}{2}(5.6 + 5) = 5.3$ which is a close approximation of $\sqrt{28}$. Now if 28 is divided by 5.3, the resulting quotient is 5.28. When this new quotient is averaged with the new divisor, the resulting quotient 5.29 is very near to the true square root of 28. When 5.29 is multiplied by itself, the resulting product is 27.9821. Hence we can conclude that the square root of 28 is 5.29.

For a second example let us find the square root of 161. Our first guess is 12 so if we divide by 12 we obtain a quotient of 13.4. The average of these two numbers is 12.7. This average, 12.7, is used as our second divisor and produces a quotient of 12.68. The average of 12.7 and 12.68 is 12.69, which we will assume to be the square root of 161, for when 12.69 is multiplied by itself the product is 161.0361.

A simple method of finding square roots makes use of tables of square roots and the assumption (though a false one) that the increase in the squares of numbers is proportional to the numbers themselves. This is called the interpolation method. In other words, if we have a number which is halfway between two numbers (whose square roots are known) then the square root of the given number is also halfway between the two known square roots. For instance, since we know the square roots of 4 and 9, we will assume that the square root of 5 is $\frac{1}{5}$ of a unit more than the square root of 4. The square root of 107 is $\frac{7}{21}$ of a unit more than the square root of 100, or 10.33. The square root of 17 is $4\frac{1}{9}$, of 18 is $4\frac{2}{9}$, or of 20 is $4\frac{4}{9}$, and so on.

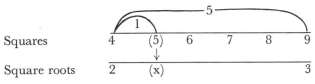

Squares	4	(5)	6	7	8	9
Square roots	2	(x)				3

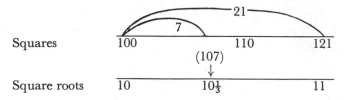

Squares	100		110	121
		(107)		
		↓		
Square roots	10	$10\frac{1}{3}$		11

If the squares of numbers (from 0 to 10) are graphed on the co-ordinate system as ordinates using the numbers as abscissas then we see that the true picture of the function $y = x^2$ is parabolic.   Readings can be made from this graph which will be more accurate than those obtained by the interpolation method above.   In the accompanying graph, we enter the table along an ordinate and find the corresponding abscissa on the x scale.   We find the square root of 20 to be approximately 4.5 and the square root of 75 to be about $8\frac{3}{5}$.   An extension of this graph would prove invaluable.

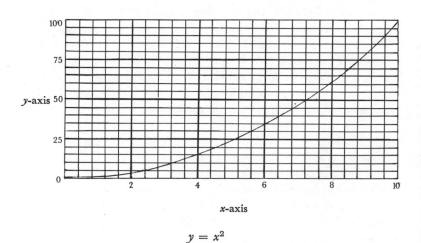

$$y = x^2$$

Now we should like to present the mechanical method for determining the square root of any number to decimal values.   We know that the square root of a one- or two-place number is a one-place number, the square root of a three- or four-place number is a two-place number, and the square root of a five- or six-place number is a three-place number, and so on.   Therefore, we begin by marking the number into periods of two places—beginning at the decimal point and moving in both directions.   It might be necessary to annex a zero to the decimal part for the number of decimal places must be an even number. Let us find the square root of 55,696.

1. Mark off in groups of 2. (Note that the integral part of the root will be in hundreds).

2. Determine the square root of the number in the first group. Put 2 in answer space above 5.

$$\begin{array}{r} 2 \\ \sqrt{5'56'96} \\ 4 \\ \hline 1\ 56 \end{array}$$

3. Square 2, subtract from 5. Remainder is 1.

4. Bring down the next group 56, making 156.

5. Multiply the answer by 20, obtaining 40.

6. Use 40 as a trial divisor of 156. This produces a quotient of 3. Place 3 in the answer space.

7. Add the 3 to the 40, making 43, and then multiply 43 by 3. Write this product, 129.

$$\begin{array}{r} 2\ 3 \\ \sqrt{5'56'96} \\ 4 \\ \hline 1\ 56 \\ 1\ 29 \\ \hline 27\ 96 \end{array}$$

40
+ 3
43

8. Subtract 129 from 156, leaving 27, and bring down the last group, making the number 2796.

9. Multiply the entire answer by 20: $20 \times 23 = 460$.

10. Use 460 as a trial divisor of 2796. This division results in a quotient of 6. Place 6 in in the answer space.

11. Add 6 to 460 making 466 and multiply 6×466, giving 2796.

$$\begin{array}{r} 2\ 3\ 6 \\ \sqrt{5'56'96} \\ 4 \\ \hline 1\ 56 \\ 1\ 29 \\ \hline 27\ 96 \\ 27\ 96 \\ \hline \end{array}$$

460
+ 6
466

12. Hence the square root of 55,696 is 236.

EXERCISES

SET 17

1. Find the square roots of these numbers by the method of approximations so as to find the I (integer) value in the formula $\sqrt{N} = I +$ fraction.

193   567   861   1523   10736

2. Find the greatest common divisor of the following sets of numbers:

135, 225, 280   144, 216   352, 420
96, 72, 120, 200   156, 184   198, 792
120, 132, 144   504, 904   3072, 7680

3. Find the G. C. D. of the following pairs of numbers by three distinct methods:

(a) 102, 255   (b) 1540, 2860   (c) 4522, 4845

4. Find the lowest common multiple of the following sets of numbers:

16, 20, 30	48, 52	15, 25, 35, 45
36, 48, 84	92, 96	20, 40, 50, 70
3, 17, 306	102, 85	13, 26, 52, 91

5. Determine which of the following numbers are prime:

283   239   1623   3227   751   941   3719   953

6. Substitute a numeral for the zero in the number 74,980 so that it is exactly divisible by 4, 6, and 9 at the same time.

7. Perform the following divisions directly without the use of paper and pencil:

| 480 ÷ 10 | 8400 ÷ 25 | 4440 ÷ 5 | 1700 ÷ 50 | 60,000 ÷ 200 |
| 7200 ÷ 10 | 11,200 ÷ 25 | 1240 ÷ 5 | 3200 ÷ 50 | 990,000 ÷ 300 |

8. Which of the following represent even numbers:

122 (five) 429 (eleven) 2244 (seven) 3333 (nine) 101021 (three)

9. Replace the X's in the number 4,2XX,X24 so that it will be divisible by both 8 and 9.

Replace the X's in 3,5XX,28X so that it will be divisible by both 5 and 9.

Replace the X's in 45X,XXX so that it will be divisible by 2, 3, 4, 5, 6, 8, and 9.

10. Explain why 43,608 is divisible by 4 and by 8.

11. How many sets of consecutive odd prime numbers are there less than 100?

12. What single-digit numbers are exact divisors of the following numbers?

428   7,165   200,169   3,440,692   92,150,784

13. Find the square root of 115 by (*a*) interpolation, (*b*) approximation, (*c*) the square root method.

CHAPTER 5

OPERATIONS WITH COMMON FRACTIONS

5.1 What Are Fractions?

Up to this point in the text we have been concerned with the fundamental operations with integers (whole numbers). Now we shall discuss and learn how to work with a new kind of number, one which is not an integer. This number can be less than an integer, equivalent to an integer, or it can be more than an integer. Numbers which are different from integers can be written in either of two forms, namely, as common fractions or as decimal fractions. This chapter will be concerned with interpretations of and operations with common fractions.

The word fraction comes from the Latin word *frangere* which means to fracture or to break. If a numeral made up of either one or several units is broken into parts, then the size of these parts, with respect to the whole, is given a number name of suitable description. The number names are fractions. There are usually *three* interpretations given to common fractions.

5.2 A Fraction Describes the Size (Magnitude) of One or More of the Equal Parts of a Whole

A part of something might represent a part of a single object or a part of a group of objects. A child might share his one candy bar with his buddy or a business man might share his profits with two co-owners. In the first case the buddy would receive a share of a single thing while in the second case a co-owner would receive a share of a quantity of things. When a whole thing is cut, divided, or broken into two parts of the same size, the size of each part is "one-half," and when a whole thing is divided into three parts of equal size, the size of each part is "one-third." Thus the little boy received one-half of the candy bar and the merchant received one-third of the profits.

One-half of a candy bar represents the size of one of the two equal pieces into which the bar has been broken.

One-third of the profits represents the size of one of the three equal parts into which the profit has been divided.

one-half of a bar	one-half of a bar

one-third of the profits	one-third of the profits	one-third of the profits

A candy bar
(representation)

Several thousand dollars profit
(representation)

Three-fourths of a cake represents three of the parts when the cake has been cut into four equal pieces. Three-fourths of the total num-number of games represents three of the parts if the total number of games is divided into four equal groups.

A cake (representation)   20 games (representation)

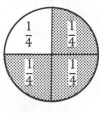

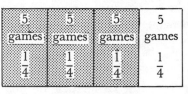

¾ of 1 thing   ¾ of 20 things

A fraction should always tell us the number of equal parts into which the whole has been divided, the size or name of each of the equal parts, and the number of equal parts under consideration. The number of equal parts into which a unit has been divided reveals the size of the parts and is called the *denominator* ("nominate" means to name). The denominator names the part. The number of parts which are being used, the number with which we are concerned, is called the *numerator* ("enumerate" tells how many). The numerator and denominator are called the terms of the fraction.

In the fraction $\frac{3}{4}$, the 4 tells us that the whole has been divided into 4 equal parts, the size of the part is one-fourth, and the quantity of parts represented or under consideration is 3. The 4 is the denominator and 3 is the numerator; the 3 and the 4 are the terms of the fraction.

A common fraction is always written with two parts, a numerator and a denominator. The numerator is written first; then a horizontal line is written directly under it and the denominator is written below the line. The correct way to write common fractions is:

$$\frac{\text{Numerator}}{\text{Denominator}}$$

and not

$$\text{Numerator/Denominator.}$$

Then the correct way to write the fraction one-half is $\frac{1}{2}$ and not 1/2 (which can be mistaken for the integer 112), and one-eighteenth should be written as $\frac{1}{18}$ and not 1/18 (which could be interpreted as eleven-eighths or even 1,118).

The common interpretation, then, of the common fraction $\frac{5}{9}$ means that some one quantity has been divided into 9 equal parts (that is, divided into 9 smaller equal sub-groups) and we are using or are concerned with 5 of them. In other words $\frac{5}{9}$ means five one-ninths.

One unit

| $\frac{1}{9}$ | $\frac{1}{9}$ | $\frac{1}{9}$ | $\frac{1}{9}$ | $\frac{1}{9}$ | $\frac{1}{9}$ | $\frac{1}{9}$ | $\frac{1}{9}$ | $\frac{1}{9}$ |

$\frac{5}{9}$ of one

When working with fractions students should first learn the meaning and use of the *unit* fraction, a fraction whose numerator is 1. Fractions with numerators different from 1 are called *non-unit* fractions or *multi-unit* fractions with preference given to the former. And attention must be directed to the fact that the size of various fractional parts represents the unit of measurement when things are counted. When we say we want $\frac{3}{4}$ of a pie we divide the pie into fourths first and then take 3 of the pieces (of size one-fourth). Or we might divide the pie into fourths and remove one-fourth. The part remaining represents $\frac{3}{4}$ of the whole pie. In any event we must either manually or visually divide the pie into 4 equal pieces. In like manner, should we wish to measure off $\frac{3}{8}$ of a yard of ribbon we need to measure off one piece which is $\frac{1}{8}$ yard long (divide the whole yard into 8 pieces of the same length) and measure off another part equal in length to this one-eighth yard, and then another, for $\frac{3}{8}$ means 3 one-eighths. We measure off $\frac{1}{8}$ and another $\frac{1}{8}$ and another $\frac{1}{8}$ in order to obtain $\frac{3}{8}$ of a yard of ribbon. If we say that in one season the New York Yankees won $\frac{5}{7}$ of their regularly scheduled games—154 games—we first divide the total number of games into 7 equal parts, we find $\frac{1}{7}$ of the whole amount and then count out 5 of these one-sevenths. One-seventh of the 154 games is 22 games, two-sevenths of them would be 2 × 22, three-sevenths of them would be 3 × 22, and five-sevenths of them would be 5 × 22 or 110 games.

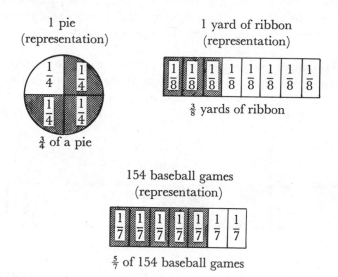

1 pie
(representation)

$\frac{3}{4}$ of a pie

1 yard of ribbon
(representation)

$\frac{3}{8}$ yards of ribbon

154 baseball games
(representation)

$\frac{5}{7}$ of 154 baseball games

Most of the work done with fractions is done with the very ordinary everyday fractions like halves, fourths, sixths, eighths, tenths, twelfths, and sixteenths. Fractions like sevenths, ninths, elevenths, seventeenths, and so on, are included as classroom problems for the purpose of developing depth in understanding and power in computation and for the sake of variety, but they are seldom encountered in real life. One would hardly ever cut a pie into thirteenths but an attempt to do so either in the concrete or picture stage will prove entertaining and enlightening. Research studies reveal that over 90 per cent of the fractions used in general business practice are the ones listed in the opening sentence of this paragraph.

When working with unit fractions from the same whole or from wholes of the same size one must be cognizant of relative sizes. One must learn in a logical fashion that if a pie is cut into thirds, the pieces will be smaller than the pieces of size one-half (of the same pie). Also, that a fourth of a pie is smaller than a third of a pie (of the same size), but there will be more pieces of the pie. Sixths are smaller than fifths, eighths smaller than sixths, tenths smaller than eighths, sixteenths smaller than eighths, etc., when they come from the same or equal wholes. If a whole thing is cut into pieces of size one-sixth, there will be more pieces than if the same whole is cut into fifths. When comparing unit fractions of the same or equal wholes, the fraction with the larger denominator represents the size of the smaller piece. Of the same or equal wholes $\frac{1}{2} > \frac{1}{3} > \frac{1}{4} > \frac{1}{5} > \frac{1}{6} > \frac{1}{7} > \frac{1}{8}$, etc.*

An emphasis on this phase of comparing unit fractions of the same whole will lead students to conclude that it takes two halves of an object to make up the whole object, three thirds of an object to make up the whole object, and that four fourths is equal to one. Thus if one eats $\frac{3}{5}$ of a cake there will be $\frac{2}{5}$ of the cake remaining, and if one has $\frac{7}{12}$ of a yard of ribbon he will need $\frac{5}{12}$ of a yard more to make up a whole yard of ribbon.

When the numerator of a fraction is the same as the denominator of the fraction, then that fraction has a value equal to 1.

$$\frac{5}{5} = 1 \qquad \frac{8}{8} = 1 \qquad \frac{12}{12} = 1$$

Coincidentally, if the numerator of a fraction is twice the denominator, then the fraction has a value of 2. Thus $\frac{4}{2}$ and $\frac{6}{3}$ and $\frac{8}{4}$ and $\frac{12}{6}$ are all equal to 2 and hence are equal to each other.

Every fraction has many equivalent forms for there are many names for the same number. For instance, the quantity $\frac{1}{2}$ can be expressed as $\frac{4}{8}$, $\frac{30}{60}$, $\frac{121}{242}$, etc; $\frac{5}{8}$ can be expressed as $\frac{10}{16}$, $\frac{15}{24}$, $\frac{500}{800}$, etc.; and $\frac{20}{80}$ can be expressed as $\frac{10}{40}$, $\frac{40}{160}$, $\frac{5}{20}$, $\frac{30}{120}$, etc.

* The symbol > means "is greater than." Thus $\frac{1}{2} > \frac{1}{3}$ is read "$\frac{1}{2}$ is greater than $\frac{1}{3}$."

A number line will help to establish more firmly this fact and other relationships between fractions.

0			1			2

0	$\dfrac{1}{2}$	$\dfrac{2}{2}$	$\dfrac{3}{2}$	$\dfrac{4}{2}$

0	$\dfrac{1}{4}$	$\dfrac{2}{4}$	$\dfrac{3}{4}$	$\dfrac{4}{4}$	$\dfrac{5}{4}$	$\dfrac{6}{4}$	$\dfrac{7}{4}$	$\dfrac{8}{4}$

0	$\dfrac{1}{8}$	$\dfrac{2}{8}$	$\dfrac{3}{8}$	$\dfrac{4}{8}$	$\dfrac{5}{8}$	$\dfrac{6}{8}$	$\dfrac{7}{8}$	$\dfrac{8}{8}$	$\dfrac{9}{8}$	$\dfrac{10}{8}$	$\dfrac{11}{8}$	$\dfrac{12}{8}$	$\dfrac{13}{8}$	$\dfrac{14}{8}$	$\dfrac{15}{8}$	$\dfrac{16}{8}$

$$\frac{1}{4} = \frac{2}{8} \qquad \frac{1}{2} = \frac{2}{4} = \frac{4}{8} \qquad \frac{3}{4} = \frac{6}{8} \qquad \frac{5}{4} = \frac{10}{8} \qquad \frac{3}{2} = \frac{6}{4} = \frac{12}{8}$$

5.3   A Fraction Is an Indicated Division

A fraction can be interpreted as a division of one number by another. The line separating the numerator and the denominator is called a division line and represents the operation of dividing the numerator by the denominator.   The fraction ¾ means that 3 things are to be divided into 4 equal parts.   In order to show this we must divide each of the three things into four equal parts and then regroup these pieces into 4 equal parts or groups.

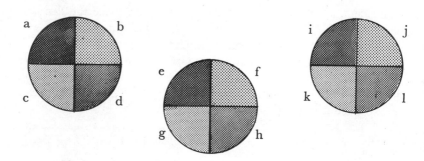

Here are three things divided into 4 equal parts each.   These pieces must be redistributed into 4 equal groups.

Group 1	Group 2	Group 3	Group 4
Put a here	Put b here	Put c here	Put d here
e	f	g	h
i	j	k	l

We see that in each of the four groups we have 3 one-fourths so $\frac{3}{4} = 3 \div 4 = 3$ one-fourths.

Let us interpret $\frac{5}{9}$ as an expression (of a fraction) indicating division. We must begin with the assumption that the numerator represents 5 concrete things which are to be divided into 9 equal parts.

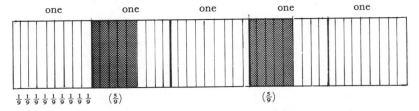

one   one   one   one   one

$\frac{1}{9}\frac{1}{9}\frac{1}{9}\frac{1}{9}\frac{1}{9}\frac{1}{9}\frac{1}{9}\frac{1}{9}\frac{1}{9}$ $(\frac{5}{9})$ $(\frac{5}{9})$

If these 5 things are divided into 9 equal parts we must first divide each one into 9 equal parts.   That will give us 45 smaller pieces each of the same size and named "one-ninths."   If these are divided into 9 equal groups there will be 5 pieces in each part, hence 5 one-ninths. Therefore $\frac{5}{9} = 5 \div 9 = 5$ one-ninths.

We can safely conclude that if a quantity is to be divided into a certain number of equal parts (the division interpretation of fractions) the end result will be the same as if we take that fractional part of one. If $6 is to be distributed equally among 8 boys each boy will receive 6 one-eighths of a dollar. ($\$\frac{6}{8}$)   The discerning student will be able to identify this division concept of a fraction as analogous to the partitioning aspect of division; the dividend is concrete, the divisor is abstract, and the final result is homogeneous in kind with the dividend or numerator of a fraction.

5.4   A Fraction Is a Ratio

If a fraction is interpreted as division with both the numerator and denominator representing the same kind of units then we have division as measurement.   We are making a comparison (which we call the ratio concept) between two quantities of the same kind. The fraction $\frac{2}{3}$ can mean a relationship of 2 things to 3 things of the same kind.   The relationship between the width of a room and its length might be 2 to 3.   For every 2 feet of width there are 3 feet of length.   This relationship is expressed as a ratio in fractional form and means that the number of feet in the width is two-thirds of the number of feet in the length of the rectangle.

$$\text{width}\ \boxed{\qquad\qquad\qquad\text{length}\qquad}$$

If a baseball team plays 154 games and wins 98 of them, then the ratio of the games won to the number of games played is 98 to 154, which is commonly written as $\frac{98}{154}$.   The relationship can also be written as 98 : 154 and is interpreted as 98 out of 154.

Sometimes the ratio is a comparison of parts of the whole and can be translated into a comparison of any part to the entire amount.   If a baseball team wins 5 games and loses 9, then the ratio of the games won to the games lost is $\frac{5}{9}$ or 5 to 9.   In other words, for every 5 games won the team lost 9.   Also, the ratio of the number of games won to the number of games played is 5 to 14; the team won $\frac{5}{14}$ of the total number of games played.   The fraction $\frac{2}{3}$ could be interpreted as representing the ratio of the number of males in our college to the number of females in the college.   If for every 2 males there are 3 females, the fraction $\frac{2}{3}$ represents the ratio between the two sexes of a population.   And if 4 out of 9 marbles are red and the others are blue, then the fraction $\frac{4}{5}$ shows that the number of red marbles is $\frac{4}{5}$ of the number of blue ones or $\frac{4}{9}$ of all.

There are many times in our everyday life when we make use of the ratio interpretation of fractions.   A pint has the same relationship to a gallon as 1 has to 8, the ratio of a foot to a yard is 1 to 3, the yard has the same ratio to a rod as 2 has to 11, and the ratio of one dozen to one gross is $\frac{1}{12}$. If Bill is 10 years old and his father is 40 years old, then the ratio of their ages is $\frac{1}{4}$. What will be the ratio between their ages in 20 years? What was it 5 years ago?

Bill's age now   1111111111
Father's age now   11111111111111111111111111111111111111111

5.5   Kinds of Fractions

Common fractions can be classified according to their form as either *simple, complex,* or *compound.* The simple fraction is one whose terms are integers such as $\frac{3}{4}$, $\frac{7}{11}$, $\frac{2}{9}$, etc. Most of the computations dealing with fractions are performed with simple fractions. If one or both terms of a fraction are non-integral, then the fraction is said to be complex such as $\frac{1\frac{1}{2}}{3}$, $\frac{5\frac{1}{4}}{7\frac{1}{4}}$, etc., but if one or both terms of the fraction involve some operation, then the fraction is said to be *compound.*   Fractions like $\frac{7\frac{1}{4} - \frac{1}{2}}{1\frac{1}{2} + \frac{1}{4}}$ and $\frac{5 \div \frac{1}{4}}{3 \times \frac{1}{2}}$ are compound and can be thought of as a sub-class of complex fractions.

There is also a classification of fractions in terms of their values. A fraction whose value is less than one is called a *proper* fraction, but if the value is equal to one or greater than one, then the fraction is said to be *improper.*   A proper fraction has a numerator which is less than the denominator. Fractions like $\frac{4}{7}$, $\frac{3}{5}$, and $\frac{18}{19}$ are called *proper* while $\frac{6}{5}$, $\frac{8}{8}$, and $\frac{16}{12}$ are *improper fractions.*   An improper fraction can always be expressed as an integer or as an integer plus a proper fraction, and when changed to the latter form is called a *mixed number.* Fractions which are equal in value but have different forms are called *equivalent* fractions. The fractions $\frac{8}{16}$, $\frac{5}{10}$, $\frac{4}{8}$, and $\frac{1}{2}$ are said to be equivalent. The fraction $\frac{5}{10}$ makes reference to 5 of the 10 equal parts of a whole, while $\frac{4}{8}$ refers to 4 of the 8 equal parts of the same whole; both quantities, however, are equivalent to $\frac{1}{2}$. These fractions are said to be equal in value though different in names and in meaning. Surely $\$\frac{1}{2}$ will buy just as much as $\$\frac{2}{4}$, but the latter refers to two coins while the former suggests only one. In one case we are talking about 1 half dollar and in the other we refer to 2 quarters. *Ordinary* fractions are those which are used in everyday personal and business affairs. Fractions like halves, thirds, fourths, and eighths are of the common ordinary variety and are often called *ruler* fractions, too.

5.6   Changing the Form of a Fraction

When performing operations with fractions it is often necessary to change the name of a fraction while keeping its value constant. Some authors define this change in form without a change in value as a reduction process.   The writer prefers to call this process simply a changing or a regrouping process.   Surely when $\frac{2}{4}$ is expressed as $\frac{1}{2}$ there has been a change in name, for instead of seeing or talking about fourths one now visualizes the half.   A change, a regrouping, or a renaming has taken place.   Since reduction might imply "making smaller," the term *changing* is recommended instead.   The principle involved in this changing process is often called the Golden Rule of fractions and implies the principle of compensation.   The Rule: Both terms of a fraction can be multiplied (or divided) by the same non-zero number without changing the value of the fraction.

When one changes $\frac{3}{4}$ to eighths the pieces will be half the size but there will be twice as many.

$$2 \times \frac{1}{2} \text{ of } \frac{3}{4} = \frac{6}{8} \qquad \text{Result:} \frac{2 \times 3}{2 \times 4} = \frac{6}{8}$$

When one changes $\frac{4}{6}$ to thirds the pieces will be twice as big but there will be half as many.

$$\frac{2 \times \frac{4}{6}}{2} \qquad \text{Result:} \quad \frac{4 \div 2}{6 \div 2} = \frac{2}{3} = \frac{\frac{1}{2} \times 4}{\frac{1}{2} \times 6} = \frac{2}{3}$$

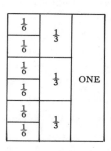

ONE			
$\frac{1}{2}$		$\frac{1}{2}$	
$\frac{1}{4}$	$\frac{1}{4}$	$\frac{1}{4}$	$\frac{1}{4}$
$\frac{1}{8}$ $\frac{1}{8}$	$\frac{1}{8}$ $\frac{1}{8}$	$\frac{1}{8}$ $\frac{1}{8}$	$\frac{1}{8}$ $\frac{1}{8}$

$\frac{3}{4}$ is equivalent to 6 one-eighths or $\frac{6}{8}$.

$$\frac{4}{6} = \frac{2}{3}.$$

To change fourths to eighths we multiply the denominator by 2 (we really multiply fourths by $\frac{1}{2}$), hence we must multiply the numerator by 2 also to maintain the equality of the two fractions. To change $\frac{3}{8}$ to sixteenths we must multiply the denominator by 2, hence we must also multiply the numerator by 2 so

$$\frac{3}{8} = \frac{6}{16} \text{ for } \frac{2 \times 3}{2 \times 8} = \frac{6}{16}$$

The effect of multiplying both the numerator and denominator by 2 has the effect of multiplying by $\frac{2}{2}$ or 1, which does not change the value of the number.

To change a fraction in terms of sixths to eighteenths we must multiply both the numerator and denominator by 3; to change thirds to sixths we multiply both terms by 2, and so it goes. We determine first the multiple of the denominator which will change the fraction to the required denomination and then multiply the numerator by that number also. Let us change $\frac{4}{15}$ to seventy-fifths. Since 75 is the fifth multiple of 15 we multiply both terms of the fraction by 5.

$$\frac{5 \times 4}{5 \times 15} = \frac{20}{75} \quad \text{Then } \frac{4}{15} = \frac{20}{75}$$

The rationalization can be shown by the regrouping process. Let us take the number quantity $\frac{3}{4}$ and express it as the sum of unit fractions. Then break each of the unit fractions into two pieces of the same size (eighths) and express the entire amount in terms of unit fractions. We can readily see that $\frac{3}{4}$ is equivalent to the fraction quantity $\frac{6}{8}$.

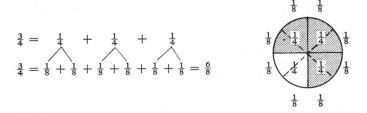

Students should be able to discover for themselves that the number of fourths in a number is half the number of eighths, that the number of halves is half the number of fourths, that the number of thirds is one-third the number of ninths, etc. This regrouping process changes a fraction so that the denomination is larger in size though the denominator is smaller (as a number) than the original denominator. Should one wish to change $\frac{4}{8}$ to an equivalent fraction he can express the quantity in larger denominations (with smaller denominators) such as in fourths or halves. Eighths can be changed into fourths or halves, tenths can be changed into fifths and into halves, and twelfths can be converted to sixths, fourths, thirds, and halves. Sometimes certain denominations are more convenient choices than others. For instance, the fraction $\frac{8}{12}$ can be changed conveniently into thirds ($\frac{2}{3}$), but if it were changed to fourths the numerator would be a mixed number, a non-integer $\left(\frac{2\frac{2}{3}}{4}\right)$. We usually convert fractions into forms such that their terms will be integers.

To change a fraction into simpler terms (with a smaller denominator and hence fewer parts) we ascertain what divisor of the given denominator will produce the required denominator. To change eighteenths to sixths we would have to divide 18 by 3 to obtain 6. Then we divide both the numerator and denominator by that number.

Change $\frac{12}{18}$ to sixths. Solution: $\frac{12}{18} = \frac{?}{6}$ $\frac{12 \div 3}{18 \div 3} = \frac{4}{6}$ Thus $\frac{12}{18} = \frac{4}{6}$.

Both terms of the fraction can be divided by the same number, different from zero, without any change in the value of the fraction. These divisions can be performed all at once by a composite divisor or they can be done in succession by prime number divisors. Should one wish to change a fraction in terms of thirty-sixths to simpler terms he might see that both terms of the fraction could be divided by 12 or he could divide successively by 2, 2, and 3. In either case he ought to be able to show equivalence of value.

$$\frac{24 \div 12}{36 \div 12} = \frac{2}{3} \quad \text{or} \quad \frac{24 \div 2}{36 \div 2} = \frac{12}{18}, \quad \frac{12 \div 2}{18 \div 2} = \frac{6}{9}, \quad \frac{6 \div 3}{9 \div 3} = \frac{2}{3}$$

Another interpretation of this conversion might enhance one's understanding of the process. If we wish to change $\frac{3}{8}$ to sixteenths we could rationalize as follows:

$$\frac{3}{8} = 3\left(\frac{1}{8}\right). \quad \text{Now } \frac{1}{8} = \frac{2}{16}.$$

Therefore $3\left(\frac{1}{8}\right) = 3\left(\frac{2}{16}\right)$ and $3\left(\frac{2}{16}\right) = \frac{6}{16}$ so $\frac{3}{8} = \frac{6}{16}$.

Another example: $\frac{5}{6} = \frac{?}{18}$

Analysis: $\frac{5}{6} = 5\left(\frac{1}{6}\right)$. Now $\frac{1}{6} = \frac{3}{18}$, so $5\left(\frac{1}{6}\right) = 5\left(\frac{3}{18}\right)$ and $5\left(\frac{3}{18}\right) = \frac{15}{18}$.

Then $\frac{5}{6} = \frac{15}{18}$.

The principles we have just explained for changing any fraction to a new fraction with a given denominator can be applied in the same manner to express any fraction in a new form with a given numerator. Should one have $\frac{3}{4}$ of a watermelon (he should have 3 pieces of size $\frac{1}{4}$ presumably) and have a need for 9 pieces he would have to cut each one-fourth into 3 equal parts. That would give him 9 pieces whose size would be one-third of the original size. We have changed $\frac{3}{4}$ to $\frac{9}{what}$? We see that to change our original fraction we must multiply the original numerator by 3. Then we must, in turn, multiply the denominator by 3 also. This will produce $\frac{9}{12}$.

$$\frac{3}{4} = \frac{9}{?} \qquad \frac{3 \times 3}{3 \times 4} = \frac{9}{12}$$

In like manner, if we are considering the number $\frac{15}{20}$ and want to change it to only 3 pieces, we would divide both the terms by 5.

$$\frac{15 \div 5}{20 \div 5} = \frac{3}{4}$$

A fraction is in its simplest terms when there is no common integral divisor of both the numerator and denominator. Fractions like $\frac{3}{4}, \frac{9}{16}, \frac{20}{21}$, etc., have no common divisors of both the numerator and denominator. In the fraction $\frac{9}{16}$ both terms have divisors but there is no number which will divide both of them and produce an integral result. Therefore since the terms are relatively prime the fraction is said to be in its simplest terms.

EXERCISES

SET 18

1. Express each of the following fractions as the sum of unit fractions in at least two different ways:

$$\frac{7}{9} \qquad \frac{5}{16} \qquad \frac{23}{24} \qquad \frac{31}{32} \qquad \frac{5}{11} \qquad \frac{2}{19} \qquad \frac{19}{28}$$

2. Show an interpretation of $\frac{5}{6}$ as division and also as a ratio.

3. Which of the following sets of fractions are equivalent?

(a) $\dfrac{5}{12}\quad\dfrac{10}{24}$ (c) $\dfrac{12}{18}\quad\dfrac{6}{9}\quad\dfrac{20}{30}$ (e) $\dfrac{2\frac{1}{2}}{10}\quad\dfrac{25}{100}\quad\dfrac{1}{4}$

(b) $\dfrac{3}{9}\quad\dfrac{2}{6}\quad\dfrac{30}{90}$ (d) $\dfrac{5}{8}\quad\dfrac{15}{24}\quad\dfrac{20}{32}$ (f) $\dfrac{5\frac{1}{2}}{100}\quad\dfrac{55}{1000}\quad\dfrac{5}{100}$

4. Show that 5 one-sevenths is smaller than 5 one-sixths of a whole.
Show that 11 one-eighths is larger than 9 one-eighths of a whole.
Show by use of a line drawing that $\frac{4}{5}$ is larger than $\frac{3}{4}$.
Show by use of a number line that $\frac{2}{3}$ is equivalent to $\frac{6}{9}$.

5. Classify the following as to kind both as to form and value.

$$\frac{5}{8}\quad\frac{9}{8}\quad\frac{17}{11}\quad\frac{5}{6}\quad\frac{4\frac{1}{4}}{9}\quad\frac{2+3}{7}\quad\frac{2\frac{1}{4}}{3\frac{1}{2}}\quad\frac{9}{9}\quad\frac{1}{213}\quad\frac{7-7}{14}$$

6. Write the following as fractional parts of a whole:

24 minutes	5 months	4 fingers	7 eggs
3 days	73 cents	1 glove	3 ounces
43 square inches	3 quarts	1500 pounds	91 years

7. The term "cancellation" descriptive of an operation appears to be in disrepute. Can you tell why?

8. Show that the use of an incorrect procedure will change the following to equivalent fractions in simpler terms:

$$\frac{16}{64}\quad\frac{19}{95}\quad\frac{26}{65}\quad\frac{22}{121}\quad\frac{44}{143}$$

9. Supply the missing terms in the sets of equivalent fractions:

$$\frac{12}{8}=\frac{30}{?}\quad\frac{6}{8}=\frac{?}{20}\quad\frac{5}{16}=\frac{?}{24}\quad\frac{50}{75}=\frac{10}{?}\quad\frac{4}{15}=\frac{?}{60}$$

$$\frac{24}{48}=\frac{?}{8}\quad\frac{11}{121}=\frac{?}{143}\quad\frac{24}{21}=\frac{8}{?}\quad\frac{192}{216}=\frac{?}{45}\quad\frac{200}{300}=\frac{?}{400}$$

10. Simplify the following expressions:

$$\frac{3\frac{1}{2}}{9}\quad\frac{2\frac{1}{2}}{3\frac{1}{4}}\quad\frac{7\frac{1}{4}}{8\frac{1}{4}}\quad\frac{3\frac{1}{2}}{3\frac{1}{2}}\quad\frac{4\frac{1}{4}}{44}\quad\frac{9+\frac{1}{2}}{9-\frac{1}{2}}\quad\frac{2}{\frac{1}{2}+\frac{1}{2}}$$

11. Simplify the following by making use of the Euclid algorism:

$$\frac{204}{595}\quad\frac{435}{696}\quad\frac{1573}{1815}\quad\frac{835}{1503}$$

5.7 Changes Involving Mixed Numbers

A mixed number is, as the name implies, composed of two kinds of numbers, an integer and a fraction. The number can be written entirely as a fraction, in which case it becomes an improper fraction, but it cannot be expressed as an integer only. Our first consideration will be that of changing a mixed number into a fraction. Let us take the number $4\frac{1}{2}$ and transform it or regroup it into fractional parts and express the entire amount in fractional form. We can change the given amount conveniently into halves, fourths, eighths, etc., but it is more desirable to express $4\frac{1}{2}$ as halves. To do this we regroup the 4 whole parts into $1 + 1 + 1 + 1$ and then regroup each of these ones into halves. Then $4\frac{1}{2}$ becomes $\frac{2}{2} + \frac{2}{2} + \frac{2}{2} + \frac{2}{2} + \frac{1}{2}$ which when combined becomes $\frac{9}{2}$.

Pictorially the solution will look like this:

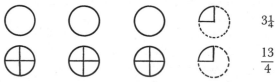

$$4\frac{1}{2} = \frac{9}{2}$$

If the example were $3\frac{1}{4}$ we would follow a similar approach. We would change the integral part into fractional parts thus: 3 becomes $\frac{4}{4} + \frac{4}{4} + \frac{4}{4}$ and then $3\frac{1}{4}$ becomes $\frac{4}{4} + \frac{4}{4} + \frac{4}{4} + \frac{1}{4}$ which in turn becomes $\frac{13}{4}$. The transformation is clearly discernible in picture form.

$$3\frac{1}{4}$$

$$\frac{13}{4}$$

To change a mixed number to an improper fraction we first express the whole number in fractional parts (in agreement with the given fractional parts) and then combine the given fractional amount. Should we wish to change $5\frac{2}{3}$ to thirds we would first change the 5 into thirds and then add the given two thirds. Since there are 3 thirds in one, then there will be 5 times 3 or 15 thirds in 5. Fifteen thirds and 2 thirds are 17 thirds. $5\frac{2}{3} = \frac{17}{3}$. In short, multiply the given denominator or size of the parts by the whole number and then add in the numerator. This number gives you the numerator of the improper fraction whose denominator is the given denominator.

$$3\frac{2}{5} = \frac{3 \times 5 + 2}{5} = \frac{17}{5} \qquad I + \frac{N}{D} = \frac{I \times D + N}{D} \qquad 4\frac{2}{7} = \frac{28 + 2}{7} = \frac{30}{7}.$$

The reader probably learned to multiply the integer by the denominator and then add in the numerator. This procedure will lead to the correct numerator (if the operations are performed correctly), but there is no justification for this order of operation. The correct procedure is to change the integral part to fractional parts and then combine with the given fractional parts. The emphasis should be on developing an understanding of the mathematical ideas and principles involved rather than on mechanical manipulations.

For another example, let us express $6\frac{4}{5}$ as an improper fraction.

1. Change 6 to fifths. $6 = \dfrac{?}{5}$

2. How many one-fifths are there in 6? $6 = \dfrac{30}{5}$

3. Add in the $\dfrac{4}{5}$: $\dfrac{30}{5} + \dfrac{4}{5}$

4. Then $6\dfrac{4}{5} = \dfrac{34}{5}$

If the numerator of a fraction is the same as or is equal to the denominator, the fraction has a value of one. If the numerator has a value which is greater than the value of the denominator, the value of the fraction is more than 1. Such fractions are called improper fractions and can easily be changed to mixed numbers. The fraction $\frac{7}{4}$ might have more meaning to the reader if changed to $\frac{4}{4} + \frac{3}{4}$ or 1 and $\frac{3}{4}$ than if left in its fractional form. The fraction $\frac{11}{3}$ might have more meaning to a student if it is expressed as the sum of a whole number and a fraction. To do this we remove groups of thirds, 3 at a time, from the given amount of 11 thirds until there are no more complete groups of 3 thirds left or simply until we have removed all the whole units (ones). We can do this 3 times and there will be $\frac{2}{3}$ left. Therefore $\frac{11}{3}$ becomes in turn $\frac{3}{3} + \frac{3}{3} + \frac{3}{3} + \frac{2}{3} = 1 + 1 + 1 + \frac{2}{3}$ or finally $3\frac{2}{3}$.

Pictorially the latter example can be represented as follows:

$$\underbrace{\bigcirc\bigcirc\bigcirc}_{\frac{3}{3}} \quad \underbrace{\bigcirc\bigcirc\bigcirc}_{\frac{3}{3}} \quad \underbrace{\bigcirc\bigcirc\bigcirc}_{\frac{3}{3}} \quad \underbrace{\bigcirc\bigcirc}_{\frac{2}{3}} \quad \frac{11}{3}$$

$$1 \quad + \quad 1 \quad + \quad 1 \quad + \quad \frac{2}{3} \quad = 3\frac{2}{3}$$

5.8 Comparison of Fractions

It is often necessary in everyday experiences to compare the relative sizes of two or more fractional quantities—to find the larger or smaller of two given amounts. There are several ways to do this and each will be illustrated here.

1. Express the fractions in the same denominations (equal denominators) and then compare their numerators.

2. Represent the given quantities linearly—on the same line diagram—and then compare their distances (or amounts) from the starting point.

3. Express the fractions as decimal fractions (of the same number of decimal places—same denominations) and compare them.

4. Express the fractions with equal numerators—the same number of pieces—and then compare the size of the pieces (compare denominations).

5. Find the differences between the given fractions and unity and compare the differences.

Method 1. Given the two fractional amounts $\frac{2}{11}$ and $\frac{3}{17}$, which is larger? Express both fractions as 187ths—the smallest integral common denominator.

$$\frac{2}{11} = \frac{34}{187} \quad \text{and} \quad \frac{3}{17} = \frac{33}{187}$$

When we compare thirty-four 187ths with thirty-three 187ths we find that the first amount is larger; therefore $\frac{2}{11}$ is larger than $\frac{3}{17}$. There is a short cut for doing problems of this kind. Multiply the first numerator by the second denominator and the second numerator by the first denominator. If the first product is the greater, then the first fraction is the larger of the two fractions. Compare $D_2 \times N_1$ with $D_1 \times N_2$. Should one wish to compare $\frac{3}{5}$ with $\frac{4}{7}$ the two fractions would be changed to thirty-fifths. This means that both the terms of the first fraction would be multiplied by 7 and both terms of the second one multiplied by 5. In other words we would have 7×3 compared with 5×4 (since both these amounts represent thirty-fifths). Since $7 \times 3 > 5 \times 4$, the fraction $\frac{3}{5}$ is the larger.

$$\frac{3}{5} \; ? \; \frac{4}{7}$$

$$\frac{3}{5} \diagdown\!\!\!\!\diagup \frac{4}{7}$$

Method 2. Given the fractional amounts $\frac{2}{3}$ and $\frac{3}{4}$, which is larger? Draw two lines of equal length. Divide one into 3 equal parts and

mark off two of them. Divide the other line into 4 equal parts and
mark off 3 of them. When we compare the two line segments we
see that the quantity $\frac{3}{4}$ is larger than $\frac{2}{3}$ if both represent parts of the
same quantity or of equal quantities.

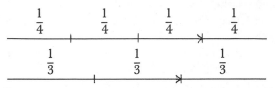

A basic principle which might be pointed out here is the fact that
if two or more numbers can be placed on the same number scale,
the one farther to the right is the largest.

$$-5 \quad -4 \quad -3 \quad -2 \quad -1 \quad 0 \quad 1 \quad 2 \quad 3 \quad 4 \quad 5 \quad 6$$

$$5 \text{ is greater than } \quad 2 \qquad 5 > 2$$
$$1 \text{ is greater than } -2 \qquad 1 > -2$$
$$-2 \text{ is greater than } -5 \qquad -2 > -5$$

Generalization: $a \qquad b \qquad 0 \qquad x \qquad y$

y is greater than either x, b, 0, or a. x is greater than either 0, b, or a.
b is greater than a but is less than 0, x, or y.

As a variable number approaches zero from the right it is getting
smaller. As it approaches zero from the left it is getting larger. As
a variable number moves to the right on a number scale it is increasing
in size. Therefore if two numbers are on a number line, the one to the
right is the larger.

$$0 \underline{\qquad\qquad \overset{\tfrac{1}{4}}{\underset{\tfrac{1}{5}}{\quad}} \left(\tfrac{1}{3}\right) \underset{\tfrac{2}{5}}{\quad} \overset{\tfrac{1}{2}}{\quad} \underset{\tfrac{3}{5}}{\quad} \left(\tfrac{2}{3}\right) \overset{\tfrac{3}{4}}{\underset{\tfrac{4}{5}}{\quad}} \qquad\qquad} 1$$

$\frac{1}{3}$ is greater than $\frac{1}{4}$; $\frac{2}{3}$ is greater than $\frac{3}{5}$; $\frac{4}{5}$ is greater than $\frac{2}{3}$.

Method 3. Given the fractional amounts $\frac{4}{5}$ and $\frac{17}{20}$, which is
larger? Though the concept of decimal fractions has not been
treated up to this point in the text the student ought to remember how
to change common fractions to decimal fractions. One concept of
the common fraction is that of division so if we divide the numerators
by their respective denominators we obtain the two decimal fractions

.80 and .85. Since .85 is larger than .80 we conclude that $\frac{17}{20}$ is larger than $\frac{4}{5}$.

Method 4. Given the two fractions $\frac{3}{5}$ and $\frac{2}{3}$, which is larger? Change both of the fractions so that they will have equal numerators. The first fraction becomes $\frac{6}{10}$ and the second one becomes $\frac{6}{9}$. The first quantity represents 6 pieces of size one-tenth and the latter represents 6 pieces of size one-ninth. Since the piece of size one-ninth is larger than the one-tenth, $\frac{1}{9} > \frac{1}{10}$, then $6(\frac{1}{9}\text{'s})$ represents an amount larger than 6 $(\frac{1}{10}\text{'s})$. Therefore $\frac{2}{3}$ is larger than $\frac{3}{5}$.

Method 5. Given the fractional quantities $\frac{5}{7}$ and $\frac{7}{9}$, which is larger? Compare the differences between the given quantities and unity (or some other convenient amount). When we compare $\frac{5}{7}$ with 1 we see that we need $\frac{2}{7}$ more to make 1 and when comparing $\frac{7}{9}$ with 1 we see that we need $\frac{2}{9}$ more to make 1. Since the amount $\frac{2}{9}$ is smaller than $\frac{2}{7}$ we know that conversely $\frac{7}{9}$ is larger than $\frac{5}{7}$.

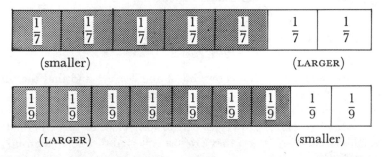

This method illustrates the principle or axiom relating to inequalities. The axiom states: "If unequals are subtracted from equals the remainders will be unequal but in reverse order."

$$1 \;=\; 1 \quad \text{equals}$$

$$\frac{2}{9} \;<\; \frac{2}{7} \quad \text{unequals}$$

$$\frac{7}{9} \;>\; \frac{5}{7} \quad \text{unequals}$$

Should one wish to make a comparison among three or more fractions, there is still the possibility of comparing them two at a time until one is certain of their relative sizes. If of three fractions *a*, *b*, and *c* it can be determined that *a* is greater than *b* and *b* is greater than *c*, then we know that $a > b > c$. But if *a* is greater than *b* and *c* is also greater than b we have not yet determined the relationship between a and c. We must then compare the latter two fractions, and when we know which of these two is the larger we will then know the relationship between a, b, and c.

5.9   Addition and Subtraction of Fractions

One of the fundamental laws governing the addition of whole numbers is the principle that only like things can be added or grouped together into a group with a single number property. This law also becomes the fundamental principle for the addition and subtraction of common fractions. Only like fractions can be combined, either by addition or subtraction, into a single fraction. We can combine one-third and one-third (of the same or equal wholes) to obtain two one-thirds in the same manner that we combine one apple and one apple to get a new group containing two apples.

1 apple	1 third	$\frac{1}{3} + \frac{1}{3} = \frac{2}{3}$	$\frac{1}{3}$
+ 1 apple	+ 1 third		$+ \frac{1}{3}$
2 apples	2 thirds		$\frac{2}{3}$

In like manner we can show that $\frac{4}{9}$ and $\frac{1}{9}$ are $\frac{5}{9}$ and that the sum of $\frac{3}{11}$ and $\frac{4}{11}$ is $\frac{7}{11}$. The pictorial representation for the addition of like fractions is very simple. Let us look at $\frac{1}{4} + \frac{1}{4} + \frac{1}{4}$. If the representative pieces are regrouped to form a whole or a part of a whole, the sum is $\frac{3}{4}$, but if they are just collected they form a group of 3 ($\frac{1}{4}$'s).

$$\frac{1}{4} + \frac{1}{4} + \frac{1}{4} = \frac{3}{4} \qquad \frac{1}{4} + \frac{1}{4} + \frac{1}{4} = 3\left(\frac{1's}{4}\right)$$

Varied experiences with the addition of like fractions should lead to all types of examples in which the sum is either less then, equal to, or greater than 1. In every case the sum should be expressed in simplest terms unless the requirements of the problem dictates otherwise. Thus sums of $\frac{6}{8}$, $\frac{5}{5}$, and $\frac{9}{6}$ should normally be expressed $\frac{3}{4}$, 1, and $1\frac{1}{2}$ respectively.

By definition, the numerator of a fraction expresses the number of parts and the denominator tells us the size of each part. Therefore in adding and subtracting fractions of like denominations we are concerned only with the numerators, the quantities of things which are to be regrouped. We combine the numerators only (as the signs dictate) when adding and subtracting fractions because these represent amounts; the denominator merely represents the name of the pieces we are combining. The number thus obtained expresses the number of parts in the final result; the size of the parts remains the same as before. We express the result in the same denomination. If we are adding fifths, the sum will be fifths, and if we are subtracting sevenths, the difference will be sevenths.

$$\frac{1}{5} + \frac{2}{5} = \frac{3}{5} \qquad \frac{5}{7} - \frac{3}{7} = \frac{2}{7}$$

One of the most difficult operations to perform in the realm of fractions is the addition (or subtraction) of fractions which are unlike —which have different denominations. This type of example may take one of several forms:

1. Fractions which are related $\qquad \frac{1}{4} + \frac{1}{8}$
   (one denominator is a multiple of the other)

2. Fractions which are unrelated $\qquad \frac{1}{3} + \frac{2}{5}$
   (the denominators are relatively prime)

3. Fractions which have a common factor $\qquad \frac{4}{9} + \frac{5}{12}$

Though authors of elementary school arithmetic texts suggest different approaches to each of these types, the writer believes that principles and practices which are general in nature and which will cover all types of addition examples should be presented.

Experience with fraction boards or fraction charts or equivalent fractions should enable students to determine intuitively (by inspection) that halves and thirds can both be measured by pieces of size one-sixth—that they can both be converted to sixths and then combined. If a piece of size one-third is cut into two equal pieces and the piece of size one-half is cut into three equal pieces, the several pieces will be of the same size. When these are grouped to form a whole, it can be shown that one more piece of the same size (we already have

5 pieces) will complete the whole. Therefore since it takes 6 pieces of this size to make unity each piece is of size one-sixth.

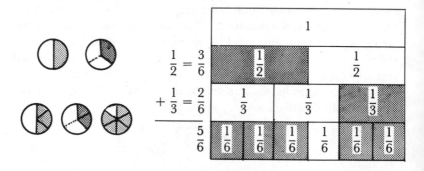

From the use of concrete and semi-concrete materials students should soon discover that halves and fifths can both be expressed as tenths, that fourths and fifths can both be changed to twentieths, thirds and fourths can be changed to twelfths, etc. A common denominator, though not necessarily the smallest possible one for two fractions, can be obtained by multiplying the given denominators together. Thus eighths and ninths can be changed to seventy-seconds and fifths and sixths can both be changed to thirtieths. Sixths and eighths can be expressed as forty-eighths though twenty-fourths would be the smallest common denominator.

The general rule applicable for finding the common denominator for two or more fractions is to try the smallest given denomination (the largest denominator). If this cannot be used for a common denominator then multiply it by 2 and try a new number. If this does not work, multiply the largest denominator by 3, and then by 4, and so on until some multiple of the largest denominator has been found which is a multiple of all the given denominators. The commmon denominator is always a multiple of the largest denominator (if one uses the largest denominator for the common denominator he is using the first multiple of the largest denominator).

When adding eighths and twelfths try using the larger denominator 1×12. Then try 2 times 12 to see if that number is a multiple of both 8 and 12. Since it is, then 2×12 or 24 is the lowest common denominator for the denominations, eighths and twelfths. Then to add $\frac{3}{8}$ and $\frac{5}{12}$ we must change them to $\frac{9}{24}$ and $\frac{10}{24}$ respectively before combining them. The sum is $\frac{19}{24}$.

This method is advantageous for finding the common denominator of 3 or more fractions. Let us add $\frac{5}{6} + \frac{4}{9} + \frac{7}{12}$. If we follow the above rule we first try 12. This will not work for we cannot (conveniently) change ninths to twelfths. Then we try 2×12 or 24. This will not do either. Next we try 3×12 or 36. This time we find that 36 is a multiple of all three of the given denominators so we express each of the given fractions as thirty-sixths.

$$1 \times \frac{5}{6} \quad \frac{5}{6} = \frac{(6) \times 5}{(6) \times 6} = \frac{30}{36}$$

$$1 \times \frac{4}{9} \quad \frac{4}{9} = \frac{(4) \times 4}{(4) \times 9} = \frac{16}{36}$$

$$1 \times \frac{7}{12} \quad \frac{7}{12} = \frac{(3) \times 7}{(3) \times 12} = \frac{21}{36}$$

$$\frac{67}{36} = \frac{36}{36} + \frac{31}{36} = 1\frac{31}{36}$$

The sum is $\frac{67}{36}$ which is $\frac{36}{36}$ and $\frac{31}{36}$ which equals 1 and $\frac{31}{36}$.

Though this method is the one generally recommended for finding the lowest common denominator (L.C.D.), the reader might find value in one or all of the following suggestions. The first of these is the factoring method. Let us use the previous example for our first illustration. Add $\frac{5}{6}$, $\frac{4}{9}$, and $\frac{7}{12}$. Begin by factoring the denominators.

$$\frac{5}{6} = \frac{5}{2 \times 3}$$

$$\frac{4}{9} = \frac{4}{3 \times 3}$$

$$\frac{7}{12} = \frac{7}{2 \times 2 \times 3}$$

Now for the lowest common denominator we must use all the different factors the greatest number of times they appear in any one number. All the different factors are 2 and 3. Since 2 appears at most 2 times (twice in 12) and 3 appears at the most 2 times (twice in 9) we must use 2×2 times 3×3 for our L.C.D. This product is 36. The student should see that this procedure is identical with finding the lowest common multiple of a set of numbers and is explained in section 4.13.

The factoring process can be conveniently performed by an algorism commonly referred to as continued short division. Let us use the same example for our first illustration. Write the denominators and begin to divide by prime numbers (such as 2, 3, 5, etc.) which will divide at least two of the numbers. If it is not a divisor of a number, write that number along with the quotients (bring it down). Divide by 2. Then divide by 3.

$$\begin{array}{r} 2 \overline{)\ 6 - 9 - 12} \\ 3 - 9 - \ 6 \end{array} \qquad \begin{array}{r} 2 \overline{)\ 6 - 9 - 12} \\ 3 \overline{)\ 3 - 9 - \ 6} \\ 1 - 3 - \ 2 \end{array}$$

L.C.D. $= 2 \times 3 \times 1 \times 3 \times 2 = 36$

Since there are no more divisors which will divide two or more of the remaining numbers, then the product of these divisors and quotients will be the L.C.D. Hence $2 \times 3 \times 1 \times 3 \times 2$, which is 36, is the L.C.D.

Another example:

$$\text{Add } \frac{1}{12} + \frac{1}{15} + \frac{1}{18}$$

Write the denominators and begin the process of dividing by prime numbers.

$$\begin{array}{r} 2 \overline{)\ 12 - 15 - 18} \\ 6 - 15 - \ 9 \end{array} \quad \begin{array}{r} 2 \overline{)\ 12 - 15 - 18} \\ 3 \overline{)\ 6 - 15 - \ 9} \\ 2 - \ 5 - \ 3 \end{array} \quad \begin{array}{r} 2 \overline{)\ 12 - 15 - 18} \\ 3 \overline{)\ 6 - 15 - \ 9} \\ 2 - \ 5 - \ 3 \end{array} = 180$$

Remember that when a number cannot be divided exactly it is brought down. Now the lowest common denominator for twelfths, fifteenths, and eighteenths is the product of 2, 3, 2, 5, and 3. This product is 180 so the L.C.D. is 180, and the three fractions above become $\frac{15}{180}$, $\frac{12}{180}$, $\frac{10}{180}$ for a total of $\frac{37}{180}$.

Find the L.C.D. for these fractions:

$$\frac{5}{24} + \frac{7}{20} + \frac{4}{25}$$

$$\begin{array}{r} 2 \overline{)\ 24 - 20 - 25} \\ 2 \overline{)\ 12 - 10 - 25} \\ 5 \overline{)\ 6 - \ 5 - 25} \\ 6 - \ 1 - \ 5 \end{array} = 600$$

L.C.D. $= 2 \times 2 \times 5 \times 6 \times 1 \times 5 = 600$

There is still another method for finding the lowest common denominator when adding three or more fractions. Sometimes it will be more convenient to find the sum of any two fractions first and then add the third fraction to this sum. The sum of thirds and fourths will be twelfths. To add fifths to this sum we would have to express these fractions as sixtieths for 60 is the lowest common multiple of 5 and 12.

An example: $\frac{1}{3}$ A suggested solution: $\frac{1}{3} = \frac{4}{12}$

$\frac{1}{4}$ $+ \frac{1}{4} = \frac{3}{12}$

$+ \frac{1}{5}$ $\frac{7}{12} = \frac{35}{60}$

Now add the other fraction $\frac{1}{5} = \frac{12}{60}$

$\frac{47}{60}$

Though the addition of three fractions is discussed here the reader should remember that problems of this nature seldom occur in real life situations and should not be practiced to the exclusion of more useful exercises. However, a knowledge of the procedures and principles suggested here should prove beneficial to all.

5.10   Addition and Subtraction of Mixed Numbers

The addition of two or more mixed numbers presents a few new difficulties. Yet if one understands the principles involved in the addition of fractions then he will be able to apply them to the addition of mixed numbers. According to the principle of likeness we add the fractional parts first and then add the integral parts. Before doing this it might be necessary to rewrite the entire mixed number (when changing it to an equivalent form). If the sum of the fractional parts is equal to an integer or an integer plus a fractional part, then the integral parts of the sums are combined.

There are many types of mixed-number additions, the simplest of which is the addition of an integer to a mixed number. Add 4 to $4\frac{1}{2}$. The solution of this example ought to be obvious. Then there is the type in which the fractional parts are like fractions. Add $3\frac{3}{4} + 1\frac{1}{4}$. If we add the fractional parts we get 1 which when combined with the integers gives a sum of 5. The most difficult example is the type in which the fractional parts are unlike. We must first add the fractional parts (methods of changing unlike fractions to like fractions already have been given in this chapter) and then combine the integers.   Let us combine $1\frac{1}{5}$ with $2\frac{3}{4}$.   To combine the fractional parts we must first express the fractions as twentieths.

$$1\tfrac{1}{5} = 1\tfrac{4}{20}$$
$$+\ 2\tfrac{3}{4} = 2\tfrac{15}{20}$$
$$\overline{\phantom{+\ 2\tfrac{3}{4} = 2}\tfrac{19}{20}}$$

Add the fractions—

Add the integers—   3

The sum of $1\frac{1}{5}$ and $2\frac{3}{4}$ is $3\frac{19}{20}$

$$1 \quad + \quad \tfrac{1}{5} \qquad\qquad 2 \qquad + \quad \tfrac{3}{4}$$

Subtraction examples offer difficulties of two types; those in which the fractional part of the subtrahend is smaller than the fractional part of the minuend and those in which the reverse is true.   In the former case the subtraction should present no problem if the fractional parts are first changed to equivalent fractions.   First we subtract the fractional parts and then we find the difference between the integral parts.   Subtract $3\frac{3}{5}$ from $7\frac{3}{4}$.

$$7\tfrac{3}{4} = 7\tfrac{15}{20}$$
$$-\ 3\tfrac{3}{5} = 3\tfrac{12}{20}$$
$$\overline{\phantom{-\ 3\tfrac{3}{5} = }4\tfrac{3}{20}}$$

The second type of example requires some alteration of the minuend before the subtraction can be performed.   This alteration or change can be done either by the decomposition technique or the equal-additions method both of which have been explained in Chapter 2.   Subtract $4\frac{5}{8}$ from $9\frac{1}{4}$.

By the decomposition method:

$$9\tfrac{1}{4} = \quad 9\tfrac{2}{8} = \quad 8 + \tfrac{8}{8} + \tfrac{2}{8} = \quad 8\tfrac{10}{8}$$
$$-4\tfrac{5}{8} = -4\tfrac{5}{8} = -4\tfrac{5}{8} \qquad\qquad = -4\tfrac{5}{8}$$
$$\overline{\phantom{-4\tfrac{5}{8} = -4\tfrac{5}{8} = -4\tfrac{5}{8} \qquad\qquad =\ \ }4\tfrac{5}{8}}$$

By the equal-additions method:

$$9\tfrac{1}{4} = \quad 9\tfrac{2}{8} \quad \text{(add 1 in the form of } \tfrac{8}{8}) = \quad 9\tfrac{10}{8}$$
$$-4\tfrac{5}{8} = -4\tfrac{5}{8} \quad \text{(add 1)} \qquad\qquad\quad = -5\tfrac{5}{8}$$
$$\overline{\phantom{-4\tfrac{5}{8} = -4\tfrac{5}{8} \quad \text{(add 1)} \qquad\qquad\quad =\ }4\tfrac{5}{8}}$$

The equal-additions approach can be used to change the subtrahend into an integer.   If the example is $9 - 6\frac{2}{3}$ we can add $\frac{1}{3}$ to both terms so that the example becomes $9\frac{1}{3} - 7$. Result is $2\frac{1}{3}$. If the example is $12\frac{1}{4} - 3\frac{3}{4}$ we can add $\frac{1}{4}$ to both terms so that the example becomes, without any change in the difference, $12\frac{1}{2} - 4$, or $8\frac{1}{2}$.

$$9\frac{1}{4} = 9\frac{2}{8} \text{ (add } \tfrac{3}{8}\text{)} \qquad 9\frac{5}{8}$$
$$-4\frac{5}{8} = 4\frac{5}{8} \text{ (add } \tfrac{3}{8}\text{)} \qquad \underline{-5}$$
$$\phantom{-4\frac{5}{8} = 4\frac{5}{8} \text{ (add } \tfrac{3}{8}\text{)} \qquad} 4\frac{5}{8}$$

EXERCISES

SET 19

1. Change the following to mixed numbers in their simplest form:

$$\frac{6}{4} \qquad \frac{17}{5} \qquad \frac{13}{12} \qquad \frac{27}{4} \qquad \frac{11}{8} \qquad \frac{20}{4} \qquad \frac{14}{8} \qquad \frac{10}{3} \qquad \frac{34}{32}$$

2. Change the following to improper fractions:

$$2\frac{1}{2} \quad 4\frac{1}{3} \quad 5\frac{2}{3} \quad 8\frac{1}{4} \quad 16\frac{2}{3} \quad 102\frac{4}{5} \quad 7\frac{1}{6} \quad 3\frac{2}{5} \quad 1\frac{7}{8} \quad 12\frac{3}{16}$$

3. Show the following equivalents in pictorial representations:

$$2\frac{2}{3} = \frac{8}{3} \qquad \frac{12}{5} = 2\frac{2}{5}$$

4. From the following pairs of fractions, select the one which has the larger value.

$$\frac{5}{9} \; \frac{2}{3} \qquad \frac{7}{11} \; \frac{2}{3} \qquad \frac{4}{15} \; \frac{3}{11} \qquad \frac{11}{13} \; \frac{15}{17} \qquad \frac{7}{12} \; \frac{4}{7} \qquad \frac{3}{82} \; \frac{7}{191}$$

5. Find the L.C.D. for
   (a) eighths, sixths, and fourths.
   (b) thirds, fifths, and ninths.
   (c) twelfths, tenths, and fifteenths.
   (d) halves, thirds, fifths, and sixths.
   (e) eighths, twelfths, thirty-seconds.

6. Compare the fractions $\frac{5}{8}$, $\frac{2}{3}$, $\frac{13}{20}$ by the 5 methods suggested in this chapter.

7. Combine the following:

$$\frac{7}{8} + \frac{9}{16} + \frac{1}{2} \qquad \frac{5}{12} + \frac{3}{16} + \frac{1}{8} \qquad \frac{7}{16} + \frac{5}{8} + \frac{9}{24}$$

$$\frac{4}{6} + \frac{3}{10} - \frac{2}{5} \qquad \frac{9}{10} + \frac{3}{4} - \frac{5}{8} \qquad \frac{11}{12} - \frac{5}{6} + \frac{1}{4} - \frac{1}{3}$$

8. From the sum of $\frac{1}{2}$ and $\frac{1}{4}$ subtract their difference.
   What quantity is $\frac{1}{4}$ more than seven-eighths?
   When $\frac{5}{8}$ is expressed as thirty-seconds there will be __ of them of size ___.
   Subtract the sum of $\frac{5}{8}$ and $\frac{3}{4}$ from the sum of $\frac{11}{12}$ and $\frac{5}{6}$.

9. Could all of the following be expressed as 240ths?

$$\frac{1}{60} \qquad \frac{3}{80} \qquad \frac{5}{24} \qquad \frac{7}{12} \qquad \frac{1}{2} \qquad \frac{17}{240} \qquad \frac{13}{30} \qquad \frac{42}{180}$$

10. Draw a number line from 0 to 2 and on it show all the halves, fourths, thirds, fifths, and sixths.

11. Simplify by the use of the Golden Rule of fractions.

$$\frac{\frac{3}{4} + \frac{5}{8}}{\frac{3}{16} + \frac{1}{4}} \qquad \frac{\frac{1}{12} + \frac{7}{8}}{\frac{9}{16} - \frac{1}{4}} \qquad \frac{2\frac{1}{6} + \frac{4}{3}}{\frac{1}{12} + 1\frac{5}{9}} \qquad \frac{\frac{3}{40} + \frac{7}{50}}{\frac{9}{40} - \frac{3}{50}}$$

12. Compare $\frac{5}{9}$ with $\frac{6}{11}$ by comparing their excesses over $\frac{1}{2}$.

13. Simplify the following:

$$\frac{172}{16} \qquad \frac{18 + 2\frac{2}{3}}{2} \qquad \frac{5\frac{1}{2} + 3\frac{1}{4}}{\frac{1}{2}} \qquad \frac{381}{37} \qquad \frac{3212}{4}$$

$$8\frac{1}{3} - \frac{1}{9} \qquad \frac{114}{133}$$

14. Demonstrate whether the following statements are true or false as they relate to proper fractions.

(a) If the numerator is multiplied by 2 the value of the fraction is doubled.

(b) If the denominator is multiplied by 2 the value of the fraction is doubled.

(c) If the numerator is divided by 3 the value of the fraction is divided by 3.

(d) If the denominator is divided by 3 the value of the fraction is tripled.

(e) If both the numerator and denominator are increased by the same number the value of the fraction is increased.

(f) If there are two numbers on a number line between 0 and 1 the number nearer to 1 is the larger.

15. Show that if (in a division example)

(a) only the dividend is doubled the quotient is doubled.

(b) only the divisor is doubled the quotient is halved.

(c) both the dividend and divisor are doubled the quotient is unchanged.

(d) only the dividend is tripled the quotient is tripled.

(e) only the divisor is tripled the quotient is divided by 3.

(f) both the divisor and dividend are tripled the quotient is unchanged.

(g) only the dividend is increased the quotient is increased.

(h) only the divisor is increased the quotient is decreased.

5.11   Multiplication of Common Fractions

We have pointed out elsewhere in this text that multiplication is the process of performing addition if the addends are alike. Were we to find the sum of $12 + 12 + 12$ we could write the three addends in a column and add them. However, we notice that we have used the addend (12) three times so we say "3 times 12" or simply "3 twelves." We recall that the multiplicand represents a number of concrete things while the multiplier is abstract and tells us how many times we have used the multiplicand as an addend. This principle applies also to multiplication examples and problems in which either one or both of the factors are fractions.

For our first example we will multiply a fraction by an integer, the fraction being the multiplicand and the integer the multiplier (integer × fraction). A problem: I ate $\frac{1}{4}$ of a cherry pie. I liked it so well that I ate another $\frac{1}{4}$ of the pie. I was still hungry and I ate another $\frac{1}{4}$ of the same cherry pie. How much pie did I eat? The solution of the problem is reached by adding $\frac{1}{4}$, $\frac{1}{4}$, and $\frac{1}{4}$. The total amount of pie which I ate is represented by $\frac{1}{4} + \frac{1}{4} + \frac{1}{4} = \frac{3}{4}$ or is the same as 3 one-fourths. In other words I ate 3 pieces of pie and each was $\frac{1}{4}$ of a pie. This can be expressed as

$$\frac{1}{4}$$
$$\times\ 3$$

or 3 × $\frac{1}{4}$ or 1 fourth + 1 fourth + 1 fourth. In any case the result will be $\frac{3}{4}$ of a pie. In pictures this can be represented as

which is 3 × $\frac{1}{4}$, or $\frac{3}{4}$.

Now let us discuss the type of example in which the fraction is used as the multiplier and the integer is the multiplicand (fraction × integer). Let us illustrate by assuming that we can pick 12 apples from a tree 3 different times, 12 apples from a tree 2 different times, 12 apples from a tree 1 time, but we cannot pick 12 apples from a tree one-half times. But $\frac{1}{2}$ times 12 apples is 6 apples. We first took 3 of the groups of 12 apples, then 2 of the groups of 12 apples, and finally just 1 group of 12 apples. We see that 3 of the 12 apples means the same thing as 3 times 12 or 3 groups of 12 apples. The "times" idea and the "of" idea are synonymous and mean multiplication. The $\frac{1}{2}$ times 12 or $\frac{1}{2}$ × 12 means $\frac{1}{2}$ of 12. Therefore $\frac{1}{2}$ times 12 apples is 6 apples, for $\frac{1}{2}$ of 12 apples is 6 apples.

Let us suppose we are asked to find $\frac{1}{4}$ times $3. This must be interpreted as "Find $\frac{1}{4}$ of $3," which in turn asks us to find $\frac{1}{4}$ of each of the 3 dollars and then to combine the results.   In picture form the analysis would look like this:

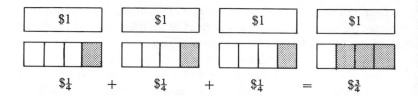

In the solution of the problem we discover that the answer is in dollars (which we knew at the outset) and that the addends are $\frac{1}{4}$.   The final solution or algorism resolves itself into $3 \times \$\frac{1}{4}$, the product of a fraction by an integer, and once again we see the commutative law in operation.

Students should discover that when they multiply a fraction by an integer the product can take one of several forms.   It can be (a) a proper fraction which can be simplified such as $\frac{1}{8} \times 6 = 6 \times \frac{1}{8} = \frac{6}{8}$, which is equivalent to $\frac{3}{4}$; it can be (b) a fraction which is equivalent to a whole number such as $\frac{3}{4} \times 8 = 8 \times \frac{3}{4} = \frac{24}{4}$, which is equivalent to 6; and it can be (c) a fraction which can be expressed as a mixed number such as $\frac{5}{7} \times 3 = 3 \times \frac{5}{7} = \frac{15}{7}$, which is equivalent to $2\frac{1}{7}$.

One of the most difficult concepts for young people to grasp is the multiplication of a fraction by a fraction.   Children grow up with the idea that multiplication is a process of magnifying or enlarging a given amount and that the final answer (product) is always larger than either of the given factors and they are partially correct.   But this principle applies to the multiplication of whole numbers only. Multiplication of a fraction by a fraction implies taking only a part of a given amount.   Naturally 5 sixes are more than 6, and 5 halves are more than $\frac{1}{2}$, but $\frac{5}{6}$ of 6 is less than 6 (only a part of 6) and $\frac{5}{6}$ of $\frac{1}{2}$ is less than $\frac{1}{2}$ (only part of $\frac{1}{2}$).   If we multiply a given number by 1 we get that same number for our product.   If we multiply by a number whose value is less than 1 we ought to obtain a number whose value is less than the original multiplicand.   Then $\frac{4}{5}$ of 8 is less than 8; $\frac{4}{5}$ of 1 is less than 1; and $\frac{4}{5}$ of $\frac{3}{7}$ is less than $\frac{3}{7}$.

If one is asked to find $\frac{1}{2}$ of 16 he is supposed to divide 16 into two parts of equal size; $\frac{1}{2}$ of 16 is the same as $16 \div 2$. Then in like manner $\frac{1}{2}$ of $\frac{1}{2}$ means that the $\frac{1}{2}$ is divided into two parts of equal size.   We must first define unity (1) and then divide it into two parts of the same or equal size so as to define our multiplicand $\frac{1}{2}$. We will draw a rectangle and call it 1. With a vertical line we will divide it into two rectangles, of equal size, which we designate as $\frac{1}{2}$. Now we will divide the one-half into two equal parts by drawing a horizontal line. Thus we have $\frac{1}{2}$ of $\frac{1}{2}$. To ascertain the size of the part we must find its relationship to the whole (unity). If we extend the horizontal line across the rectangle we find that we have divided the original rectangle into 4 equal parts (fourths) and the $\frac{1}{2}$ of $\frac{1}{2}$ represents one of these equal parts. Therefore $\frac{1}{2}$ of $\frac{1}{2}$ is $\frac{1}{4}$ or $\frac{1}{2} \times \frac{1}{2} = \frac{1}{4}$.

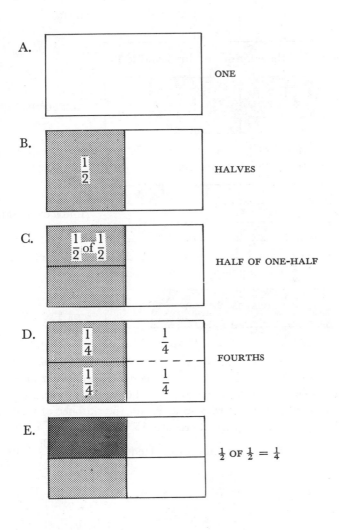

A second example: Now let us find $\frac{2}{3}$ of $\frac{4}{5}$ or multiply $\frac{2}{3} \times \frac{4}{5}$. Begin by defining unity (one).

A.

ONE

With vertical lines divide the rectangle into 5 equal parts.

B.

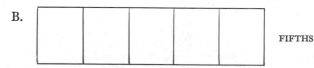

FIFTHS

Shade in 4 of these for our multiplicand is $\frac{4}{5}$.

C.

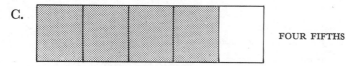

FOUR FIFTHS

Since we want $\frac{2}{3}$ of $\frac{4}{5}$ we must now divide the fifths into thirds. We should do this with horizontal lines.

D.

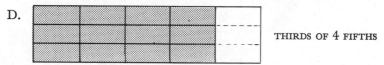

THIRDS OF 4 FIFTHS

Now since we want 2 thirds of the four-fifths we select the top 2 rows and cross-hatch the top two-thirds of the four-fifths.

E.

$\frac{2}{3}$ OF $\frac{4}{5}$

To determine our result we count the number of little rectangles and find that our result is 8 small units which are as yet unnamed. To find their size we must continue the horizontal lines through the entire unit rectangle in order to ascertain the number of rectangles of equal area in 1. Since there are 15 we know that each little rectangle is of size one-fifteenth. Hence $\frac{2}{3}$ of $\frac{4}{5} = \frac{8(1)}{15}$ or $\frac{8}{15}$.

$$\frac{2}{3} \times \frac{4}{5} = \frac{8}{15}.$$

The students should be ready to generalize now that the *product of two fractions is equal to the product of their numerators divided by the product of their denominators.*

5.12 Multiplications Involving Mixed Numbers

Occasionally it is necessary to multiply a mixed number by an integer or to multiply an integer by a mixed number.   If it is convenient to do so, we perform the multiplications directly, but if not, we express the mixed number as a fraction and then proceed as if multiplying two fractions.   If the problem is to find $2\frac{1}{3} \times 9$ we can do it directly.   We find 2 times 9 and then add this result to $\frac{1}{3}$ of 9. This gives us the sum of 18 and 3 which is 21.
Other examples:

$$4\tfrac{1}{5} \times 10 = 40 + 2 = 42 \qquad 8\tfrac{1}{2} \times 6 = 48 + 3 = 51$$
$$4 \times 10 + \tfrac{1}{5} \times 10 \qquad\qquad 8 \times 6 + \tfrac{1}{2} \times 6$$

The multiplication of a mixed number by an integer can often be performed directly, too.   According to the distributive law the example $6 \times 5\frac{1}{3}$ means 6 fives and 6 one-thirds or $30 + 2$ for a total of 32.
Other examples:

$$4 \times 3\tfrac{1}{4} = 12 + 1 = 13 \qquad 12 \times 2\tfrac{1}{6} = 24 + 2 = 26$$

If the fractional part times the multiplicand is not integral, one can express the mixed-number multiplier as a fraction and then multiply. For example, multiply $3\frac{1}{3} \times 4$.   Express $3\frac{1}{3}$ as $\frac{10}{3}$ and multiply $\frac{10}{3} \times \frac{4}{1}$.   This becomes $\frac{40}{3}$ or $13\frac{1}{3}$.   Multiply 6 by $3\frac{2}{5}$.   Express the multiplier as $\frac{17}{5}$ and proceed to multiply: $\frac{17}{5} \times \frac{6}{1} = \frac{102}{5} = 20\frac{2}{5}$.

Most of the real problems which ask one to find a fractional part of a mixed expression can be solved directly.   The fractional part of the integer is obtained and then to this is added the fractional part of the fraction.   Find $\frac{1}{2}$ of $4\frac{2}{3}$.   Our multiplicand is $4\frac{2}{3}$ and we want $\frac{1}{2}$ of it. We take half of 4 which is 2 and half of $\frac{2}{3}$ which is $\frac{1}{3}$.   Then $\frac{1}{2}$ of $4\frac{2}{3}$ must be $2\frac{1}{3}$.

All examples involving multiplications where the factors are a fraction and a mixed number can be solved by changing the mixed number to an improper fraction and then by multiplying the fractions together.

$$5\tfrac{1}{2} \times \tfrac{1}{4} = \tfrac{11}{2} \times \tfrac{1}{4} = \tfrac{11}{8} \text{ or } 1\tfrac{3}{8}$$
$$\tfrac{3}{4} \times 2\tfrac{1}{5} = \tfrac{3}{4} \times \tfrac{11}{5} = \tfrac{33}{20} \text{ or } 1\tfrac{13}{20}$$

A casual glance at the two types of solutions ought to convince the most doubting student of the efficacy of the direct method whenever it is convenient to use it.   We should resort to the fractional forms only when it is absolutely necessary.

Directly	Fractional Form
$\tfrac{1}{2} \times 4\tfrac{2}{3} = 2 + \tfrac{1}{3}$	$\tfrac{3}{5} \times 2\tfrac{7}{8} = \tfrac{3}{5} \times \tfrac{23}{8} = \tfrac{69}{40} = 1\tfrac{29}{40}$
$4\tfrac{1}{4} \times \tfrac{3}{4} = 3 + \tfrac{3}{16}$	$2\tfrac{4}{9} \times \tfrac{2}{3} = \tfrac{22}{9} \times \tfrac{2}{3} = \tfrac{44}{27} = 1\tfrac{17}{27}$

The last type of example which involves the multiplication of fractions is the type in which both the multiplier and multiplicand are mixed numbers. Both the factors can be changed to improper fractions and then multiplied. For illustrative purposes let us find the cost of $8\tfrac{1}{3}$ yards of ribbon at $2\tfrac{1}{2}$ cents per yard. We know that the answer will be in cents, and that it will be more than 16 cents (for 8×2 cents $= 16$ cents).
Solution:

$$8\tfrac{1}{3} \times 2\tfrac{1}{2} \qquad 8\tfrac{1}{3} = \tfrac{25}{3} \qquad 2\tfrac{1}{2} = \tfrac{5}{2}$$
$$\tfrac{25}{3} \times \tfrac{5}{2} = \tfrac{125}{6} = 20\tfrac{5}{6} \text{ (cents)}$$

The cost will be 21 cents.

Often the product of two mixed numbers can be found directly without changing them to improper fractions. For illustrative purposes let us find the product of $8\tfrac{1}{3} \times 6\tfrac{1}{2}$. A study of this example clearly reveals the necessity for use of the distributive law, for the $6\tfrac{1}{2}$ is to be multiplied by both 8 and $\tfrac{1}{3}$. If we multiply $6\tfrac{1}{2}$ by 8 we get 48 and 4 which is 52, and if we multiply $6\tfrac{1}{2}$ by $\tfrac{1}{3}$ we get 2 and $\tfrac{1}{6}$ which is $2\tfrac{1}{6}$. Now if we add their two partial products we obtain $54\tfrac{1}{6}$ for the total product.

$$8\tfrac{1}{3} \times 6\tfrac{1}{2} = \begin{cases} 8 \times 6\tfrac{1}{2} = 52 \\ \\ \tfrac{1}{3} \times 6\tfrac{1}{2} = \dfrac{2\tfrac{1}{6}}{54\tfrac{1}{6}} \end{cases}$$

Let us show another algorism for this type of example.

Multiply $\quad 4\frac{3}{4} \qquad 4 + \frac{3}{4}$

$\qquad\quad \times 8\frac{3}{4} \qquad 8 + \frac{3}{4}$

$$\begin{array}{ll} \frac{9}{16} & (\frac{3}{4} \times \frac{3}{4}) \\ 3 & (\frac{3}{4} \times 4) \\ 6 & (8 \times \frac{3}{4}) \\ 32 & (8 \times 4) \\ \hline 41\frac{9}{16} & \end{array}$$

Multiplication involving common fractions can also be performed with the use of decimal fractions if they can be converted easily to equivalent decimal fractions. The method will be explained in the next chapter; one example here will suffice.

Multiply $4\frac{3}{4} \times 5\frac{2}{5}$ Solution:

$$\begin{array}{r} 5.4 \\ \times\ 4.75 \\ \hline 270 \\ 378 \\ 216 \\ \hline 25.650 \end{array}$$

EXERCISES

SET 20

1. Find the products:

$7 \times \frac{2}{3}$ $12 \times \frac{2}{9}$ $15 \times \frac{4}{5}$ $9 \times \frac{8}{7}$ $25 \times \frac{3}{4}$ $17 \times \frac{8}{11}$ $4 \times \frac{3}{13}$

$\frac{6}{7} \times 14$ $\frac{3}{5} \times 105$ $\frac{4}{9} \times 180$ $\frac{5}{12} \times 144$ $\frac{3}{8} \times 15$ $\frac{5}{6} \times 10$ $\frac{2}{9} \times 1$

2. Multiply by changing to improper fractions:

$8 \times 3\frac{2}{3}$ $12 \times 4\frac{1}{5}$ $2 \times 3\frac{1}{3}$ $4 \times 3\frac{5}{6}$ $21 \times 4\frac{2}{7}$ $35 \times 2\frac{3}{5}$

3. Multiply directly:

$10 \times 4\frac{4}{5}$ $5\frac{2}{5} \times 40$ $9 \times 3\frac{2}{3}$ $7\frac{1}{4} \times 8$ $5\frac{1}{3} \times 27$ $32 \times 3\frac{1}{8}$

4. Write out and solve three word problems illustrating a fraction multiplied by an integer.

5. Write out and solve three word problems illustrating a mixed number multiplied by a fraction.

6. Change to improper fractions and multiply:

$4\frac{2}{5} \times 6\frac{1}{3}$ $8\frac{1}{2} \times 9\frac{1}{3}$ $2\frac{2}{3} \times 3\frac{1}{4}$ $13\frac{1}{4} \times 15\frac{1}{4}$

7. Multiply directly:

$8\frac{1}{2} \times 6\frac{1}{2}$ $4\frac{1}{3} \times 9\frac{1}{4}$ $16\frac{2}{3} \times 10\frac{3}{4}$ $12\frac{2}{3} \times 12\frac{1}{4}$

8. Multiply:

$\frac{2}{3} \times \frac{4}{5} \times \frac{4}{7}$ $\frac{4}{5} \times \frac{2}{3} \times \frac{15}{16}$ $\frac{3}{16} \times \frac{3}{4} \times \frac{8}{9}$ $\frac{5}{6} \times \frac{2}{7} \times \frac{21}{10}$

9. Without copying the examples, write the products:

$2\frac{1}{2} \times 2\frac{1}{2}$ $4\frac{1}{2} \times 6\frac{1}{2}$ $8\frac{1}{2} \times 10\frac{1}{2}$
$5\frac{1}{2} \times 6\frac{1}{2}$ $8\frac{1}{2} \times 8\frac{1}{2}$ $7\frac{1}{2} \times 2\frac{1}{2}$

10. Find the products:

$8\frac{1}{3} \times 2\frac{1}{2} \times 2\frac{1}{25}$ $5 \times \frac{2}{15} \times \frac{3}{7} \times \frac{1}{4}$
$2\frac{1}{3} \times 5\frac{4}{5} \times 1\frac{1}{7}$ $4\frac{1}{2} \times 3\frac{1}{3} \times \frac{12}{13}$

11. Show by a picture representation that $3 \times 2\frac{3}{4} = 8\frac{1}{4}$
12. Prove by a picture diagram that $\frac{4}{7} \times \frac{3}{5} = \frac{12}{35}$
13. Prove by a picture diagram that $\frac{2}{3} \times \frac{3}{4} = \frac{1}{2}$
14. Select the larger product from these pairs of products:

$\frac{1}{2}$ of 3 or $\frac{1}{4}$ of $\frac{1}{2}$ $2\frac{1}{2} \times 3$ or $2 \times 3\frac{1}{2}$
$7\frac{1}{3} \times 10$ or $10 \times 7\frac{1}{3}$ $3\frac{1}{4} \times 4\frac{1}{3}$ or $4\frac{1}{3} \times 3$
$2\frac{1}{2} \times 6 \times 8\frac{1}{3}$ or $3\frac{1}{3} \times 10\frac{1}{2} \times 3$ $12\frac{1}{2} \times 5\frac{1}{2}$ or $6\frac{1}{2} \times 10\frac{1}{2}$

15. The Univac can multiply two 13-digit numbers in $\dfrac{1}{30,000}$ of a second and add the same two numbers in half the time. How long does it take the Univac to add the two numbers?

16. Given the set of unit fractions, $\frac{1}{2} \ \frac{1}{3} \ \frac{1}{4} \ \frac{1}{5} \ \frac{1}{6} \ \frac{1}{7}$, show that any one of these fractions results from adding the adjacent numerators for a new numerator and adding the adjacent denominators for a new denominator. This property is known as Farey's Theorem.

5.13   Division of Common Fractions

In a previous chapter the concept of division was given two interpretations; namely, measurement and partitioning. We use the measurement idea or concept when we wish to know how many times the divisor is contained in the dividend or can be removed from the dividend. We are interested in finding the number of groups when we know the size of each group. We use the part-taking idea when we want to divide a given amount into a given number of groups, when we need to find the size of each group knowing the number of groups. The example, "How many 3-cent stamps can I buy with 15 cents?" is an illustration of measurement division while the example, "If 15 apples are distributed equally among 3 boys, how many apples will each boy receive?" is an illustration of partitioning division. An understanding of both of these concepts is essential for an understanding of division examples involving fractions.

Let us begin by discussing the example in which an integer is divided by a fraction and use for our illustration $4 \div \frac{1}{2}$. The example asks us one of two questions, (a) How many pieces of size $\frac{1}{2}$ are there in 4 whole pieces? or (b) When 4 is divided into $\frac{1}{2}$ part, what is the size of each part? Since the second question has no answer, the only interpretation we can give the example is one of measurement: "How many halves are there in 4?" However, the example could illustrate the ratio concept of fractions.

There are three commonly accepted methods for solving the example, $4 \div \frac{1}{2}$, and we will illustrate them here.

(a) *The common denominator method.* Express both the dividend and the divisor in the same kind of units and divide the numerators.

4 is the same as $\frac{8}{2}$ or 8 halves.

$\frac{1}{2}$ is already expressed in halves. Then our problem becomes: How many groups of size one-half are contained in or can be taken out of 8 halves? The answer is obviously 8.

$$8 \text{ halves} \div 1 \text{ half} = 8 \qquad \frac{8 \text{ halves}}{1 \text{ half}} = 8$$

(b) *The diagrammatic method* or solution by diagram. The answer is found by counting. Draw 4 whole things (of the same size). Cut them into halves. Count the number of halves. There are 8 of them. Therefore there are 8 pieces of size $\frac{1}{2}$ in 4.

One half   →
Two halves ⟶
Three halves ⟶
Four halves ⟶
Five halves ⟶
Six halves ⟶
Seven halves ⟶
Eight halves ⟶

(c) *The inversion method.* The dividend is multiplied by the divisor inverted (the reciprocal of the fraction).

$4 \div \frac{1}{2} =$ We know there are 2 halves in 1.
$4 \times \frac{2}{1} =$ In 4, there will be 4 times 2 halves $4 \times \frac{2}{1} = 8$ or 8 halves.

Let us solve one more example three different ways.   How many $\frac{3}{4}$ are there in 6?

(*a*) Since $6 \div \frac{3}{4}$ is the same as $\frac{24}{4} \div \frac{3}{4}$ we have $24 \div 3 = 8$.

(*b*) Draw six whole things.   Divide them into fourths.   Now regroup them into groups containing 3 one-fourths.   This can be done 8 times.   Therefore $6 \div \frac{3}{4} = 8$.

Count them.

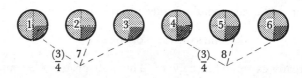

(*c*) There are 24 fourths in 6.   When these are grouped in fourths, naturally there will be 24 of them.   When they are packaged in groups containing 2 fourths, there will be only half as many.   When they are grouped in sets containing 3 fourths, there will be only one-third as many.   Thus

$$6 \div \tfrac{3}{4} = 6 \times 4$$

(for the number of fourths) now multiplied by $\frac{1}{3}$ for there will be one-third as many (as there are fourths).

Thus

$$6 \div \tfrac{3}{4} = \tfrac{1}{3} \ \text{of } 6 \times 4$$

or

$$\frac{6 \times 4}{3} \quad \text{which is the same as} \quad 6 \times \tfrac{4}{3}.$$

The inversion method can be rationalized also by the use of complex fractions.   Let's write the example as $\dfrac{6}{\frac{3}{4}}$ and multiply both terms of the fraction by 1.   We will carefully choose our 1 to be $\dfrac{\frac{4}{3}}{\frac{4}{3}}$.   Therefore $\dfrac{\frac{4}{3}}{\frac{4}{3}} \times \dfrac{6}{\frac{3}{4}} = \dfrac{\frac{4}{3} \times 6}{1}$ or, by use of the commutative law, $6 \times \frac{4}{3}$.   Therefore $6 \div \frac{3}{4} = 6 \times \frac{4}{3} = 8$.

The second type of division example is the type in which the dividend is a fraction and the divisor is an integer.   For an illustrative example let us divide $\frac{1}{2}$ by 2: $\frac{1}{2} \div 2$. Since there are no whole pieces of size 2 in the given amount of $\frac{1}{2}$, the example is more easily interpreted as partitioning. We are asked to divide the given amount into two equal parts.

(*a*) The common-denominator approach gives us this solution:

$$\tfrac{1}{2} \div 2 = \tfrac{1}{2} \div \tfrac{4}{2} = 1 \text{ half} \div 4 \text{ halves} = \tfrac{1}{4}$$

Were one interested in the measurement aspect of this type of example he would discover that the common fraction $\frac{1}{4}$ can be interpreted as a ratio, that the ratio of $\frac{1}{2}$ to 2 is the same as 1 to 4. In other words, the first quantity is $\frac{1}{4}$ of the second one, the second number is 4 times the first, and there is $\frac{1}{4}$ of 2 in the given amount $\frac{1}{2}$.

(*b*) The diagrammatic approach suggests that we begin with a given amount of $\frac{1}{2}$ and that we divide it into two equal parts. It is easily discernible that the resulting quantity is $\frac{1}{4}$.

ONE

$$\frac{1}{2} \qquad\qquad \frac{1}{2}$$

(*c*) The inversion method is explained by recognizing the fact that to divide anything into two equal parts is synonymous with taking $\frac{1}{2}$ of the given amount. Thus $\frac{1}{2} \div 2$ is the same as taking $\frac{1}{2}$ of $\frac{1}{2}$ or $\frac{1}{2} \times \frac{1}{2} = \frac{1}{4}$

For a second example to illustrate the division of a fraction by an integer let us divide $\frac{3}{4}$ by 5: $\frac{3}{4} \div 5$.

(*a*) By the common-denominator approach we have

$$\tfrac{3}{4} \div 5 = \tfrac{3}{4} \div \tfrac{20}{4} =$$

$$\frac{3 \text{ fourths}}{20 \text{ fourths}} = 3 \text{ fourths} \div 20 \text{ fourths} = 3 \div 20 = \frac{3}{20}$$

(*b*) By the use of diagrams we must first set up the dividend $\frac{3}{4}$ and then divide this into 5 equal parts. One of these 5 equal parts represents $\frac{3}{20}$ of the whole one.

$\frac{1}{5}$ OF $\frac{3}{4}$

ONE

$\frac{1}{20}$

$\frac{1}{4}$ $\frac{1}{4}$ $\frac{1}{4}$ $\frac{1}{4}$

(*c*) To divide a number by 5 is equivalent to taking $\frac{1}{5}$ of it (another rationalization of the inversion method).

$$\frac{3}{4} \div 5 \text{ is the same as } \frac{1}{5} \text{ of } \frac{3}{4} = \frac{3}{4} \times \frac{1}{5} = \frac{3}{20}$$

The third type of problem involving division of fractions is the kind in which both the dividend and divisor are fractions. The simplest illustration of this type is the example in which the dividend is larger than the divisor, as in the problem, "How many bandages each $\frac{1}{6}$ of a yard long can be cut from a piece of material $\frac{2}{3}$ of a yard long?"

This problem can be solved, too, by the three methods outlined previously.

(*a*) *The common-denominator method.*

$$\frac{2}{3} \div \frac{1}{6} = \frac{4}{6} \div \frac{1}{6} \quad \frac{4 \text{ sixths}}{1 \text{ sixth}} = 4 \text{ sixths} \div 1 \text{ sixth} = 4.$$

There will be 4 bandages.

(*b*) *The diagrammatic solution.* We clearly see the necessity for expressing the dividend $\frac{2}{3}$ in sixths in order to make the measurement or make the comparison. We want to know how many pieces of a given length can be cut from a larger piece.

$\dfrac{1}{6}$	$\dfrac{1}{6}$	$\dfrac{1}{6}$	$\dfrac{1}{6}$	$\dfrac{1}{6}$	$\dfrac{1}{6}$

$\dfrac{1}{3}$		$\dfrac{1}{3}$		$\dfrac{1}{3}$	

———————————————— one ————————————————

There are 4 one-sixths in $\frac{2}{3}$.

(c) *The inversion method.* Since we are required to find the number of one-sixths in a given amount we multiply the given amount by 6. There are 6 sixths in 1 whole yard of material, therefore in $\frac{2}{3}$ of a yard there will be 6 times $\frac{2}{3}$ (or $6 \times \frac{2}{3}$) for $\frac{12}{3}$ or 4 pieces of size one-sixth. Therefore: $\frac{2}{3} \div \frac{1}{6} = \frac{2}{3} \times \frac{6}{1} = 4$.

It is apparent from previous learnings that when the divisor is larger than the dividend, the quotient will be less than 1, there will not be any integral part to the answer. The dividend is only a part of the given divisor and hence the answer is written in fractional form. This fact is of paramount importance in the treatment of the second type of example, which involves dividing a fraction by another which is larger than the dividend, for example, $\frac{4}{7} \div \frac{5}{7}$.

A problem which will illustrate the given example might read something like this: "John is to work at the grocery store 5 days per week. If he works 4 days, what part of the required time does he work?" The solution to the problem is easy if we use the common-denominator method: 4 sevenths $\div$ 5 sevenths $= \frac{4}{5}$.

Let us solve a problem of this type in each of the three ways already discussed. "Mrs. Brown's fruit cake recipe calls for $\frac{3}{8}$ pound of raisins. She has $\frac{1}{4}$ of a pound of raisins on hand. What part of the recipe can she make?"

(a) *The common denominator method*:

$$\frac{1}{4} \text{ lb} \div \frac{3}{8} \text{ lb is the same as } \frac{2}{8} \text{ lb} \div \frac{3}{8} \text{ lb}$$

$$\frac{2}{8} \div \frac{3}{8} = 2 \text{ (eighths)} \div 3 \text{ (eighths)} = \frac{2 \text{ (eighths)}}{3 \text{ (eighths)}} = \frac{2}{3}$$

Mrs. Brown will be able to make $\frac{2}{3}$ of the recipe. The reader should note that we do not use the concrete terms or labels in the solution of the problem—in the algorism the terms are considered abstract.

(*b*) *The diagrammatic method.* How many times (what fractional part of) does the given amount $\frac{1}{4}$ contain the divisor $\frac{3}{8}$?

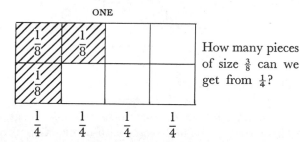

How many pieces of size $\frac{3}{8}$ can we get from $\frac{1}{4}$?

Since the $\frac{1}{4}$ is only two thirds of the $\frac{3}{8}$, there is only $\frac{2}{3}$ of a three-eighths in one-fourth. There is a ratio of 2 to 3. One needs 3 pieces of a given size but there are only 2 available. Hence the quotient two-thirds.

(*c*) *The inversion method.* First we must find out how many one-eighths there are in $\frac{1}{4}$. This can be done by multiplying $\frac{1}{4} \times \frac{8}{1}$. There are 2 one-eighths in $\frac{1}{4}$. Now if these one-eighths are packaged 3 at a time (there won't be a complete package), there will be one-third as many $\frac{3}{8}$'s as $\frac{1}{8}$'s. Then $\frac{1}{3}$ of $2 = \frac{2}{3}$. Since $\frac{1}{4} \div \frac{3}{8} = \frac{1}{4} \times \frac{8}{3} = \frac{2}{3}$, there will be $\frac{2}{3}$ of a package of the required size.

Let us say another word about the inversion method. We know that if the divisor in any division problem is doubled, then our quotient will be half as large as previously. Also, if we make the divisor three times its original size, then the quotient will be one-third as much, and so on. If we divide by one-fifth and obtain a quotient, then when we divide that same dividend by three-fifths, the quotient should be one-third as much. If we divide a number by one-seventh, and then later by five-sevenths, our second answer should be one-fifth of the former.

Illustrations:

$24 \div 6 = 4$ $\qquad\qquad$ $36 \div 3 = 12$

$24 \div 12 = 2$ (divisor twice as $\qquad$ $36 \div 9 = 4$ (divisor three big, quotient half $\qquad\qquad\qquad\qquad\qquad$ times as big, as much) $\qquad\qquad\qquad\qquad\qquad\qquad\qquad$ quotient one-third as much)

If $30 \div \dfrac{1}{5} = 150$

Then $30 \div \dfrac{2}{5} = \dfrac{1}{2} \text{ of } \left(30 \div \dfrac{1}{5}\right) \text{ or } \dfrac{1}{2}(30 \times 5) = \dfrac{30 \times 5}{2} = 75$

Then $30 \div \dfrac{3}{5} = \dfrac{1}{3} \text{ of } \left(30 \div \dfrac{1}{5}\right) \text{ or } \dfrac{1}{3}(30 \times 5) = \dfrac{30 \times 5}{3} = 50$

Then $30 \div \dfrac{4}{5} = \dfrac{1}{4} \text{ of } \left(30 \div \dfrac{1}{5}\right) \text{ or } \dfrac{1}{4}(30 \times 5) = \dfrac{30 \times 5}{4} = 37\tfrac{1}{2}$

In these examples we first find the number of fifths by multiplying the dividend by 5 (the denominator) and then divide by the size of the group or the number of fifths (which number is the numerator). Thus the number 21 would contain 147 one-sevenths $(21 \div \tfrac{1}{7} = 147)$ but only one-third that many three-sevenths. $21 \div \tfrac{3}{7}$ becomes 21×7 and it must then be divided by 3. Written as a complete algorism we have $21 \div \tfrac{3}{7} = 21 \times \tfrac{7}{3}$ which is 49.

5.14 Division Involving Mixed Numbers

This last type of problem involving the division of fractions is the division of mixed numbers. Since it is quite absurd to divide a given amount into a number of non-integral parts, we must interpret the division of mixed numbers as the measurement-type division. However, if the divisor is an integer then we can employ the partitioning interpretation. The example $2\tfrac{1}{2} \div 4$ might be interpreted either of two ways:

(a) Divide $2\tfrac{1}{2}$ pies among 4 boys. How much pie will each one get?

(b) If I have $\$2\tfrac{1}{2}$, how many yards of silk can I buy if silk costs $\$4$ per yard?

Since we have discussed the division of fractions rather systematically and thoroughly in this chapter it should suffice here if we treat all of the various types of examples involving division of mixed numbers in a single discussion.

TYPES OF EXAMPLES

I. Mixed number divided by an integer. Integer smaller.
$$6\tfrac{3}{4} \div 3$$

II. Mixed number divided by an integer. Integer larger.
$$3\tfrac{3}{4} \div 6$$

III. Integer divided by a mixed number.   Integer smaller.

$$2 \div 4\tfrac{1}{4}$$

IV. Integer divided by a mixed number.   Integer larger.

$$9 \div 3\tfrac{1}{2}$$

V. Mixed number divided by a mixed number.   Divisor smaller.

$$2\tfrac{1}{2} \div 1\tfrac{1}{4}$$

VI. Mixed number divided by a mixed number.   Divisor larger.

$$1\tfrac{2}{3} \div 2\tfrac{2}{3}$$

The solution of all examples involving division of non-integral numbers can be facilitated by the application of the Golden Rule of fractions.   Surely after a reading of the section on division of fractions the student ought to appreciate the presentation of one simple all-inclusive method which is sound in principle and easy of execution. The principle, reiterated here, states that if both terms of a fraction are multipled by the same non-zero number there will be no change in the quotient.   Hence if we write all division examples as complex fractions we can change all of the examples to division of integers. $8 \div \tfrac{1}{2}$ gives the same quotient as $16 \div 1$ (multiply both terms by 2) and $6 \div \tfrac{2}{3}$ gives the same quotient as $18 \div 2$ (multiply by 3).

$$8 \div \frac{1}{2} = \frac{8}{\frac{1}{2}} = \frac{2 \times 8}{2 \times \frac{1}{2}} = \frac{16}{1} = 16$$

$$6 \div \frac{2}{3} = \frac{6}{\frac{2}{3}} = \frac{3 \times 6}{3 \times \frac{2}{3}} = \frac{18}{2} = 9$$

Divisions involving mixed numbers can also be changed to division of integers.   Thus $5\tfrac{1}{2} \div \tfrac{1}{4}$ becomes $22 \div 1$ (multiplying both the dividend and divisor by 4) and $8\tfrac{1}{3} \div 2\tfrac{1}{4}$ becomes $100 \div 27$ (multiplying by 12).

$$5\tfrac{1}{2} \div \frac{1}{4} = \frac{5\tfrac{1}{2}}{\frac{1}{4}} = \frac{4 \times 5\tfrac{1}{2}}{4 \times \frac{1}{4}} = \frac{22}{1} = 22$$

$$8\tfrac{1}{3} \div 2\tfrac{1}{4} = \frac{8\tfrac{1}{3}}{2\tfrac{1}{4}} = \frac{12 \times 8\tfrac{1}{3}}{12 \times 2\tfrac{1}{4}} = \frac{100}{27} = 3\tfrac{19}{27}$$

The multiplication aspect of the Golden Rule of fractions is forever useful for the simplification of division examples.

The example	$7 \div \frac{2}{3}$	$3\frac{1}{2} \div 2$	$\frac{3}{8} \div 2$	$6 \div 2\frac{2}{3}$
The transformed example	$21 \div 2$	$7 \div 4$	$3 \div 16$	$18 \div 8$
The quotient	$10\frac{1}{2}$	$1\frac{3}{4}$	$\frac{3}{16}$	$2\frac{1}{4}$

5.15 Ratio and Proportion

One of the interpretations of a fraction is called the ratio concept, with the denominator representing the base or basis of comparison. The numerator tells the number of parts we are considering while the denominator states the number of equal parts into which the unit or group was divided. Thus the fraction $\frac{4}{5}$ might mean that a whole thing is divided into 5 equal parts or a ratio of 4 to 5.

First, a ratio can be expressed in many and various forms, chief of which is the common fraction. Secondly, the ratio can always represent the amount being compared with the base one or the single unit. Also, the basis for comparison can be expressed as 100, in which case we express the ratio as a per cent. The ratio can also be expressed simply in decimal fraction form, in which case the base will be a power of 10. Thus if a cement mixture contains 2 parts of cement to 3 parts of sand, then the mixture is $\frac{2}{5}$ cement; the ratio of the amount of cement to the total amount of the mixture is 2 to 5. This ratio can be expressed as $\frac{2}{5}$ to 1, or 40 out of 100 which is 40 per cent, or simply .4. The latter ratio is usually interpreted as .4 to 1 or simply $\frac{4}{10}$ to 1, which is the same as 4 to 10.

If a college student body of 7280 students contains 3458 girls, then the ratio of the number of girls to the number of boys is 19 to 21. This means that for every 19 female students in the college there are 21 males enrolled. The ratio of the number of girls to the entire college population is 19 to 40 or $47\frac{1}{2}$ per cent.

True ratios are expressed in terms of the same kind of units, such as feet to feet, people to people, cookies to cookies, and so on. However, there are many relationships or ratios in use today which violate this principle. These expressions are merely relationships or rates and are not true ratios. The speed of an automobile can be expressed as 45 miles per 1 hour, the pressure of a gas could be 45 pounds per square inch, the cost of fresh green peas might be 45 cents per pound, the acceleration of a moving object might be 45 feet per second every second, and the blue print of a baseball diamond might be 2 inches for every 30 feet. When we say that the cost of admission to the school fair is 2 cents per year of age we are not expressing a ratio; it is merely a relationship and should not be expressed in fractional form.

Ratios are useful for solving problems, not so much when used alone, but when two or more of them can be equated. If two ratios are equal then the resulting expression is called a proportion. Thus there are four terms to a proportion, the two numerators and the two denominators. These terms are also designated as the first and last terms (called the extremes) and the second and third terms, called the means. Thus if the ratio $\frac{a}{b}$ is equal to the ratio of $\frac{c}{d}$, then the terms a and d are the extremes and b and c are the means. Now since we know that $\frac{a}{b} = \frac{c}{d}$, it is possible to multiply both members of the equation by the same non-zero value without destroying the equality. If we choose bd for the multiplier, the resulting equation becomes $ad = bc$. Thus we have developed the well-known and much used generalization regarding a proportion; namely, *the product of the means is equal to the product of the extremes*. If any three terms of a proportion are known, the use of this principle aids in the solution of the fourth term. For instance, what number has the same ratio to 18 as 5 has to 6?

Solution: Let $\frac{N}{18} = \frac{5}{6}$

Multiplying we obtain 6N = 90 (the product of the means = the product of the extremes).

Dividing by 6: N = 15

Proportions are useful in solving many types of problems. We will use them here to solve types of problems illustrated in a previous paragraph.

Problem: At a constant speed of 45 miles per hour, how far will a car travel in 7 hours?

Solution: The ratio between the distances is proportional to the times. Therefore, $\frac{45}{D} = \frac{1}{7}$ or D = 315 miles.

Problem: If the pressure of a gas is 45 pounds per square inch, what is the total pressure over an area of 11 square inches?

Solution: The ratio between the pressures is the same as the ratio between the areas. Therefore, $\dfrac{45}{P} = \dfrac{1}{11}$ or $P = 495$ pounds.

Problem: If grapefruit are marked 2 for 25 cents, how many grapefruit can be purchased for $4?

Solution: The ratio between the quantities is equal to the ratio between the amounts of money. Therefore, $\dfrac{2}{N} = \dfrac{25}{400}$. Since $25N = 800$, we find N to be 16. I can buy 16 grapefruit for $4.

Problem: If a picture 6 inches by 9 inches is to be enlarged to a length of 12 inches, what will be the corresponding height?

Solution: The ratio between the heights is the same as the ratio between the lengths. Therefore, $\dfrac{6}{H} = \dfrac{9}{12}$. Since $9H = 72$, we find $H = 8$. The height will be 8 inches.

It should be noted that in all of the illustrations we have expressed the ratios between like units, such as pressure to pressure, square inches to square inches, cost to cost, distance to distance, and so on. This is a fundamental principle of ratio and proportion problems.

EXERCISES

SET 21

1. Solve by the common denominator method:

$$\dfrac{5}{8} \div \dfrac{1}{4} \quad \dfrac{7}{16} \div \dfrac{1}{4} \quad \dfrac{3}{16} \div \dfrac{3}{5} \quad \dfrac{11}{12} \div \dfrac{1}{6} \quad \dfrac{24}{25} \div \dfrac{3}{5} \quad \dfrac{13}{16} \div \dfrac{3}{4} \quad \dfrac{1}{6} \div \dfrac{1}{5}$$

2. Solve by the use of diagrams:

$$2 \div \tfrac{1}{3} \quad 9\tfrac{1}{2} \div \tfrac{1}{2} \quad \tfrac{7}{3} \div \tfrac{2}{3} \quad 4 \div \tfrac{5}{6} \quad 2\tfrac{1}{2} \div \tfrac{5}{6} \quad 1\tfrac{1}{4} \div \tfrac{3}{8} \quad \tfrac{1}{2} \div \tfrac{1}{6}$$

3. Solve by the inversion method:

$$\tfrac{21}{22} \div \tfrac{2}{3} \quad 2\tfrac{4}{9} \div \tfrac{3}{8} \quad 4\tfrac{1}{6} \div \tfrac{2}{3} \quad 7\tfrac{1}{8} \div 2\tfrac{1}{2} \quad \tfrac{1}{2} \div \tfrac{1}{6} \quad 101\tfrac{2}{3} \div 80\tfrac{5}{9}$$

4. Solve by use of the Golden Rule of fractions:

$\frac{3}{7} \div \frac{1}{3}$ $2\frac{1}{2} \div 3\frac{1}{5}$ $\frac{2}{6} \div \frac{4}{9}$ $5\frac{1}{4} \div 3\frac{7}{8}$ $16\frac{1}{5} \div 4\frac{4}{5}$ $19\frac{2}{3} \div 4\frac{1}{3}$

5. What are the two interpretations for the example: $16 \div 2\frac{1}{2}$?
6. Show by a picture representation $\frac{3}{16} \div \frac{1}{2}$.
7. Write out two essay-type problems illustrating division of a large mixed number by a small mixed number.   Solve the problems.
8. (a) Multiply $3\frac{1}{2}$ by $4\frac{3}{4}$ and then divide the product by $2\frac{1}{2}$.
   (b) Multiply $3\frac{1}{4}$ by $3\frac{1}{2}$ and then divide the product by $1\frac{1}{2}$.
   (c) Divide 4 by $3\frac{1}{2}$ and then divide the quotient by $1\frac{1}{2}$.
   (d) Square $5\frac{1}{4}$ and then divide the product by the square of $1\frac{1}{4}$.
   (e) From the cube of $1\frac{1}{2}$ subtract the square of the same number.
   (f) From twice $3\frac{3}{4}$ subtract one-half the product of $4\frac{1}{4}$ and $2\frac{1}{4}$.
   (g) Multiply half the product of $4\frac{1}{2}$ and $4\frac{1}{4}$ by 20.
9. What suggestions can you give for checking examples involving divisions of fractions?
10. What is the remainder when $15\frac{1}{2}$ is divided by 2 (measurement division)?
11. Interpret the quotient of $7\frac{3}{4}$ in the above problem.
12. Can the dividend, divisor, and quotient in an example all be smaller than 1?
13. Mr. Jones owns the west half of the southwest quarter of the northeast quarter of section 13.   What part of a section of land does he own?   If a section of land contains 640 acres, how many acres of land does he own?
14. Define: reciprocal of a number, inversion, Golden Rule of fractions.
15. What is the remainder when $2\frac{2}{3}$ is divided by $\frac{1}{4}$?
16. Divide an inheritance of $60,000 among three heirs in the ratio of 2 to 5 to 5.
17. In a classroom there are 16 boys and 31 girls.   What is the ratio of the number of girls to the entire class membership?   Express this in hundredths.

CHAPTER 6

OPERATIONS WITH DECIMAL FRACTIONS

6.1 Introduction

In the primary grades children are introduced to a medium of exchange we call money. They learn through the use of problems in the classroom and through their experience outside the classroom that the number or symbolic representation written $5.65 means five dollars and 65 cents. The dot or point separating the number of dollars from the number of cents is often referred to as the "cents point." It separates the whole part or the number of dollars from the parts of a dollar. Numbers to the left of the point mean whole dollars while numbers to the right of the point mean parts of a dollar.

It has been clearly established in a previous chapter that the place value of a numeral is multiplied by 10 as it moves one place to the left in a number and is 100 times as much if it moves two places to the left. The value of the 5 in 50 is ten times the value of 5 for it stands for 5 tens; the 7 in 700 is 100 times the value of 7 for it stands for 7 hundreds. As we continue the system of numeration to the right, the values of the numerals decrease; that is, the denomination of each place becomes one-tenth as much as the denomination of its neighbor to the left. In the number 77 the second 7 has a value $\frac{1}{10}$ the value of the preceding 7.

Thus if we write $77.77 we read the numbers as "Seventy-seven dollars and seventy-seven cents."

$$
\begin{array}{rl}
\$77.77 = \$70.00 & \text{(seventy dollars)} \\
7.00 & \text{(seven dollars)} \\
.70 & \text{(seventy cents)} \\
\underline{.07} & \text{(seven cents)} \\
\$77.77 &
\end{array}
$$

This chapter is concerned with the study of fractions whose denominators are powers of 10. These fractions, whose denominators are not written as such, are called *decimal fractions*. The small dot is placed directly behind the ones place to designate which part of the numeral is integral and which is fractional.   This little dot is called the "*decimal point.*"   Thus 72.6 indicates that the 2 is in the ones place.

The concept of the decimal fraction .1 (one-tenth) can be developed through the use of the automobile odometer.   The odometer measures distances traveled in small units which are one-tenth of a mile. When 10 of these small units have been covered the total distance traveled is one full mile.   The mile is divided into 10 equal parts and each of these parts is written as .1 and interpreted as one-tenth of a mile.

| .1 | .1 | .1 | .1 | .1 | .1 | .1 | .1 | .1 | .1 |

.1 of a mile

One mile

Many measurements in real life are made in tenths of a unit. Distances are measured in tenths of a mile, sporting events are timed in tenths of a second, weights are recorded in tenths of a pound, temperatures are read in tenths of a degree, and rainfall is usually measured in tenths of an inch.   The student should be able to add to this list illustrations from his own experience.

6.2   Geometric and Place-value Interpretation

Since .1 means the size of one of the ten equal parts into which some one thing has been divided ($.1 = \frac{1}{10}$), then .2 must mean 2 of those equal parts and .3 must mean 3 of those equal parts.   It is quite natural for one to visualize all fraction representations as parts of wholes.   The stimulus .3 usually suggests to the reader a piece or chunk, "something in the neighborhood of one-fourth."   Students visualize the whole of an object divided into portions of size $\frac{3}{10}$ and $\frac{7}{10}$ but they should also visualize 3 distinct sections of the whole, each section being $\frac{1}{10}$ of the whole: $.3 = \frac{3}{10} = 3(\frac{1}{10})$.

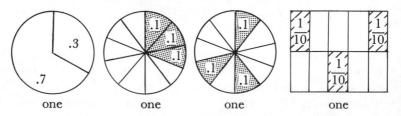

one   one   one   one

It must be pointed out that .1 means any one of the ten equal parts into which the whole has been divided. The following all represent .1 (one-tenth) of equal wholes.

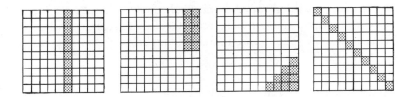

Now .2 would mean two pieces of size .1 or any two pieces pictured above. Hence .3 would mean three pieces of size .1 or any three pieces pictured above. It is safe to conclude that all four of the areas pictured or represented in the design represent .4 of one whole. Usually, however, when we speak of .4 of something we mean four pieces of the same size and shape.

The meaning of "hundredth" can be developed through the use of our money system. The dollar is composed of 100 cents, therefore each cent represents one-hundredth of a dollar. Since we know that 1 cent can be written as $.01, then 5 cents can be written as $.05 and 25 cents as $.25. We observe that one penny is .01 (one-hundredth) of a dollar and one dime is .1 (one-tenth) of a dollar. We also note that the numeral 1 occupies different places and hence different place value. In one place it means one dollar, in another it means one dime which is one-tenth of a dollar, and in another place it means one penny or one-tenth of a dime.

Dollar	Dime Tenths of a dollar	Penny Hundredths of a dollar	
1			1 dollar
	1		1 dime
		1	1 penny

As the numeral 1 is moved one place to the right in the number system its place value becomes only one-tenth of its original value. In the number 33 cents, which is composed of 30 cents and 3 cents, the second 3 has a value .1 of the value of the first three. Three cents is .1 the value of three dimes: $.03 = \frac{1}{10}$ of .30; $.03 = .1 \times .30$.

Reference to a ten-tens chart of the 100 numerals will help establish meanings and understandings. The first number in the chart represents $\frac{1}{100}$ of the group of numbers, the first ten numbers represent $\frac{1}{10}$ of the group of 100 numbers, and 100 of them represent all or $\frac{100}{100}$ of the numbers. The picture representation below shows the meaning of $\frac{1}{100}$ which is written .01.

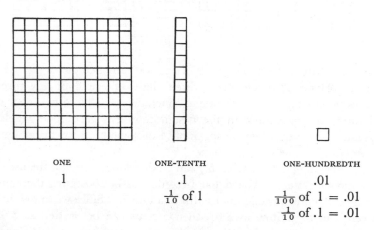

ONE	ONE-TENTH	ONE-HUNDREDTH
1	.1	.01
	$\frac{1}{10}$ of 1	$\frac{1}{100}$ of $1 = .01$
		$\frac{1}{10}$ of $.1 = .01$

If a whole is divided into 100 equal parts, then each part is called one one-hundredth. Then .07 would mean 7 of those equal parts, .23 would mean 23 of those parts, .45 would refer to 45 of those equal parts, and .99 would mean 99 of those equal parts (all but one of them, all but .01).

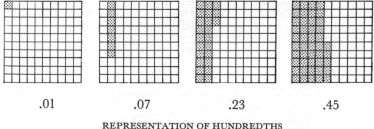

.01   .07   .23   .45

REPRESENTATION OF HUNDREDTHS

An examination of the diagrams above should show very clearly the relative sizes of ordinary decimal fractions. Naturally .07 is larger than .01; .23 is larger than .07; and .45 is larger than .23.

.1	.01	.01	.01	.01	.01	.01	.01	.01	.01	.01	.10 = .1
.1	.01										.10 = .1
.1	.01										.10 = .1
.1	.01										.10 = .1
.1	.01										.10 = .1
.1	.01										.10 = .1
.1	.01										.10 = .1
.1	.01										.10 = .1
.1	.01										.10 = .1
.1	.01										.10 = .1
$\overline{1.0}$	.1	.1	.1	.1	.1	.1	.1	.1	.1	.1	$\overline{1.00} = \overline{1.}$

A diagrammatic representation of tenths and hundredths as pictured above should prove of inestimable value in showing the relationships between 1, .1, and .01. The entire rectangle represents unity or one, each strip (row or column) represents one-tenth of one, and each small rectangle represents $\frac{1}{10}$ of each strip or $\frac{1}{100}$ of the whole rectangle.

We should be able to determine from this representation that 10 one-hundredths are equivalent to 1 tenth (10 × .01 = .1) and that 10 tenths are equivalent to 1 (10 × .1 = 1). Conclusions we can draw are that 20 hundredths are equivalent to 2 tenths which in turn is equal to the common fraction $\frac{1}{5}$, (.20 = .2 = $\frac{1}{5}$); 40 hundredths is equivalent to 4 tenths or $\frac{2}{5}$ (.40 = .4 = $\frac{2}{5}$); 50 hundredths is equivalent to 5 tenths which in turn is equal to $\frac{1}{2}$ (.50 = .5 = $\frac{1}{2}$), and other similar relationships.

When the concepts of tenths and hundredths are firmly established, the general concept of decimal fractions can be extended to include thousandths, ten-thousandths, and smaller denominations. For those interpretations a table of values would prove helpful.

	Thousands	Hundreds	Tens	Ones	Tenths	Hundredths	Thousandths	Ten-thousandths	Hundred-thousandths	Millionths	Ten-millionths	Hundred-millionths
(1)					6							
(2)					4	7						
(3)					0	0	3					
(4)					2	3	4					
(5)					0	0	0	6				
(6)					0	0	3	7				
(7)					0	0	0	0	9			
(8)					0	0	0	0	0	4		
(9)					0	0	0	0	0	0	8	
(10)		4	1	5	0	0	0	4	1	5		

A PLACE VALUE CHART

6.3 Reading and Writing Decimal Numbers

The ability to read decimal fractions is contingent upon the ability to read integral numbers. If the number is a mixed number, the integral part is read normally and the integers in the decimal part are read as if they were integral and then given their proper designation. The decimal numbers .3, .61, .573. and .004 are read as 3, 61, 573, and 4 respectively with their proper designation. The first number is read as tenths, the 61 is read as hundredths (because the last digit is in the hundredths place), the 573 represents thousandths (because the last digit is in the thousandths place) and the 4 also represents thousandths (for the same reason).

The denominations down the scale have the same prefixes as those in the other direction, but the decimal notations are hyphenated. The decimal unit .0001 $(\frac{1}{10000})$ is written as the compound word "ten-thousandths."

	Hundred	Ten		Hundred	Ten		
←Millions	Millions	Millions	Thousands	Thousands	Thousands	Hundreds Tens	ONES
				Ten-	Hundred-		
ONES	Tenths	Hundredths	Thousandths	Thousandths	Thousandths	Millionths→	

In reading decimal numbers the word *and* separates the integral part from the fractional part. The number 3.7 is read as "three *and* seven tenths," and 400.004 is read as "four hundred and four thousandths," while .404 is read "four hundred four thousandths."

The decimal numbers given in the place value chart above are read as follows:

1. Six tenths
2. Forty-seven hundredths
3. Three thousandths
4. Two hundred thirty-four thousandths
5. Six ten-thousandths
6. Thirty-seven ten-thousandths
7. Nine hundred-thousandths
8. Four millionths
9. Eight ten-millionths
10. Four hundred fifteen and four hundred fifteen millionths

It is possible for misunderstandings to arise when one hears a decimal number being read, for he can misinterpret the fractional part. Should one hear the number "seven hundred thousandths" he does not know if the speaker means 7 units of size one hundred thousandths or 700 units of size one-thousandth. It could be either .00007 or .700.

Because of the difficulty one might encounter in copying the non-zero digits in the proper places, decimal fractions are often read in terms of a sequence of digits with the decimal point called "point." Thus "point four zero one" definitely means (.401) four hundred one thousandths. Were it read in the regular way it might be mistaken for .400 or four hundred one-thousandths.

Let us add further to the interpretation of decimal fractions by expressing them as powers of ten and expressing the whole as the sum of its parts.

Thousands	Hundreds	Tens	Ones	•	Tenths	Hundredths	Thousandths
1	1	1	1		1	1	1

$$1000 \quad = 10^3$$
$$100 \quad = 10^2$$
$$10 \quad = 10^1$$
$$1 \quad = 10^0$$
$$.1 \quad = 10^{-1}$$
$$.01 \quad = 10^{-2}$$
$$.001 \quad = 10^{-3}$$

←	10^3	10^2	10^1	10^0	10^{-1}	10^{-2}	10^{-3}	→
	2	3	4	7	8	9	3	

The number in the box is composed of: Two thousand three hundred forty-seven and eight tenths and nine hundredths and three thousandths: 2,347.893.

Two thousand	2000	$= 2 \times 1000$
Three hundred	300	$= 3 \times 100$
Four tens	40	$= 4 \times 10$
Seven ones	7	$= 7 \times 1$
Eight tenths	.8	$= 8 \times .1$
Nine hundredths	.09	$= 9 \times .01$
Three thousandths	.003	$= 3 \times .001$
	2347.893	

$$2347.893 = 2(10^3) + 3(10^2) + 4(10^1) + 7(10^0) + 8(10^{-1}) + 9(10^{-2}) + 3(10^{-3}).$$

The correct way to read the number is: "Two thousand three hundred forty-seven and eight hundred ninety-three thousandths."

Thousands 10^3	Hundreds 10^2	Tens 10^1	Ones 10^0	Tenths 10^{-1}	Hundredths 10^{-2}	Thousandths 10^{-3}
3	4	5	7	6	8	

This number is read: "Three thousand four hundred fifty-seven and sixty-eight hundredths." When it is decomposed into its component parts we have:

3 thousand	3000	3 (1000)	3×10^3
4 hundred	400	4 (100)	4×10^2
5 tens	50	5 (10)	5×10^1
7 ones	7	7 (1)	7×10^0
6 tenths	.6	6 (.1)	6×10^{-1}
8 hundredths	.08	8 (.01)	8×10^{-2}

$$3457.68 = 3000 + 400 + 50 + 7 + .6 + .08$$

Each value represents a power of 10. For values to the left the power of 10 increases by one; to the right the power of 10 decreases by one. Each place value is 10 times the value of the neighboring place to the right and is one-tenth the value of the place to the left.

6.4 Accuracy of Measurement

When one says that the width of a metal bar is .3 of an inch, one means that it is nearer to .3 inches than to .2 inches or .4 inches—it is somewhere between .2½ and .3½ inches or between .25 and .35 inches.

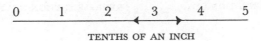

TENTHS OF AN INCH

A measurement expressed as .30 inches is different in meaning from .3 inches. Such a measure implies that the unit of measure is .01 inch and that the measurement has been expressed to the nearest integral number of hundredths. The real value lies between .29½ and .30½ inches. We say that .3 inches is correct to the nearest tenth of an inch while .30 is correct to the nearest hundredth of an inch. The latter is a more precise measurement.

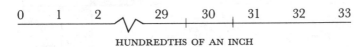

HUNDREDTHS OF AN INCH

The number .3 from an arithmetic standpoint is equal to .30 but is very different in meaning: $\frac{3}{10} = \frac{30}{100}$. If a student has 30 cents he could have that amount of money represented in any one of several ways. For instance, if he has 3 dimes he would have $\frac{3}{10}$ of a dollar for there are 10 dimes in a dollar. If he has 30 pennies he would have $\frac{30}{100}$ of a dollar for there are 100 pennies in a dollar. The .3 means 3 units of measurement each having a size of $\frac{1}{10}$, while .30 means 30 units of measurement each having a size of $\frac{1}{100}$. In the first case we have counted only 3 things while in the second case we have counted 30 things.

.3 means 3 of 10 equal parts of one whole thing. Three one-tenths.

.30 means 30 of 100 equal parts of one whole thing. Thirty one-hundredths.

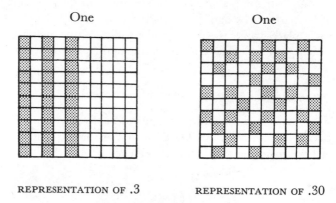

REPRESENTATION OF .3   REPRESENTATION OF .30

Just as there is a difference in meaning between $\frac{4}{8}$ of an apple and $\frac{2}{4}$ of an apple there is also a difference in meaning between .5 and .50. The former means 5 pieces of size one-tenth while the latter means 50 pieces of size one-hundredth.

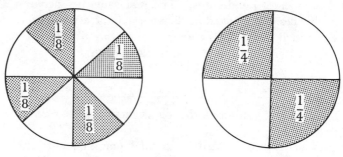

6.5 Changing Common Fractions to Decimal Fractions

Students have formed the habit of annexing zeros indiscriminately to decimal numbers and though we have just shown that such a practice affects the accuracy of the measurement, it is legitimate for arithmetical purposes. It is often necessary to change common fractions to decimal fractions and in order to do this extra places are often needed. One of the methods for changing $\frac{3}{8}$ to a decimal fraction is to divide the 3 by 8, which can be performed if we annex zeros to the 3, making it 3.000.   The algorism will look like this:

$$\frac{3}{8} = 3 \div 8 \quad 8\overline{)\,3.000} \quad .375$$

$$\begin{array}{r} .375 \\ 8\,)\,\overline{3.000} \\ 2\,4 \\ \overline{60} \\ 56 \\ \overline{40} \\ 40 \end{array}$$

Therefore $\frac{3}{8}$ = .375

$\frac{3}{8}$ is equivalent to .375

This technique is used rather extensively for conversion of common fractions to their equivalent decimal form.   Since one interpretation of a fraction is one of expressed division, one needs only to divide the numerator by the denominator to find another form of the fraction.   Students have already been introduced to this kind of problem when learning how to share an integral amount of money with a given number of people.   In the problem, "Divide $3 equally among 4 boys," the solution involves dividing $3 by 4.   This results in a direct quotient of $\frac{3}{4}$, or one might annex zeros to the decimal part and divide $3.00 by 4.   In that case the quotient would be $.75 or 75 cents.

The type of problem illustrated suggests the solution of examples of this type: Express $\frac{2}{5}$ as a decimal fraction.   Change $\frac{1}{4}$ to tenths. Write decimally: $4\frac{1}{8}$.   Seven tenths equals $\frac{?}{100}$.   Fifty out of 60 is the same as *how many* out of 100?

Every one of the fractions given above can be changed to its decimal equivalent by dividing the numerator by the denominator if sufficient zeros are annexed to the numerator.

$$5\,)\,\overline{2.0} \qquad 4\,)\,\overline{1.00} \qquad 8\,)\,\overline{1.000} \qquad 10\,)\,\overline{7.0} \qquad 60\,)\,\overline{50.00}$$

There is another way to change a common fraction to a decimal fraction (involving no new learnings).   We have already been introduced to the Golden Rule of fractions and should be completely convinced that both the numerator and denominator of a fraction can be multiplied by the same non-zero number.   Let us use this rule in changing common fractions to decimal fractions.

Change $\frac{1}{5}$ to tenths. $\frac{1}{5} = \frac{?}{10}$.   Multiply N and D by 2.

Fraction is $\frac{2}{10}$ or .2.

Change $\frac{7}{25}$ to hundredths. $\frac{7}{25} = \frac{?}{100}$.   Multiply N and D by 4.

Fraction is $\frac{28}{100}$ or .28.

Change $\frac{3}{8}$ to hundredths. $\frac{3}{8} = \frac{?}{100}$.   Multiply N and D by $12\frac{1}{2}$.

Fraction is $\frac{37\frac{1}{2}}{100}$ or $.37\frac{1}{2}$.

What must we do if we want to change $\frac{9}{16}$ to hundredths?   We must multiply both terms of the fraction by the same number.   We use a trial multiplier until we reach 6: $6 \times 16 = 96$.   We need 4 more or we need $\frac{1}{4}$ of 16.   Therefore if we multiply 16 by $6\frac{1}{4}$ we will obtain 100.   Then we must multiply 9 by $6\frac{1}{4}$ also.   This gives us $56\frac{1}{4}$. Therefore $\frac{9}{16} = \frac{6\frac{1}{4} \times 9}{6\frac{1}{4} \times 16} = \frac{56\frac{1}{4}}{100}$ or $.56\frac{1}{4}$.

This method is recommended for examples which can be converted easily to tenths, hundredths, etc.—examples which contain integral factors of powers of 10.   If the denominations are thirds, sixths, sevenths, ninths, twelfths, etc., the division operation previously explained will be more efficient.

6.6 Comparing Decimal Fractions

Young adults enter college with very hazy notions about the relative sizes of decimal fractions.   The example which had the largest number of incorrect responses by college freshmen on an inventory test given by the writer was the example which asked them to rewrite the following decimal fractions according to size beginning with the largest: .31 .302 .320.   Students seem to lack the ability to compare fractions.

As a numeral is placed farther from the decimal point, to the right, its place value becomes less and the value of the number becomes smaller, but if a numeral is annexed to a given decimal fraction the resulting fraction has been increased—something has been added (if the numeral is different from zero).   The number .08 is less than .8 but .81 is greater than .8.

.7	7 tenths	
.07	7 hundredths	one-tenth of .7
.007	7 thousandths	one-tenth of .07
.0007	7 ten-thousandths	one-tenth of .007

The numbers above are decreasing in value: .07 is smaller than .7; .007 is smaller than .07; and .0007 is smaller than .007. Now if we add something to each of the numbers, the new numbers will be larger in value than the original ones.

.7	.07	.007	.0007
.71	.072	.0073	.00078

The following numbers are arranged in order of size from the smallest to the largest:

.2   .23   .234   .2345   .7   .71   .718   .7183

If we try to find the difference between two decimal fractions for purposes of comparison, then we should be able to ascertain the larger of the two. If we were able to find the difference between .2 and .23 we would write the latter as the minuend; hence it is the larger.

Decimal fractions can also be compared if they are expressed in common denominations. To gain a better understanding of sizes of such numbers one should decompose them as tenths, hundredths, etc. As one has had much practice in reading whole numbers in a variety of ways, so should one have practice in reading decimal fractions in a number of ways. If we want to read a number as tenths we read all the numerals to the tenths column, if we want to read a number as hundredths we read all the numerals to the hundredths place, etc. The chart below shows one how to read .2468 in different ways.

	Ones •	Tenths	Hundredths	Thousandths	Ten-thousandths
A.		2	4	6	8
B.		2	4	6	8
C.		2	4	6	8
D.		2	4	6	8

A. Two and four hundred sixty-eight thousandths *Tenths*
B. Twenty-four and sixty-eight hundredths *Hundredths*
C. Two hundred forty-six and eight tenths *Thousandths*
D. Two thousand four hundred sixty-eight *Ten-thousandths*

Should we want to change a number from tenths to hundredths we fill in the hundredths place with the zero (place holder) and read it as a two-place number in hundredths.   Thus .2 becomes .20; .7 becomes .70; and .8 becomes 80 hundredths

2 tenths = 20 hundredths = 200 thousandths = 2000 ten-thousandths,

etc.

$$.2 = .20 = .200 = .2000, \text{ etc.}$$

Then, should one desire to compare .2 with .24, he can express each fraction in the same denomination, namely tenths.   The first number is 2 tenths while the latter is $2\frac{4}{10}$ tenths.   Hence .24 is larger than .2.   To compare .571 with .58, we can express both decimal fractions in terms of tenths—$5\frac{71}{100}$ tenths and $5\frac{8}{10}$ tenths—or we can express both of them in terms of hundredths—$.57\frac{1}{10}$ and .58.   The first pair of numbers can also be expressed as hundredths—.20 and .24—and the second pair can both be expressed as thousandths—.571 and .580.   It is easy to determine the larger of two numbers if they both are expressed in the same denomination.

The numbers being compared can all be expressed in the smallest denomination represented just by annexing zeros in places to the right of the given numbers.   Should one compare .6 with .63 he merely expresses .6 as .60 and compares .60 with .63.   We are certain that 63 hundredths is larger than 60 hundredths and so is larger than 6 tenths, which is its equivalent.

Compare .4, .47, and .473.

The number	The number decomposed	The number as tenths	The number as thousandths	The number ranked by size
.4	.4	4.	400.	smallest
.47	.4 + .07	4.7	470.	second
.473	.4 + .07 + .003	4.73	473.	largest

Therefore .4 < .47 < .473

6.7 Changing Decimal Fractions to Common Fractions

Since by definition a decimal fraction is just another way of writing a common fraction whose denominator is a power of 10, we need only put the definition in reverse when we want to change decimal fractions to their equivalent common fractional form.   If we have a number of one decimal place (tenths) we write the fraction with the denominator 10 and simplify the fraction as desired. Thus .3 becomes $\frac{3}{10}$ and is expressed in its simplest form, while .8 becomes in turn $\frac{8}{10}$ and then $\frac{4}{5}$. In like manner a number of only two decimal places is a number in terms of hundredths and can be written with the denominator 100 and then simplified if desired. The number .45 becomes $\frac{45}{100}$ which simplifies to $\frac{9}{20}$ when both terms of the fraction are divided by 5. The number .275 is a number in thousandths, so it can be written in common fraction form directly as $\frac{275}{1000}$. Now if both terms of the fraction are divided by 5 and then by 5 again (or divided once by 25) the resulting fraction is the simple common fraction $\frac{11}{40}$. If students understand the nature of decimal fractions they should have little trouble converting them to their common fraction form.

6.8   Repeating Decimals

Any fraction whose denominator is a power of 2, power of 5, or the product of powers of both can be expressed completely as a terminating decimal fraction. Fractions like $\frac{3}{4}$, $\frac{4}{25}$, $\frac{7}{8}$, $\frac{19}{64}$, and $\frac{121}{320}$ are of this variety; they can be expressed as pure decimal fractions. Other common fractions can never be expressed in pure decimal form. Some are the never-ending type like $\frac{3}{13}$ which repeats groups of digits, and others are the type like $\frac{2}{9}$ which, too, never terminate but repeat the same digits. The fraction $\frac{5}{7}$ can be changed to a repeating decimal fraction, for after obtaining seven quotient figures, all of the possible remainders have had an opportunity to occur. Hence if the remainder is not zero in seven divisions then repetition must take place.

It is simple enough to change a common fraction to its decimal equivalent but the reverse is much more complicated. Suppose we convert the repeating decimal fraction .3434343434... to its equivalent common fraction.

Procedure: Let N = .3434343434343434...
Multiply by 100:   100N = 34.34343434343434...

Subtracting the first equation from the second produces the equation, 99N = 34. Thus N, the original fraction, is equivalent to the common fraction, $\frac{34}{99}$. The student should observe that a multiplier is selected which causes, as a result of subsequent subtraction, the decimal part to vanish completely.

> Witness: Change .547854785478... to its equivalent common fraction form.
> Let N = .547854785478...
> Then 10,000 is the factor
>   10,000N = 5478.54785478...
> By subtraction 9,999N = 5478 and hence N = $\frac{5478}{9999}$,

which simplifies to $\frac{1826}{3333}$. From the foregoing illustrations, does it follow that .402402402... and .964964964... become respectively $\frac{402}{999}$ and $\frac{964}{999}$?

A more difficult example is the type which does not begin repeating until after one or two digits such as the decimal fraction .8333333.... Let us change this fraction to its common fraction form.

> Let   N = .83333333... or .8 + .033333333...
> Then 10N = 8.333333333... or 8. + .3333333333...

Subtracting the first equation from the second we have

$$9N = 7.5 \quad \text{or } 7.2 + .3$$

$$\text{and} \quad N = \frac{7\frac{1}{2}}{9} \quad \text{or} \frac{7.5}{9} \quad \text{or} \frac{15}{18} \quad \text{or} \frac{5}{6}$$

Therefore, .8333333... = $\frac{5}{6}$

Change .52171717171717... to a common fraction.

> Solution: Let N = .521717171717   or   .52 + .00171717171717
> Then 100N = 52.00 + .1717171711
> The difference is 99N = 51.48 + .17 or 51.65
>   Multiplying both members by 100   9900N = 5165
>   Dividing both members by 9900   N = $\frac{5165}{9900}$

which regroups into $\frac{1033}{1980}$. The student should verify the fact, by division, that $\frac{1033}{1980}$ is equivalent to .5217171717....

6.9 Some Useful Equivalents

A thorough knowledge of the relationships and equivalences of many common and decimal fractions will prove helpful in problem solving. Problems involving computations with decimal fractions can be simplified by using common fraction equivalents. Some of the most common equivalents which should be learned are listed below:

$\frac{1}{2} = .50$	$\frac{1}{4} = .25$	$\frac{1}{3} = .33\frac{1}{3}$	$\frac{1}{5} = .20$	$\frac{1}{6} = .16\frac{2}{3}$	$\frac{1}{8} = .12\frac{1}{2}$
$\frac{1}{10} = .10$	$\frac{3}{4} = .75$	$\frac{2}{3} = .66\frac{2}{3}$	$\frac{2}{5} = .40$	$\frac{5}{6} = .83\frac{1}{3}$	$\frac{3}{8} = .37\frac{1}{2}$
$\frac{1}{20} = .05$	$\frac{1}{15} = .06\frac{2}{3}$	$\frac{1}{9} = .11\frac{1}{9}$	$\frac{3}{5} = .60$	$\frac{1}{12} = .08\frac{1}{3}$	$\frac{5}{8} = .62\frac{1}{2}$
$\frac{1}{50} = .02$	$\frac{1}{16} = .06\frac{1}{4}$	$\frac{1}{30} = .03\frac{1}{3}$	$\frac{4}{5} = .80$	$\frac{5}{12} = .41\frac{2}{3}$	$\frac{7}{8} = .87\frac{1}{2}$

6.10   Families of Fractions

A set of fractions whose denominators are multiples of powers of ten are often called families of fractions. The fractions $\frac{1}{3}$, $\frac{1}{30}$, $\frac{1}{300}$, $\frac{1}{3000}$ are of this type, for the original denominator is multiplied by 10, 100, and 1000. The original fraction is multiplied successively by $\frac{1}{10}$, $\frac{1}{100}$, and $\frac{1}{1000}$ or by .1, .01, and .001. Thus there is a definite relationship between these fractions and sets of fractions like them.

If $\frac{1}{3} = .3+$ then $\frac{1}{30} = .03+$, $\frac{1}{300} = .003+$ and $\frac{1}{3000} = .0003+$. In like manner $\frac{3}{5}$, $\frac{3}{50}$, $\frac{3}{500}$, and $\frac{3}{5000}$ are respectively equivalent to .6, .06, .006, and .0006. We are all well aware of the fact that $\frac{1}{2} = .5$ and that $\frac{1}{20} = \frac{1}{10}$ of $\frac{1}{2}$ or $\frac{\frac{1}{2}}{10}$ which in turn is $\frac{.5}{10}$ or .05.

To divide a number by 10, or a power of 10, all integers must be moved to the right the number of places corresponding to the power of 10 in the divisor. To divide .5 by 10, the 5 must be placed in the hundredths place, .05. To divide .5 by 100 the number 5 moves into the column two places to the right (thousandths place) as .005. Students who say that the decimal point moves a certain number of places to the left should know that in reality the decimal point never moves—it's the numerals which change places and take on other values.

$\frac{1}{5}$	$= \frac{1}{5} \div 1$	$= .2$	$\frac{1}{2}$	$= .5$	$\frac{1}{4}$	$= .25$	$\frac{1}{8}$	$= .125$
$\frac{1}{50}$	$= \frac{1}{5} \div 10$	$= .02$	$\frac{1}{20}$	$= .05$	$\frac{1}{40}$	$= .025$	$\frac{1}{80}$	$= .0125$
$\frac{1}{500}$	$= \frac{1}{5} \div 100$	$= .002$	$\frac{1}{200}$	$= .005$	$\frac{1}{400}$	$= .0025$	$\frac{1}{800}$	$= .00125$

An understanding of these relationships should be coveted by the most discerning students.

6.11   Fractions in Other Bases

In the decimal system we use the "decimal point" to separate the whole from the fractional part, to identify the ones place.   If we were to use the base two the point for separation would be called the "binary point" and in the base twelve it probably would be the "duodecimal point."   If .1 in the system whose base is ten means 1 tenth, then in the base two, three, four, etc., it must mean 1 half, 1 third, 1 fourth, respectively.

In the binary system the place values to the right of the ones place have values designated by (base)$^{-1}$ or $\frac{1}{\text{base}}$, (base)$^{-2}$ or $\frac{1}{\text{base}^2}$, and so forth.   In our language these values would be called halves, fourths, eighths, sixteenths, etc., in powers of the base two.   If the base is three the place values denoting fractional parts are thirds, ninths, twenty-sevenths, etc.   Then in the base twelve the first place to the right of the ones place has a value of one-twelfth and the next one has a value of one-hundred-forty-fourth.

In base four the number .13 means 1 fourth + 3 sixteenths.
In base five the number .24 means 2 fifths + 4 twenty-fifths.
In base six the number .05 means 5 thirty-sixths.
In base nine the number .103 means 1 ninth + 3 seven-hundred-twenty-ninths.
In base three the number .2012 = $(\frac{2}{3} + \frac{0}{9} + \frac{1}{27} + \frac{2}{81})_{\text{ten}} = \frac{59}{81}_{(\text{ten})}$.

EXERCISES

SET 22

1. Show the difference in meaning between "three and one-half hundredths" and "three and one half of a hundredth."
2. Write the following decimal fractions in words:
   .200   .401   .400   .00002   .404   400.004   .910   .003003
3. Write the following in numeral form:
   six hundred ten thousandths   seven hundred thousandths
   six hundred ten-thousandths   one-fourth of a hundredth
   six hundred ten ten-thousandths   five hundred-thousandths
   six hundred ten and ten thousandths   three hundred ten tenths
4. How many complete tenths in each of the following:
   .3   .35   .350   .305   3.5   35   3.500   3.05   350

5. Change the following to the duodecimal scale and write as duodecimal fractions:

$$\frac{1}{4} \qquad \frac{1}{3} \qquad \frac{1}{2} \qquad \frac{3}{4} \qquad \frac{2}{3} \qquad \frac{5}{6}$$

6. Show that .1001 (two) = .21 (four)
7. Add the following in base five: .1 + .1 + .3
   What would the sum be in base four? in base six?
8. Copy and complete the table of equivalent values.

$$\frac{1}{2} = .5 \qquad \frac{1}{20} = \qquad \frac{1}{200} = \qquad \frac{1}{2000} =$$
$$\frac{3}{5} = .6 \qquad \frac{3}{50} = \qquad \frac{3}{500} = \qquad \frac{3}{5000} =$$
$$\frac{7}{8} = .875 \qquad \frac{7}{80} = \qquad \frac{7}{800} = \qquad \frac{7}{8000} =$$
$$\frac{1}{9} = .11+ \qquad \frac{1}{90} = \qquad \frac{1}{900} = \qquad \frac{1}{9000} =$$

9. Change the following decimal fractions to simple common fractions:
   .250   .70   .65   .245   .15   1.350   .00025
   .3   .00004   .0050   .4900   .002   .0101   .5050
10. Place the following numbers on the same number line:
   $\frac{1}{2}$ .65   1.15 $\frac{5}{6}$ .89   .333 $\frac{267}{1000}$ $\frac{81}{82}$ .09
11. Write the numerals of exercise No. 9 from the largest to the smallest.
12. Select the smallest number from each set: (a) 1.80 1.08 10.8
   (b) .045 .04 .0405 (c) .56 .4 .80 (d) .16 1.6 .0160 (e) $\frac{4}{9}$ $\frac{5}{12}$ $\frac{3}{8}$
   (f) $\frac{2}{11}$ $\frac{3}{17}$ $\frac{1}{5}$ (g) $\frac{5}{3}$ $1\frac{1}{2}$ 16 tenths.
13. Show by division that $\frac{2}{13}$ becomes a repeating decimal fraction.
14. Express as common fractions: (a) .272727... (b) .79127912...
   (c) 4.121212...
15. Which of the following can be expressed as repeating decimal fractions:

$$\frac{4}{9} \qquad \frac{5}{17} \qquad \sqrt{2} \qquad \pi$$

6.12 Addition of Decimal Fractions

Learning to add and subtract decimal fractions ought to follow easily when the meanings of decimal fractions are well defined. We must recall the basic principle of addition, namely, that only like things can be added. We remember that when we add books to a new pile or quantity of books the total represents a quantity of books, that thirds added to thirds will give a new group of thirds, that hundreds added to hundreds will give a new group of hundreds, etc. From this principle we conclude that tenths added to tenths will give a new group of tenths, but let us test the hypothesis. Combine .3 of a cup of sugar with .4 of a cup of sugar. How much sugar will there be? Since the problem implies putting things together, we use the addition operation. Let us add .3 cup with .4 cup of sugar.

$$
\begin{array}{ll}
\text{3 tenths cup sugar} & \frac{3}{10} + \frac{4}{10} = \frac{7}{10} \qquad 3(\frac{1}{10}) \\
\underline{+ \text{ 4 tenths cup sugar}} & \underline{+ \; 4(\frac{1}{10})} \\
\text{7 tenths cup sugar} & 7(\frac{1}{10})
\end{array}
$$

Therefore we can safely conclude that tenths added to tenths will give tenths.

.3 cup sugar

\+ .4 cup sugar

.7 cup sugar

The fact can be further verified by use of a diagram. If we lay out .3 of a unit and to it add .4 of that same unit, we will have .7 of the same unit.

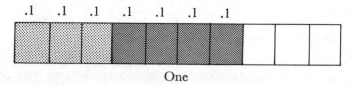

One

Let us solve a problem involving tenths. "John walked .4 of a mile in the morning, .4 of a mile in the afternoon, and .2 of a mile in the evening. What was the total distance traveled that day?" Since the problem suggests combining quantities of the same kind we ought to use the addition operation.

Add: .4 of a mile   4 tenths of a mile

.4 of a mile   4 tenths of a mile

.2 of a mile   2 tenths of a mile

10 tenths of a mile or 1 whole mile

$\frac{4}{10} + \frac{4}{10} + \frac{2}{10} = \frac{10}{10}$, which equals 1. Therefore .4 + .4 + .2 = 1.

Let us illustrate the problem graphically:

0   .1   .2   .3   .4   .5   .6   .7   .8   .9   1.0   1.1   1.2

.4   .4   .2

We can see from the above that when the number of tenths equals ten we have reached unity, that $\frac{11}{10}$, $\frac{12}{10}$, $\frac{13}{10}$, etc., are more than 1 and are, respectively, 1.1, 1.2, and 1.3. The sum of .6 and .7 is 13 tenths or 1.3. Tenths represent only one decimal place, one place to the right of the ones column. Since we usually put only one numeral in each column, then when we obtain a two-digit number for the sum a portion of it is converted to ones since ten tenths make one whole 1.

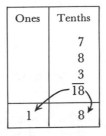

Therefore, when we add tenths we line up the numerals in their proper columns, the ones in the ones place and the tenths in the tenths place (this amounts to keeping the decimal points lined one under the other) and then add the respective columns. We add the tenths column and record the number in the tenths place. If the sum is equal to or greater than 10 (ten tenths) we convert the result to an integer and a certain number of tenths remaining. Witness:

$$.6 \; \tfrac{6}{10} \qquad .8 \; \tfrac{8}{10} \qquad .8 \; \tfrac{8}{10} \qquad .5 \; \tfrac{5}{10} \qquad 1.8 \; \tfrac{18}{10} \qquad .7 \; \tfrac{7}{10}$$
$$\underline{+ \; .7 \; \tfrac{7}{10}} \quad \underline{+ \; .9 \; \tfrac{9}{10}} \quad \underline{+ \; .8 \; \tfrac{8}{10}} \quad \underline{+ \; .5 \; \tfrac{5}{10}} \quad \underline{+ \; .3 \; \tfrac{3}{10}} \quad \underline{+ \; 1.9 \; \tfrac{19}{10}}$$
$$1.3 \; \tfrac{13}{10} \qquad 1.7 \; \tfrac{17}{10} \qquad 1.6 \; \tfrac{16}{10} \qquad 1.0 \; \tfrac{10}{10} \qquad 2.1 \; \tfrac{21}{10} \qquad 2.6 \; \tfrac{26}{10}$$

We can develop a similar case for addition of hundredths. We add only like things; therefore we add hundredths to hundredths. For instance, "If the rainfall on Monday morning was .03 of an inch and in the afternoon it was .04 of an inch, what was the total amount of rainfall for the entire day?" An analysis of the problem suggests that we combine .03 with .04. We can use common fractions to show that the result will be $\tfrac{7}{100}$ or .07.

Thus .03 + .04 = .07

$$\frac{3}{100} + \frac{4}{100} = \frac{7}{100} \qquad \begin{array}{r} .03 \text{ of an inch} \\ + \; .04 \text{ of an inch} \\ \hline .07 \text{ of an inch} \end{array} \qquad \begin{array}{r} 3 \text{ hundredths} \\ + \; 4 \text{ hundredths} \\ \hline 7 \text{ hundredths} \end{array}$$

The total amount of rainfall was .07 of an inch.

Let us solve a few more examples. Forty-two hundredths and 23 hundredths will be (42 + 23) hundredths or 65 hundredths. Seventy hundredths and 30 hundredths will be (70 and 30) hundredths or 100 hundredths, which is 1. Eighty-four hundredths and 33 hundredths will be 117 hundredths, $\frac{117}{100}$ or 1 and 17 hundredths.

$$
\begin{array}{cccc}
.42 & .70 & .84 & .27 \\
+\ .23 & +\ .30 & +\ .33 & +\ .35 \\
\hline
.65 & 1.00 & 1.17 & .62 \\
\end{array}
$$

Since 100 hundredths is one, then we write 1 in the ones column and fill in other columns with zeros to denote absence of those units in the number 1.

Ones	Tenths	Hundredths
	6 3	4 6
1 .	0	0

The example illustrated in the box clearly shows that 84 hundredths is the same as .8 plus .04 and that .33 is composed of 3 tenths and 3 hundredths. So we add the numbers in the hundredths column and if we obtain more than 10 hundreths or exactly 10 hundredths, then we write a 1 in the next column (tenths place). If we add the tenths column and obtain more than 10 tenths or exactly 10 tenths, then we have a 1 in the next column. Our number system is based on ten, and ten of any power of ten will give us one of the next higher power of ten, and one more is added to the column adjacent to the left.

Ones	Tenths	Hundredths
	8 3	4 3
	11	7
1	1	7

We can readily see that the addition of decimal fractions is similar to the addition of whole numbers. We add the respective columns, the tens, the ones, the tenths, the hundredths, etc., and make changes or regroupings when they are necessary. Let us solve an example which involves some mixed decimal numbers. Combine 53.25 + 27.87. One ought to see a close similarity which this problem bears to problems of adding money. The idea of regrouping (carrying) as it is applied to the addition of decimal numbers is just an application of previously learned ideas and principles.

Example:

Tens	Ones	‖ Tenths	Hundredths
5	3	2	5
2	7	8	7
7	10	10	12

53.25
+ 27.87

Solution

```
  1 1 1
  5 3. 2 5
+ 2 7. 8 7
  8 1. 1 2
```

2 Write 2, carry 1.

11 ← 1 Write 1, carry 1.

11 ← 1 Write 1, carry 1.

8 (7 + 1 = 8)

| 8 | 1 | • | 1 | 2 |

```
  7.8946
+ 8.4279
      15
      11
      11
      12
      15
 16.3225
```

If the principle of adding like quantities is clearly understood and adhered to, the student should have no difficulty in extending the principle to the addition of thousandths, ten-thousandths, and to lower orders of decimal numbers.

Frequently there arises a situation in which one is asked to combine fractional parts of different denominations like tenths and hundredths. For instance, if a metal rod .75 of a foot long is welded to one which is .8 of a foot long, how long will the new rod be? The solution of the problem is obtained by adding .75 feet and .8 feet. We will have to add tenths and hundredths, which we cannot do until these numbers are expressed in like denominations.

From our experience with the addition of common fractions we recall that we can find a lower denomination to which we can express the given denominations. In this case the lower denomination is "hundredths." We express .8 as .80, for $\frac{80}{100}$ is equivalent to $\frac{8}{10}$ and though there is a difference in interpretation it is considered correct practice to change the form of one or more of the given fractions so that all will be alike. Now we add .75 to .80.

The algorism:

$$
\begin{array}{l}
.8 \\
+\ .75 \\
\hline
\end{array}
\qquad
\text{Solutions:}
\qquad
\begin{array}{l}
.8\ =\ \frac{8}{10}\ =\ \frac{80}{100} \\
+\ .75\ =\quad\ \frac{75}{100} \\
\hline
\qquad\qquad\ \frac{155}{100}\ \text{or}\ 1\frac{55}{100}
\end{array}
\qquad
\begin{array}{l}
.8\ =\ .80 \\
+\ .75\ =\ .75 \\
\hline
\qquad\ 1.55
\end{array}
$$

The rod will be 1.55 feet long.

Decimal fractions are nearly always measured numbers and hence if we can make one measurement in thousandths it stands to reason that we can make other measurements in thousandths. Hence it seems foolish to ask students to find the sum of .7 inches and .345 inches. The problem might arise in a real life situation but it is considered better practice to express measured numbers in the same denominations. The type of problem in which one adds numbers of different denominations is referred to as the addition of "ragged decimals" and because these are rare in real life situations they have little place in arithmetic texts. One illustration here should suffice.

$$
\begin{array}{l}
\text{Add: } 34.5 \\
\qquad\ 3 \\
\qquad\ 2.006 \\
\qquad\ 1.9 \\
\hline
\end{array}
\qquad
\text{Solutions:}
\qquad
\begin{array}{l}
34\frac{5}{10}\ =\ 34\frac{500}{1000}\ =\ 34.500 \\
3\quad\ =\ 3\qquad\ =\ 3.000 \\
2\frac{6}{1000}\ =\ 2\frac{6}{1000}\ =\ 2.006 \\
1\frac{9}{10}\ =\ 1\frac{900}{1000}\ =\ 1.900 \\
\hline
40\frac{1406}{1000}\ \text{or}\ 41.406 \\
41\frac{406}{1000}
\end{array}
$$

6.13 Subtraction of Decimal Fractions

Suggestions for the subtraction of decimal fractions are similar to those already presented for the addition of decimal fractions. The basic principle to be employed is that only like quantities can be subtracted. Hence it will often be necessary to convert from one denomination to a smaller denomination—to express all quantities in the same denomination—in order to perform the subtractions. If the subtrahend and minuend are given in like terms there is no particular difficulty.   We will subtract tenths from tenths, hundredths from hundredths, and so on.

Witness: Subtract .4 inches from .7 inches.

$$\begin{array}{l} .7 \\ -.4 \\ \hline \end{array} \qquad \frac{7}{10} - \frac{4}{10} = \frac{3}{10}$$

7 tenths (inches)
$-$ 4 tenths (inches)
3 tenths (inches)

Therefore   .7 inches
$-$ .4 inches
.3 inches

If the numbers are not expressed in the same denomination we can annex zeros to fill spaces for convenience in making arithmetical computations.   From a rope .75 feet long cut a piece .3 of a foot long. How much will be left?

From .75 feet   .75   .75 $= \frac{75}{100}$ $= .75$
Tale .3 feet $-$ .3 $-$ .3 $= \frac{30}{100}$ $= .30$
$\frac{45}{100}$ .45

There will be .45 of a foot left.

Perhaps the most difficult type of example involving the subtraction of decimal fractions is the type in which some transformation or change must be made to the minuend before the subtractions can be performed to completion; in other words, if some of the numerals in the subtrahend are larger than the numerals of the same denomination in the minuend.   Let us subtract .378 from .502.

$$\begin{array}{l} .502 \\ -.378 \\ \hline \end{array}$$

.502 = 5 tenths + 0 hundredths + 2 thousandths
.378 = 3 tenths + 7 hundredths + 8 thousandths

= 4 tenths + 10 hundredths + 2 thousandths
= 3 tenths + 7 hundredths + 8 thousandths

= 4 tenths + 9 hundredths + 12 thousandths
= 3 tenths + 7 hundredths + 8 thousandths

It is not until we reach the final transformation that all of the subtractions can be performed.   We obtain 1 tenth + 2 hundredths + 4 thousandths or .124.   Therefore .502 $-$ .378 = .124 and the algorism might take one of these forms:

.502 = .5 + .00 + .002 = .4 + .10 + .002 = .4 + .09 + .012
.378 = .3 + .07 + .008 = .3 + .07 + .008 = .3 + .07 + .008

.502 = . 5 0 2 = . 4'0 2 = . 4 9'2 = . 5'0'2 = .50'2
.378 = . 3 7 8 = . 3 7 8 = . 3 7 8 = . 3 7 8 = .37 8

The decomposition method ought to be easy to rationalize with decimal numbers in view of the extensive work we have had with the rationalization of decomposition with whole numbers. Let us reiterate that adjacent places in our number system differ by a power of ten; that 10 of any power of ten makes 1 of the next higher power of ten and forces a 1 into the next column to the left. Ten hundreds make a thousand. Put the system in reverse and we find that 1 of a certain power of ten will produce or is equal to 10 of the next lower power of ten, that is, 1 hundred is equal to 10 ones, 1 tenth is equal to 10 hundredths, etc. Students should be aware of and able to extend this table of equivalents:

1 hundred	= 10 tens		100	= 10 (10)
1 ten	= 10 ones		10	= 10 (1)
1 one	= 10 tenths		1	= 10 (.1)
1 tenth	= 10 hundredths		.1	= 10 (.01)
1 hundredth	= 10 thousandths		.01	= 10 (.001)

Before we leave the topic of subtraction of decimal fractions there is one more word that ought to be added and a suggestion given. In the chapter on Subtraction of Whole Numbers we discussed the method commonly called the "Equal Additions" method, in which one adds the same amount to both the minuend and subtrahend before making or doing the subtractions. If we add 10 tenths to one number and 1 to the other we have not altered the difference between the two numbers. Let us apply this method to the solution of $7.2 - 3.8$.

7.2	7 and .2	Now add in 10 (.1) making it 7 and 12 tenths
3.8	3 and .8	Now add in 1 making it 4 and 8 tenths

Now in the latter form the subtractions can be performed obtaining 3.4. The algorism would look like this:

Ones	Tenths
7	2
3	8

becoming

Ones	Tenths
7	12
4	8
3	4

When the student understands the equal-additions method he will shorten his computations and his verbalization into this simple pattern:

Example: 3.451
          − 1.678
          ───────
               3   8 from 11 is 3
               7   8 from 15 is 7
               7   7 from 14 is 7
               1   2 from 3 is 1
          ───────
           1.773

The computer should be encouraged to check his subtraction examples. We have pointed out in Chapter 2 that subtraction examples can be checked by:

1. Adding the remainder to the subtrahend. If the sum is equal to the minuend then we conclude that the remainder is correct.
2. Subtracting the remainder from the minuend. If the difference obtained is equal to the subtrahend we conclude that the solution is correct.
3. The process known as "casting out nines" or the single-digit check. If the sum of the digits when reduced to one figure in the subtrahend is subtracted from the sum of the digits in the minuend (also when reduced to one figure) and is equal to the sum of the digits in the remainder (when reduced to one figure) we conclude that the solution is correct.

EXERCISES

SET 23

1. Add $4.5 + 5\frac{1}{2} + 33\frac{1}{3} + 8\frac{1}{3} + 2.1$.
   Add $.2 + \frac{1}{2}$ of $\frac{3}{5} + \frac{1}{3}$ of $.3$.
   Add $3.4 + \frac{7}{8} + \frac{3}{5} + 4\frac{1}{2} + 2$.
2. Which is larger? (a) $\frac{30}{51}$, $16 \div 27$, or $1 - .543296$. (b) $\frac{1}{3}$ of $.92$ or $\frac{1}{4}$ of $.92$. (c) $8 - 1.35$ or $7 - .65$. (d) 2.3 hundredths or 23 thousandths.
3. Subtract by the decomposition method:

.895	16.785	12.203	3.903	.452	71.426	.09
.237	3.196	33.047	1.287	.27	65.268	.063

4. Subtract by using the "equal additions" method:

6.24	1.004	103.201	103.201	421.0	20.03	60.70
3.08	.298	72.014	102.991	28.3	4.27	2.25

5. Find the difference between the following pairs of numbers and express the results correct to the nearest hundredth.

$\frac{2}{3}$ and $\frac{4}{5}$ $\frac{4}{11}$ and $\frac{5}{13}$ $\frac{7}{9}$ and $\frac{7}{8}$ $\frac{11}{12}$ and $\frac{13}{15}$

6. Which number does not belong in this set:

.02$\frac{1}{2}$ $\frac{1}{40}$ 2$\frac{1}{2}$ hundredths   25 thousandths $\frac{2.5}{10}$

Make up an example like the one just given.

7. Add and check by using the excess-of-nines check.

.456	1.342	.0452	.675	9.468	12.208	17.6
.234	3.324	.1126	.638	11.309	12.687	9.9
.612	5.678	7.3165	.541	8.628	19.427	6.3

8. Add the following in base five.

.03	.11	.33	.24	1.24	3.33	.404	32.11
.02	.12	.03	.12	1.42	3.33	.441	23.14

9. Subtract the following numbers which are written in the scale of nine.

1.8	3.08	21.16	23.12	47.316	88.18	108.035
1.3	1.17	14.08	3.08	23.707	22.22	10.027

10. Determine the base in which each of these operations has been performed:

(a)   1.3   (b)   21.23   (c)   7.20   (d)   12.23   (e)   10.25
     + 1.4   + 23.44   − 2.88   − 4.67   − 2.78
     ───────   ─────────   ────────   ────────   ────────
       3.1   100.22   4.21   5.34   7.47

11. Without copying the examples estimate their sums:
    (a) 11.1569 + 1.203 + 23.119 + 40.7005 + 30.2222
    (b) .56 + .46 + .78 + .33 + .23 + .89
    (c) 2.1 + 4.1 + 4.0 + 4.6 + 7.7 + 6.2 + 8.9
    (d) .222 + .344 + .552 + .978 + .669 + .455

6.14. Multiplication of Decimal Fractions

Multiplications and divisions performed with decimal fractions are similar to the same operations when performed with whole numbers. The operations are performed as if the numbers involved were integers and then compensations are made for the fact that some or all of the numbers are not integers. We treat the example, 4.5 × 4.5, as if the numbers were 45 × 45, perform the multiplications, and then place or position the decimal point. Even though there is a higher-decade addition involved in the multiplications these operations are carried out as if there were no decimal points in the numbers.

We begin the study of this unit by multiplying a decimal fraction by an integer, then proceed to the example of multiplying an integer by a decimal fraction, and then finally we use a decimal fraction for both the multiplier and the multiplicand. A problem illustrating the first type might be about Johnny who rode his bicycle from his home to his school .2 of a mile, then .2 of a mile to the grocery store, and then .2 of a mile from the store to his home. How far did he ride on his bicycle?

Solutions: .2 miles   .2 miles + .2 miles + .2 miles = .6 miles
            .2 miles
            .2 miles   .2 + .2 + .2 = .6   The distance is .6 miles.
            .6 miles

$\frac{2}{10} + \frac{2}{10} + \frac{2}{10} = \frac{6}{10}$ $3 \times \frac{2}{10} = \frac{6}{10}$

.2 miles

.2 \/ .2

            .2 miles
          × 3
          .6 miles

Let us also see what will happen when .7 is multiplied by 32. We multiply 32 times 7 which is 224 and since the 7 represents tenths, the product will be in tenths. Then 224 tenths expressed as a common fraction is $\frac{224}{10}$, which is equivalent to $22\frac{4}{10}$ or 22.4. Now we generalize a rule, namely, that to multiply a fraction in tenths by an integer, multiply as if both the numbers were integers and then point off one decimal place in the product (associate one decimal place with the decimal fraction *tenths*).

$$\begin{array}{r} .7 \\ \times\ 32 \\ \hline 14 \\ 21 \\ \hline 22.4 \end{array}$$

It should follow with little or no explanation that a mixed number involving tenths when multiplied by an integer will also give an answer containing tenths. Thus 3 × 4.1 ought to be 12.3, and 5 × 11.1 ought to be 55.5. If $3\frac{1}{8}$ when multiplied by 5 is $5\frac{5}{8}$, it is only natural that if $3\frac{1}{10}$ is multiplied by 5 the product will be 15 and $\frac{5}{10}$ or 15.5. Thus 5 × 3.1 = 15.5. This fact can be verified by addition.

Our second illustration consists of multiplying a number involving hundredths by an integer. The type can be introduced by a problem like this: Find the total length of 3 pieces of steel each .65 inches long. The analysis of the problem suggests either the addition or the multiplication operation. Let us use both.

.65 inches	.65 inches	(.6 + .05)	.15
.65 inches	× 3	× 3	1.8
.65 inches	1.95 inches	1.8 + .15	= 1.95
1.95 inches			

Therefore, hundredths when multiplied by a whole number will contain hundredths in the product. Point off two places from the right and locate the decimal point.

A sheet of paper is .004 of an inch thick. What will be the combined thickness of 2 sheets of paper? of 4 sheets of paper? The problem illustrates the product of a number involving thousandths by an integer. By a common-sense approach it should appear that 4 thousandths and 4 thousandths ought to be 8 thousandths and that 4 times 4 thousandths ought to be 16 thousandths.

We multiply decimal numbers by whole numbers by assuming that the multiplicands are whole numbers, too, and proceed accordingly. We must have the same kind of units in the product as we have in the multiplicand; they are both homogeneous. In other words, we have just as many decimal places in the product as we have decimal places in the multiplicand.

$2 \times .4 = \quad .8$	$2 \times .04 = \quad .08$	$300 \times 9.1 \quad = 2730.0$
$7 \times .6 = \quad 4.2$	$7 \times .06 = \quad .42$	$65 \times 1.65 \quad = \quad 107.25$
$12 \times .9 = 10.8$	$12 \times .09 = 1.08$	$8 \times 1.111 = \quad 8.888$

The multiplication of a decimal number by an integer can easily be rationalized by the use of the addition algorism. If the multiplier is an integer, then we know that we have used the multiplicand as an addend a given number of times. Now when the multiplier takes a different form, it is impossible to show that we use the addend a fractional number of times. If the multiplier is .2 we cannot use a given addend .2 times; if the multiplier is .13 we cannot use a given addend .13 times; if the multiplier is .234 we cannot use a given addend .234 times. In other words, if the multiplier is a fraction, either common or decimal, we must take a specified part of the addend. If we multiply 86 by ½ we take a part of 86; if we multiply 64 by ⅜ we take a part of 64; if we multiply 900 by .34 we must take a part of 900, which in this case is $\frac{34}{100}$ of 900.   When the multiplier is a decimal fraction (a pure decimal fraction) we are taking a part of the multiplicand.   Hence we must conclude that in problems of this type our product will be smaller than the original multiplicand.

If we want to multiply an integer by a number involving tenths let us introduce the problem with this story: It requires 3 yards of material for a new blouse.   If .2 of the material is used for the collar, how much material is needed for the collar?   Since the multiplier is a fraction we are actually taking a part of the multiplicand.   It is impossible for us to set up the problem as an addition example, for we cannot show 3 yards as an addend 2 tenths times.   Let us approach the solution of the problem diagrammatically.

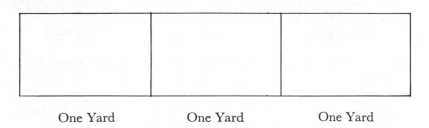

One Yard   One Yard   One Yard

Since we want only .2 of this amount, we must theoretically divide the entire piece of material into tenths and then cut off the required 2 tenths of the entire piece.   The diagram will look like this:

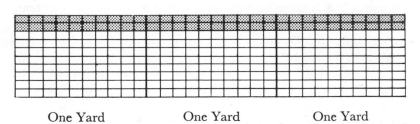

One Yard   One Yard   One Yard

A careful study of the diagram will reveal that we are actually taking 2 tenths of the first yard, 2 tenths of the second yard, and 2 tenths of the third yard.   In other words, we are taking 2 tenths of each of 3 yards.   The original problem of multiplying .2 × 3 yards results in multiplying .2 yards by 3 or 3 × .2 yards.   And this example has already been explained fully in a previous section. Since the multiplicand is expressed in tenths, the product must be expressed in tenths also. And the product is .6 (yards). Let us point out here that it might be more practical to cut off the .6 of a yard from the end of the piece of material, that we use just .6 of the first yard which we have proved is equivalent to the 2 tenths of the entire piece. The diagram then can be changed to look something like this:

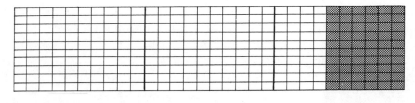

One Yard   One Yard   One Yard

The solution of the above problem illustrates again the use of the commutative law, for the algorism suggests that .2 × 3 became really 3 × .2.

There are many instances when one is asked to find one or more hundredths of a number, but most of these examples involve the use of per cents (which will be discussed in Chapter 7). If we want to know .35 of a certain number we usually want 35 per cent of that number. Inasmuch as the topic of percentage is usually introduced after some work in multiplying by hundredths we must find some problem from business or industry which does not mention per cent. This problem will serve our purposes. From a total of 7200 A and P store employees, .85 of them belong to the Labor Union. How many belong to the union?

The analysis of the problem suggests that only a part of them (not all of them) belong to the Labor Union. This fractional part is 85 hundredths, or more than ¾ of them. Thus our answer should be in the neighborhood of 6000 or more, something between 6000 and 7000, let us say. By multiplication we find that our answer is in hundredths so we must point off two decimal places. We multiply .85 times 7200 which is the same as 7200 × 85 hundredths. Therefore we multiply the integers and obtain 612000 which must be expressed as hundredths. Therefore the product of .85 × 7200 is 6120.00. Therefore 6120 of the employees belong to the union.

The solution can be verified by the use of common fractions.

$$.85 \times 7200 = \tfrac{85}{100} \times 7200 = 85 \times 72 = 6120$$

So far in this discussion we have dealt with examples in which only one of the factors is a decimal number. Now we shall discuss the examples in which both factors are decimal numbers and we will begin with the problem of multiplying a decimal number involving tenths by a decimal number involving tenths. Here is our introductory problem: Mr. Jones spends .3 of his monthly income for overhead (lights, gas, telephone) and .2 of this amount is spent for the operation of his gas stove. What part of his monthly income is spent for gas?

Draw a rectangle to represent Mr. Jones's entire monthly income. Divide this into ten equal parts and shade in three of them. Three of the ten equal parts represents .3 of the total amount. Now since we are interested in .2 of this .3 we divide the .3 into ten equal parts by use of horizontal lines and then color in two of these ten equal parts. Thus the colored area represents .2 of .3 of the whole amount. When we count the number of small sections we find that there are six of them, and since the diagram reveals that each small section represents $\tfrac{1}{100}$ of the whole, then .2 × .3 = .06.

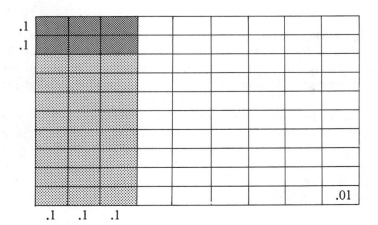

This can be verified by the use of common fractions.

$$\frac{2}{10} \times \frac{3}{10} = \frac{6}{100}$$

Thus we conclude that tenths multiplied by tenths results in hundredths.

$$.3 \times .5 = .15 \qquad .6 \times .7 = .42$$
$$.2 \times .4 = .08 \qquad .9 \times .9 = .81$$

It should be pointed out here that $\frac{1}{10}$ of anything is equivalent to dividing that amount by 10. Taking .1 of .3 is equivalent to $.3 \div 10$ or .3 divided into 10 equal parts. This division can be illustrated on a line by dividing each of the 3 tenths into 10 equal parts.

To find .1 of .3 we must take .1 of each of the 3 tenths and then regroup the several parts. One-tenth of .1 is .01 and so we obtain 3 separate one-hundredths. Therefore $.1 \times .3 = .03$

To develop the rule for multiplying a decimal number involving hundredths by a decimal number involving tenths, let us use this story: Mr. Brown has .85 (eighty-five hundredths) of an acre of land for gardening. He planted .3 of the lot into potatoes. What part of the acre of land was used for potatoes?

The analysis of the problem can be similar to the preceding illustration of multiplication of tenths by tenths. Let us begin by taking .1 of 85 hundredths, which means to divide .85 into 10 equal parts. Now we want 3 of these parts, for we want .3 of .85. The number .85 can be interpreted as $8\frac{1}{2}$ tenths or $.8\frac{1}{2}$, and so .3 of $8\frac{1}{2}$ tenths ought to give a product in hundredths.

$$.3 \times .8\tfrac{1}{2} = .25\tfrac{1}{2} \qquad \frac{3}{10} \times \frac{8\frac{1}{2}}{10} = \frac{25\frac{1}{2}}{100}$$

Now $\frac{1}{2}$ of a hundredth is the same as $.01 \div 2$ which is .005. When this amount is added to .25 we have .255 or 255 thousandths. Therefore $.3 \times .85 = .255$ and Mr. Brown planted .255 of an acre of potatoes, and we have shown that tenths times hundredths gives thousandths.

$$\frac{3}{10} \times \frac{85}{100} = \frac{255}{1000} \text{ or } .255$$

Let us see how to multiply a decimal number involving hundredths by a decimal number involving hundredths. This problem will do: Mr. Black had a steel rod .43 yards long. He cut off .25 of it for a window prop. How long was the window prop?

If we were to estimate the length of the prop we would think "$\frac{1}{4}$ of 43 hundredths is about 11 hundredths." Therefore .25 × .43 is in the neighborhood of .11. Let us solve the problem by the use of common fractions.

$$\frac{25}{100} \times \frac{43}{100} = \frac{1075}{10000} = .1075$$

If we solve the problem by using decimal fractions we should obtain the same result. The algorism becomes

.43 (yards)
× .25

and we perform the multiplications as if the numbers were integers and obtain the product of 1075. Since the product must be in the neighborhood of .11 (according to our estimated product) we place the decimal point before the 1 for a product of .1075 which represents .1075 yards. When we multiply hundredths by hundredths the product will be hundred-hundredths or ten-thousandths which is the name of the fourth place to the right of the ones column or place.

General Rule. In the multiplication of decimal fractions point off as many decimal places in the product as there are decimal places in the multiplicand and multiplier together (the product can be rounded off to fewer places however).

.3 × 1.11 = .333	.25 × .25 = .0625
.2 × .123 = .0246	1.02 × .02 = .0204
1.1 × 1.21 = 1.331	.002 × .003 = .000006

EXERCISES

SET 24

1. Perform the multiplications and then round off the results to the nearest hundredth:

.47	.46	.89	.56	.56	6.36	13.45	21.07
× .41	× .84	× .75	× .28	× .96	× 1.47	× 1.49	× 21.07

2. Find the height of a stack of 23 manuscripts each of which is 2.65 inches thick.

3. A metal washer is .457 inches thick.   What is the combined thickness of 75 washers?

4. The rainfall in Baltimore for the year 1956 averaged 4.47 inches per month.   What was the total rainfall for the year?

5. A meter is equivalent to 39.37 inches.   If a basketball player is 1.9 meters tall, what is his height in inches?

6. A cubic foot of water weighs approximately 62.5 pounds.   What is the weight of 42.5 cubic feet of water?

7. Multiply each number in the first column by the numbers in the column headings, and then find the sum of each column.

	10	100	.01	1000	.1
3.7					
22.9					
.04067					
.4					
7.					

8. Without performing the operations give an estimate of the products.

2.11 × 3.12	12.30 × 12.49	400.04 × .211
7.14 × 8.09	25.12 × 25.07	300.03 × .221
6.99 × 8.06	60.04 × 70.03	705.03 × .401
.456 × .456	.011 × .307	200.4 × .2 × .06
.204 × .204	.031 × .306	489.67 × .3 × .1111
.412 × .612	.049 × .304	.29 × .39 × .49 × .99

9. Round off each of the following decimal fractions (a) to the nearest number of tenths, (b) to the nearest number of hundredths, and (c) to the nearest number of thousandths:
.4678   .6077   .4555   2.8305   45.606038   11.1368   .7

10. Estimate both the sum and product of the numbers in exercise No. 9.

6.15   Division of Decimal Fractions

Now we have come to the fourth and last of the fundamental operations with decimal fractions, namely division.   There are many types of division examples involving decimals but the writer will discuss only a few of them and then will generalize.

It has been pointed out that if the divisor is an integer then the division example can be interpreted either as measurement or partitive division. Likewise it was demonstrated in the preceding chapter that if the divisor is a fraction, then the example is definitely one of the measurement variety. Therefore, when one encounters the example of an *integer* or a *decimal fraction* divided by a *decimal fraction*, the question asks him to find the missing *multiplier*. What number multiplied by the given divisor will produce the given dividend? The example $3 \div .1$ asks one to find the number of pieces of size .1 which can be gotten from another piece of size 3; in other words, how many one-tenths are there in 3 or how many one-tenths can be gotten out of 3? The concept is clearly one of measurement. Since we know that there are 10 tenths or 10 (.1) in 1, then there must be 20 (2 × 10) tenths in 2, and 30 (3 × 10) tenths in 3.

$$\frac{3}{1} = \frac{?}{10} \qquad \frac{3}{1} = \frac{10 \times 3}{10 \times 1} = \frac{30}{10} \text{ or } 30 \text{ tenths.}$$

Therefore there are 30 (.1) in 3.

Let us interpret the example through the common-denominator approach. Since 3 is the same as $\frac{30}{10}$ or 3.0 and since .1 is the same as $\frac{1}{10}$, then $3 \div 1$ becomes $\frac{30}{10} \div \frac{1}{10}$, which is $30 \div 1$ or 30. Therefore $3.0 \div .1 = 30$.

Since the number .2 is twice the size of .1, then the quotient of $3 \div .2$ is half the quotient of $3 \div .1$. Therefore $3 \div .2 = 15$, for $\frac{30}{10} \div \frac{2}{10} = 15$. Also $3 \div .3 = 10$; $3 \div .4 = 7\frac{1}{2}$; $3 \div .5 = 6$; and $3 \div .6 = 5$.

If we rewrite the dividend so that it will have the same denomination (just as many decimal places) as the divisor then we are justified in dropping the decimal point; we ignore the fact that the numbers are decimal numbers and proceed to divide as if we were dividing integers. Witness: $.1 \overline{)\ 3}$ becomes $1 \text{ tenth} \overline{)\ 30 \text{ tenths}}$ or $\frac{3.0}{.1}$. Now if we multiply both the numerator and denominator of the fraction by 10 the division becomes $\frac{30}{1}$, for $\frac{10 \times 3}{10 \times .1} = \frac{30}{1}$, which is the same as 30. Therefore we conclude that to divide an integer by a number involving tenths we can multiply both the dividend and the divisor by 10 and then perform the operation.

Let us continue by dividing an integer by a decimal number in hundredths and use for our illustration the problem which asks us to find the number of 25-cent pieces in $12. The problem can also be interpreted as:

How many 25-cent pieces can be gotten from 1200 cents?
How many quarter dollars can be gotten in exchange for 12 dollars?
What is $12 divided by $.25?
Divide $12 by 25 cents.
Divide $12 by $¼.

This type of division is interpreted as measurement, for both the dividend and divisor are of the same denomination. For our division example in which the divisor is a decimal fraction involving hundredths we choose the algorism .25 $\overline{)\,12.00}$ which becomes 25 $\overline{)\,1200}$ after we have multiplied both the divisor and dividend by 100. We find it convenient to express the divisor as an integer.

$$.25\,\overline{)\,12} \qquad\qquad 25\,\overline{)\,1200}$$

$$
\begin{array}{r}
4 \\
25\,\overline{)\,1200} \\
100 \\
\hline
200
\end{array}
$$

$$
\begin{array}{r}
48 \\
25\,\overline{)\,1200} \\
100 \\
\hline
200 \\
200 \\
\hline
\end{array}
$$

$$\$12. \div \$.25 = 48$$

The solution just outlined is a form of the common denominator method. The 12 (the dividend) was expressed in hundredths, too, since the divisor was given in hundredths. Since 12 is the same as $\frac{12}{1}$, when we multiply both terms by 100 we obtain $\frac{1200}{100}$. Then our original algorism of 12 ÷ .25 becomes $\frac{1200}{100} \div \frac{25}{100}$ or 1200 ÷ 25. When we perform the division we obtain 48. There are just as many $.25 in $12 as there are 25's in 1200.

If the problem involves division by a number containing thousandths, we have only to follow the suggestions given above. Let us change the dividend and divisor so that they will be of the same denomination and then divide as if we were dividing whole numbers.

To divide 4 by .125 we express them in common fraction form with the same denomination. If the reader follows through the several algorisms he will discover that $4 \div .125$ is the same as $4000 \div 125$.

$$\frac{4}{1} \div \frac{125}{1000} = \frac{4000}{1000} \div \frac{125}{1000} = 4000 \div 125 = 32$$

$$4 \div .125 = \quad 4 \div \frac{125}{1000} = \quad 4 \div \frac{1}{8} \quad = 4 \times \frac{8}{1} = 32$$

$$.125 \overline{\smash{)}\, 4} \quad = \quad 125 \overline{\smash{)}\, 4000} \quad = \quad 32$$

If the dividend is a decimal fraction and the divisor is an integer the problem can best be interpreted as a partitioning example. Thus if we encounter the expression $.8 \div 4$ we usually divide the .8 into 4 equal parts. A problem which fits this algorism would be: "If I have .8 of a pound of nut meats and wish to put them into 4 bags containing equal amounts, how much will there be in each bag?" This example is clearly one of part-taking, putting some in the first bag, some in the second bag, and so on, until the nut meats are all used up. We can think of .8 pounds as 8 tenths pounds and then divide by 4. One-fourth of 8 tenths pounds is 2 tenths pounds.

$$.8 \div 4 = \frac{1}{4} \text{ of 8 tenths} = \frac{.8}{4} = .2 = 4 \overline{\smash{)}\, .8}^{\,.2}$$

$$.8 \div 4 = \frac{8}{10} \times \frac{1}{4} = \frac{2}{10}$$

We note that since our original dividend contained a measurement in tenths, then our quotient must also be in tenths. When tenths are partitioned into smaller groups we ought to have tenths, or parts of tenths in each of the groups. Thus $.6 \div 2 = .3$ and $.9 \div 3 = .3$ for $\frac{1}{2}$ of 6 tenths is 3 tenths and $\frac{1}{3}$ of 9 tenths is 3 tenths.

The extension to examples in which the dividend contains hundredths ought to be simple. If half of 8 tenths is 4 tenths then it follows that half of 8 hundredths is 4 hundredths.

$$.08 \div 2 = .04 \qquad \frac{8}{100} \div \frac{2}{1} = \frac{8}{100} \times \frac{1}{2} = \frac{4}{100}$$

Mr. Jones has a plot of ground containing .96 of an acre. If he divides it into 3 equal plots, how large will each plot be? This is clearly a partitioning example in which Mr. Jones mentally portions out his land into 3 parts so as to have the same amount in each part.

$$.96 \div 3 = \frac{96}{100} \div 3 \text{ or } \frac{1}{3} \text{ of } \frac{96}{100} \text{ which is } \frac{32}{100}.$$

Remember that .96 is composed of 9 tenths and 6 hundredths. And $\frac{1}{3}$ of 9 tenths is 3 tenths and $\frac{1}{3}$ of 6 hundredths is 2 hundredths. Therefore $\frac{1}{3}$ of .96 is the same as $\frac{1}{3}$ of .9 plus $\frac{1}{3}$ of .06 or .3 + .02, which is .32.

$$3 \overline{)\,.96} \qquad \overset{.30 + .02}{3 \overline{)\,.90 + .06}} \qquad \overset{.32}{3 \overline{)\,.96}}$$

In the actual solution we divide .9 by 3 and then divide .06 by 3. The complete quotient is .32.

If we divide a number containing hundredths by an integer the quotient will be in hundredths or parts of hundredths. We perform the division as if the dividend were a whole number and then position the decimal point. Since 46 hundredths divided by 2 or separated into 2 parts will give us 23 hundredths in each part, then when the division is performed decimally, .46 ÷ 2, we should also obtain 23 hundredths, .23.

When .64 is divided by 8 we obtain .08; when we divide .64 by .64 we obtain 1; but when we divide .64 by 96 we obtain $\frac{2}{3}$ of a hundredth.

$$4 \overline{)\,.64} \qquad \overset{16 \text{ hundredths}}{4 \overline{)\,64 \text{ hundredths}}} \qquad \overset{.16}{4 \overline{)\,.64}}$$

$$17 \overline{)\,.51} \qquad \overset{3 \text{ hundredths}}{17 \overline{)\,51 \text{ hundredths}}} \qquad \overset{.03}{17 \overline{)\,.51}}$$

$$33 \overline{)\,.99} \qquad \overset{}{33 \overline{)\,\underset{3 \text{ hundredths}}{99 \text{ hundredths}}}} \qquad \overset{.03}{33 \overline{)\,.99}}$$

If a steel washer is .008 of an inch thick and is sliced through the middle, making two washers of the same thickness, how thick will each washer be? The problem is clearly one of partitioning for we take the original washer and divide it into two equal parts. Since the original washer was 8 thousandths of an inch thick, then the new washers, which will be half as thick, will be 4 thousandths of an inch thick.

$$\overset{.004}{4 \overline{)\,.016}} \quad \overset{.012}{3 \overline{)\,.036}} \quad \overset{.111}{5 \overline{)\,.555}} \quad \overset{.004}{7 \overline{)\,.028}} \quad \overset{.000\frac{1}{2}}{4 \overline{)\,.002}}$$

One of the most difficult operations which must be performed with numbers is the division of decimal fractions by decimal fractions. Too often the operations connected with this type of problem have been presented in a mechanical rather than a meaningful manner. Students have learned rules for procedures and processes but have gained little insight or understanding of these operations. It is hoped that the treatment which follows will deepen the reader's understanding of those operations.

When we want to know how many packages containing .2 of a pound can be obtained from a larger package containing .8 of a pound, we divide by .2 and obtain 4. This 4 represents 4 packages. When we divide $12 by $4 we are asking how many groups of $4 can be gotten from a group of $12. Likewise when we divide .9 by .3 we are trying to find the number of groups of 3 tenths. Since both the dividend and divisor in these separate problems are of the same denomination, we perform the division as if they were both whole numbers, always keeping in mind that the quotient represents the number of groups.

$$.9 \div .3 = \frac{9}{10} \div \frac{3}{10} = 9 \text{ tenths} \div 3 \text{ tenths} = 9 \div 3 = 3$$

Once again we make use of the law of compensation which permits one to multiply both the numerator and denominator of a fraction by the same number (different from 0). Hence in this example if we multiply both the dividend and divisor by 10 we obtain $9 \div 3 = 3$.

$$\frac{.9}{.3} = \frac{10 \times .9}{10 \times .3} = \frac{9}{3} = 3$$

Also

$$.9 \div .3 = \frac{\frac{9}{10}}{\frac{3}{10}} = \frac{10 \times \frac{9}{10}}{10 \times \frac{3}{10}} = \frac{9}{3} = 3$$

There are 3 groups of .3 in .9.

The same analogy can be carried to the solution of the problem in which both the dividend and divisor are hundredths. For instance, "How many baskets of coal weighing .17 of a ton can be gotten from a pile of coal weighing .68 of a ton?"

The solution requires the use of the division process. We make use of the measurement idea of division for we want to find the number of groups of a given size (.17 ton).

Solutions: .68 ÷ .17   68 hundredths ÷ 17 hundredths = 4

$$\frac{68}{100} \div \frac{17}{100} = 4 \qquad 17 \text{ hundredths } \overset{4}{\overline{)\,68 \text{ hundredths}}}$$

$$\frac{68}{100} \div \frac{17}{100} = \frac{68}{100} \times \frac{100}{17} = \frac{\overset{4}{\cancel{68}}}{\cancel{100}} \times \frac{\overset{1}{\cancel{100}}}{\underset{1}{\cancel{17}}} = 4$$

$$\frac{.68}{.17} = \frac{100 \times .68}{100 \times .17} = \frac{68}{17} = 4$$

$$\frac{\frac{68}{100}}{\frac{17}{100}} = \frac{100 \times \frac{68}{100}}{100 \times \frac{17}{100}} = \frac{68}{17} = 4$$

```
   .68
 − .17   (1)
   ‾‾‾
   .51
 − .17   (2)
   ‾‾‾
   .34
 − .17   (3)
   ‾‾‾
   .17
 − .17   (4)
   ‾‾‾
```

Therefore 4 baskets of coal each containing .17 of a ton can be gotten from a load containing .68 of a ton.

If both terms of the division example are of the same denomination, we perform the divisions as if they were whole numbers. Thus .45 ÷ .15 is the same as 45 ÷ 15 and 72 ÷ 12 gives the same quotient as .72 ÷ .12.

Then	.64 ÷ .16	.75 ÷ .25	.92 ÷ .46
becomes	64 ÷ 16	75 ÷ 25	92 ÷ 46

If both the dividend and divisor are expressed in thousandths the division is performed as if both the numbers were integers. Thus .008 ÷ .002 gives us the same quotient as 8 ÷ 2. This means that there are just as many pieces of size 2 thousandths in 8 thousandths as there are 2's in 8. Likewise, 9 thousandths divided by 3 thousandths must be interpreted as asking us to find the number of pieces of size 3 thousandths which can be cut from another piece of size 9 thousandths. The answer is 3.

Then .025 ÷ .005 must be 5,   for   25 ÷ 5 is 5.
And   .444 ÷ .002 must be 222, for 444 ÷ 2 is 222.

Now we come to the general case of division of decimal fractions by decimal fractions; namely the type in which the dividend and divisor are of different denominations. For instance:

(*a*) How many disks .45 inches thick can be cut from a piece of metal .9 inches thick?

(*b*) How many metal leaves .125 inches thick can be cut from a piece of metal .8 inches thick?

(*c*) Divide .4 by .25.

It is convenient for purposes of analysis as well as for purposes of computation to express both the dividend and divisor in the same denominations. Let us do this to the examples mentioned above.

(*a*)	(*b*)	(*c*)
.45) .9	.125) .8	.25) .4
.45) .90	.125) .800	.25) .40

Now we perform the divisions as if the terms were integers.

$$\frac{2}{45\,)\,90} \qquad \frac{6.4}{125\,)\,800} \qquad \frac{1.6}{25\,)\,40} \qquad \frac{4.4}{20\,)\,88}$$

The divisions are easy to perform if transformations or regroupings are made so that in every case of division of decimal fractions the divisor is made a whole number. In the example .84 ÷ .2 let us change the divisor to a whole number by multiplying it by 10. Then we must multiply the dividend by 10 also. The example becomes 8.4 ÷ 2, which gives us a quotient of 4.2. This is the same quotient we would obtain if we multiplied both terms by 100 (84 ÷ 20), or some other power of 10.

In the example .648 ÷ .08 we multiply both the dividend and the divisor by 100 so as to change the divisor into a whole number. This gives a new example, 64.8 ÷ 8, or 8.1. This is the same quotient we would obtain if we were to express both the dividend and divisor as whole numbers (multiplying both terms by 1000): 648 ÷ 80 for a quotient of 8.1.

The Golden Rule for fractions (or the law of compensation) which permits one to multiply both terms of a fraction by the same non-zero number is of inestimable value when working with division of decimal fractions.

Let us apply the rule to the solution of other examples:

$$.75 \div .5 \qquad .366 \div .61 \qquad .88 \div .002$$
$$7.5 \div 5 \qquad 36.6 \div 61 \qquad 880 \div 2$$
$$\frac{1.5}{5\,)\,7.5} \qquad \frac{.6}{61\,)\,36.6} \qquad \frac{440}{2\,)\,880}$$

The rule which enables one to make the divisor a whole number is commonly referred to as "moving the decimal point" or the *caret* method (∧). When the division of decimal fractions is taught mechanically, students are told to move the decimal point the same number of places in both the divisor and dividend so that the divisor becomes an integer. It has been pointed out elsewhere in this text that the decimal point never moves, that it is always positioned between the ones place and the tenths place. What actually happens is that one increases the size of the numbers by multiplying them by a power of 10. When this process is presented meaningfully, the student will sense the application of the Golden Rule for fractions— that both terms of the fraction can be multiplied by the same non-zero number without effect upon the quotient.

The "caret" system offers a convenience of showing a new algorism without having to rewrite the example. The author suggests the second algorism in preference to the first in the solution of the examples below:

The example: .805 ÷ .35

$$
.35. \overline{) .80.5} \qquad 35 \overline{)80.5}
$$

$$
\begin{array}{r} 2.3 \\ .35. \overline{)\ .80.5} \\ 70 \\ \hline 105 \\ 105 \\ \hline \end{array}
\qquad
\begin{array}{r} 2.3 \\ 35 \overline{)\ 80.5} \\ 70 \\ \hline 105 \\ 105 \\ \hline \end{array}
$$

The example: .72 ÷ .225

$$
\begin{array}{r} 3.2 \\ .225. \overline{)\ .720.} \end{array}
\qquad
\begin{array}{r} 3.2 \\ 225 \overline{)\ 720} \end{array}
$$

The application of the Golden Rule for fractions simplifies awkward-looking and seemingly difficult examples as illustrated below:

The quotient of   16.45 ÷ 1.35 is the same as   1645 ÷   135.
The quotient of   9.6   ÷ .008 is the same as   9600 ÷   8.
The quotient of   3.4   ÷ .35 is the same as   340 ÷   35.
The quotient of 100.025 ÷ 6.04 is the same as 100,025 ÷ 6040.
The quotient of   90.01 ÷ 1.07 is the same as   9001 ÷   107.

EXERCISES

SET 25

1. Perform the division and express the quotients correct to the nearest hundredth:

.47 ÷ .08   .456 ÷ .07   .603 ÷ .04   .67 ÷ .9
.113 ÷ .465   .648 ÷ .87   1.4324 ÷ .65   20.9 ÷ 1.756

2. Without performing the division estimate the quotients:

(a) 10.16 ÷ .201   (d) 70.05 ÷ .5   (g) 8.46 ÷ 40
(b) 72.11 ÷ 7.21   (e)   9.11 ÷ 3.16   (h) .009 ÷ .01
(c)   .8 ÷ .100   (f) 45.89 ÷ 5.09   (i) 7000 ÷ .02

3. Estimate the answers: 102 × 106 ÷ 105   9.112 ÷ 3.1 × 10
400.4 ÷ 40.12 × 3.5   40.1 × 200.5 ÷ 5000   29 × 40 ÷ 31

4. Which player has the better batting average: Jones who has made 141 hits out of 533 times at bat or Smith who has hit safely 156 times out of 580 attempts?

5. Fill in the averages (to three decimal places) for these baseball teams in the American League:

Team	Won	Lost	Average
New York	62	34	
Chicago	59	37	
Boston	53	44	
Detroit	48	48	

6. Write the decimal fraction equivalents (correct to hundredths) for the following fractions:

$$\frac{1}{6} \quad \frac{1}{7} \quad \frac{1}{8} \quad \frac{1}{9} \quad \frac{1}{10} \quad \frac{1}{11} \quad \frac{1}{12} \quad \frac{1}{15} \quad \frac{1}{80}$$

7. Which of the above fractions in exercise No. 6 are non-ending decimal fractions?

8. Rearrange according to size from smallest to largest:

(a) 786.0   78.06   807.6   80.76   7.860   67.008   8.678
(b) .564   .654   .0465   .0654   .4560   .0045   0.6654
(c) 1.001   1.003   1.030   1.100   1.0101   1.0011   1.11

9. An auto used 18 gallons of gasoline in going 380 miles. A second car used 21 gallons in going 430 miles. Which car has the better average?

CHAPTER 7

PERCENTAGE

7.1 Introduction

One of the arithmetical concepts most widely used in everyday business affairs is the concept of per cent. Contact with the concept of per cent is practically inescapable for children and adults alike these days. The purchase of tickets to a movie, baseball game, or the school play and similar amusements often reveals that an extra cost has been added to the base price. The purchase of luxury commodities, clothing, automobiles, property (real estate), and even the purchase of foodstuffs may require the payment of some additional amount in the form of a tax which eventually finds its way either to the Federal or State government, or some to both. Goods purchased at reduced prices are often sold at a discount or per cent off the regular price. The amount added to or subtracted from the original price represents a per cent of that price.

It should be recalled here that one of the fundamental interpretations of a common fraction is the ratio concept. The fraction $\frac{2}{7}$ can be interpreted as meaning "Two sevenths; $2 \div 7$; or the comparison of 2 things to 7 of the same kind." This latter idea suggests that the fraction $\frac{2}{7}$ means 2 out of every 7. The mathematical statement that a student is not in school 2 days out of 7 days (one week) illustrates one of the meanings of a fraction.

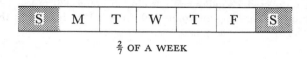

$\frac{2}{7}$ OF A WEEK

In this latter example the 7 is called the base or basis for the comparison ("base" used here is not to be confused with the base of a number system). Of the total group of 7 we are concerned with 2 of them. Therefore on the base 14 (or more correctly on the basis of 14) we are concerned with 4. Since 2 out of 7 is the constant ratio, then this relationship can be expressed with any base other then 7 (multiples of 7 are the most convenient bases). Thus

$$\frac{2}{7} = \frac{4}{14} = \frac{6}{21} = \frac{14}{49} = \frac{24}{84}, \text{ etc.}$$

Any whole number can be used as a base. Since there are 24 hours in a day and an adult is expected to sleep during 8 of them, we express the relationship between sleeping hours and number of hours in a day as $\frac{8}{24}$ (meaning 8 out of 24). This ratio can be expressed as $\frac{1}{3}$ but this statement suggests that a person sleeps 1 hour out of every 3 hours. However, $\frac{8}{24}$ is equivalent to $\frac{1}{3}$. It also is equivalent to $\frac{16}{48}, \frac{4}{12}, \frac{9}{27}$, etc. If a man buys $\frac{2}{5}$ tons of coal he is buying part of a ton of coal. This amount of coal would represent 800 pounds out of 2000 pounds or $\frac{800}{2000}$ tons. Thus $\frac{2}{5} = \frac{800}{2000}$. These examples illustrate different bases for comparison.

When we say that raw meat loses half its weight in cooking we mean that the ratio of the cooked meat to the raw meat is 1 to 2. For every 2 pounds of raw meat we now have 1 pound of cooked meat. Then 1 out of 2 implies 2 out of 4, 10 out of 20, 25 out of 50, $42\frac{1}{2}$ out of 85, 50 out of 100, and similar comparisons.

It is often convenient to change given ratio forms or relationships to equivalent ratios having 100 for their base. We can make comparisons between two or more given ratios more easily if they are expressed in the same base, and 100 is a convenient base. If we are given two relationships such as "Bill made 2 hits out of 5 times at bat and Joe made 3 hits out of 8 times at bat," we can determine which boy had the better batting record by expressing both ratios in terms of the same number of times at bat. We could express these ratios on the basis of 40 times at bat, in which case Bill's 2 out of 5 becomes 16 out of 40 and Joe's 3 out of 8 becomes 15 out of 40. Hence Bill is the better batter. We can also express the two relationships in terms of 100 and arrive at the same conclusion, for $\frac{2}{5} = \frac{40}{100}$ and $\frac{3}{8} = \frac{37\frac{1}{2}}{100}$.

When ratios are expressed in terms of 100 or hundredths they are being expressed as per cents, for "per cent" means *by the hundred* or *per hundred* or *hundredths*. One per cent represents the size of 1 of the 100 equal parts of a unit. Then $\frac{17}{100}$ (read as seventeen hundredths or seventeen one-hundredths) means 17 out of 100 which is 17 per cent which is 17 hundredths or .17. Conversely, 29 per cent means .29 or 29 hundredths or 29 out of 100 or simply $\frac{29}{100}$. The symbol for per cent is "%," which, incidentally, makes use of all the symbols in the number 100—the stroke and the two zeros.

Therefore, $\frac{31}{100} = 31\%$ and $73\% = \frac{73}{100}$ and we see that the terms "per cent" and "hundredths" are synonymous.

We have already shown by using the Golden Rule for fractions how to change the form of a fraction to any equivalent form with any desired denomination. To change $\frac{3}{20}$ to hundredths we multiply both the numerator and denominator by 5 and obtain the equivalent value $\frac{15}{100}$. Therefore $\frac{3}{20} = \frac{15}{100} = 15\%$. Every fraction, common as well as decimal, can be expressed as a per cent (as parts of 100).

$$\frac{3}{5} = \frac{?}{100} \qquad \frac{20}{20} \times \frac{3}{5} = \frac{60}{100} \qquad \frac{3}{5} = 60\%$$

$$\frac{7}{8} = \frac{?}{100} \qquad \frac{12\frac{1}{2}}{12\frac{1}{2}} \times \frac{7}{8} = \frac{87\frac{1}{2}}{100} \qquad \frac{7}{8} = 87\frac{1}{2}\%$$

Percentage is not a new topic; it is merely an extension of the concept of *fractions* which has already been presented.

7.2 Changing to Equivalent Values

It is advantageous to know how to change a relationship expressed in per cent to some other form which will permit easy computation and quick comprehension. When dealing with 50% of a group one should visualize half of the group, and when dealing with $\frac{1}{4}$ of a group one can think of 25% of it. Conversely, it is desirable to know how to convert a simple common fraction to its equivalent per cent. In other words, it is desirable to know how to convert from one form to another.

A. From a fraction to a per cent. When a fraction is expressed in its decimal form it is easy to convert such a fraction to a per cent. Since hundredths and per cent are synonymous, a fraction expressed in hundredths can be expressed immediately as per cent. The fraction .51 is interpreted as 51 per cent (51%). Since .351 is 35.1 hundredths, then .351 = 35.1%, and .007 is .7 hundredths or .7 per cent or .7%. Students should note that when a decimal fraction is changed to a per cent, the integral numbers are moved two places to the left. Thus .08$\frac{1}{2}$ becomes 8$\frac{1}{2}$ per cent (8$\frac{1}{2}$%). The integer 8 which was formerly in the hundredths place has moved two places to the left into the ones place. If one first expresses a decimal fraction as hundredths, then there will be as many per cent in the number as there are hundredths. N hundredths = N per cent.

.43 = 43%	.03 = 3%	.125 = 12.5%	1.07 = 107%
.77 = 77%	.01 = 1%	.384 = 38.4%	13.45 = 1345%
.89 = 89%	.09 = 9%	.082 = 8.2%	4.015 = 401.5%

In order to change a common fraction to a per cent we must first convert it to its equivalent decimal fraction form and then proceed as outlined above. Should one desire to convert $\frac{1}{5}$ to a per cent he should first express the fraction with a denominator, 100 (multiply both the numerator and denominator by 20). $\frac{1}{5} = \frac{20}{100}$. Now since $\frac{20}{100}$ can be written as .20, then $\frac{1}{5}$, which is equivalent to .20, becomes 20%. The fraction $\frac{2}{9}$ can be changed to hundredths by multiplying both terms of the fraction by $11\frac{1}{9}$. Then $\frac{2}{9}$ becomes $\frac{22\frac{2}{9}}{100}$ or $.22\frac{2}{9}$ which in turn equals $22\frac{2}{9}\%$. Since one interpretation of a fraction is that of an indicated quotient we can divide the numerator of a fraction by its denominator to find its decimal equivalent. Thus $\frac{3}{7}$ becomes $3 \div 7$, which becomes $.42\frac{6}{7}$, which in turn is equal to $42\frac{6}{7}\%$. The common fraction should first be changed to its decimal equivalent, expressed in hundredths, and then changed to per cent. The fraction $\frac{3}{400} = .0075$ or .75 hundredths or .75% ($\frac{3}{4}\%$) and $\frac{1}{80} = 0.125$ or 1.25 hundredths or 1.25% ($1\frac{1}{4}\%$).

$$\frac{1}{3} = .33\frac{1}{3} = 33\frac{1}{3}\% \qquad \frac{9}{40} = .225 = 22.5\% \qquad \frac{3}{95} = .031555+ = 3.1555+\%$$

$$\frac{7}{8} = .87\frac{1}{2} = 87\frac{1}{2}\% \qquad \frac{33}{200} = .165 = 16.5\% \qquad \frac{7}{60} = .116666+ = 11.6666+\%$$

B. From a per cent to a common fraction. If per cent means hundredths, then a given per cent can be expressed as hundredths and the transformation is complete except for possible simplification. Since 46% means 46 hundredths, then 46% means .46. Likewise 79% = .79 and 31% = .31 and 2% means .02. Principles already established apply throughout the whole realm of per cents and percentage problems. Since 7% means $\frac{7}{100}$ then 7% means .07, and 327% means $\frac{327}{100}$ or 3.27. It should be apparent that a certain number

of per cent gives one the same number read as hundredths.
N per cent = N hundredths.

$$17\% = \frac{17}{100} = .17 \qquad 106\% = \frac{106}{100} = 1.06 \qquad .4\% = \frac{.4}{100} = .004$$

$$1.21\% = \frac{1.21}{100} = .0121 \qquad 250\% = \frac{250}{100} = 2.50 \qquad \frac{3}{8}\% = \frac{\frac{3}{8}}{100} = \frac{3}{800}$$
$$= .00375$$

No doubt the reader has observed that in the above illustrations
we found the common fraction equivalents first before changing the
given per cent to a decimal fraction form. The given number of
per cent is expressed as the numerator of a fraction whose denominator
is 100 (or hundredths). In this way per cents can easily be seen as
both common and decimal fractions. Thus 37% must automatically
be equivalent to $\frac{37}{100}$ and .37.

Students need a thorough understanding of the concept of per cent
and a marked ability to make conversions quickly from one form to
another. They should practice on this type of exercise:

Complete the table:

Exercise	Per cent	Decimal fraction	Common fraction
1	35		
2		.65	
3			$\frac{4}{5}$

There are certain common fractions which occur frequently in
ordinary computation. These fractions have denominators of 2, 3, 5,
and multiplies of 2, 3, and 5. Since these occur so frequently in
everyday problem-solving situations, it would seem expedient for
students to learn their decimal equivalents and hence their equivalent
per cents.

Any part of 100 can be conveniently expressed as a per cent.
One-fifth of 100 is 20. Therefore $\frac{1}{5} = 20\%$. The commonly used
parts of 100 are $\frac{1}{2}, \frac{1}{3}, \frac{1}{4}, \frac{1}{5}, \frac{1}{6}, \frac{1}{8}, \frac{1}{10}, \frac{1}{12}, \frac{1}{16}$, and $\frac{1}{20}$ and multiples of the
same. Let us discover their decimal and per cent equivalents.

To begin with, let us draw a large unit consisting of 10 rows of 10
squares each. This block will contain 100 smaller squares each of

which is $\frac{1}{100}$ of the whole and 10 rows and 10 columns each of which represents $\frac{1}{10}$ or 10% of the whole.

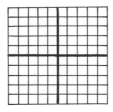

If we divide the big square down the middle we discover that $\frac{1}{2}$ of the block contains 50 squares or represents 50% of the whole. Now if we also cut the block through the middle horizontally we will be able to discover that $\frac{1}{4} = 25\%$, $\frac{2}{4} = 50\%$, and $\frac{3}{4} = 75\%$.

If one of the quarters is cut down the middle (vertically) we ascertain that $\frac{1}{8}$ is equivalent to 10 small squares and 5 one-half squares or a total of $12\frac{1}{2}$ squares. Thus $\frac{1}{8} = 12\frac{1}{2}\%$ and now from this diagram we can find all the per cent equivalents for eighths.

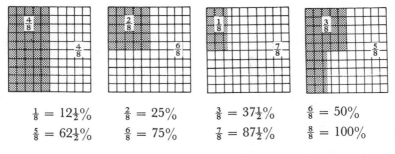

$\frac{1}{8} = 12\frac{1}{2}\%$ $\frac{2}{8} = 25\%$ $\frac{3}{8} = 37\frac{1}{2}\%$ $\frac{6}{8} = 50\%$

$\frac{5}{8} = 62\frac{1}{2}\%$ $\frac{6}{8} = 75\%$ $\frac{7}{8} = 87\frac{1}{2}\%$ $\frac{8}{8} = 100\%$

If we wanted to know the per cent equivalents for sixteenths we would divide one of the eighths into two equal parts and make use of various combinations of parts to give us all of the sixteenths family. Since $\frac{1}{8}$ is equal to $12\frac{1}{2}\%$, then $\frac{1}{16}$, which is one-half of $\frac{1}{8}$, will be one-half of $12\frac{1}{2}\%$, or $6\frac{1}{4}\%$.

7.3 Per Cent in Problem Solving

In problem-solving situations involving per cent there are three necessary elements. Since per cent represents a ratio or a comparison we see the need for a basis of comparison, an amount compared with the basis of comparison, and a resulting fraction expression. We have shown that the fraction $\frac{3}{4}$ is equivalent to 75%. This means that the ratio of 3 to 4 is the same as the ratio of 75 to 100, for 75% = $\frac{75}{100}$.

Also the fraction $\frac{3}{4}$ means $3 \div 4$, which becomes $4\overline{)\,3.00} = .75$ or 75%. We can see the numerator, the denominator, and the per cent clearly delineated in the expression $\frac{3}{4} = 75\%$.

The 4 (denominator, the basis of comparison) is called the *base*.

The 3 (numerator, the amount being compared) is called the *percentage*.

The quotient (expressed as hundredths) is changed to per cent and is called the *rate*.

From the above explanation it follows that $\dfrac{\text{percentage}}{\text{base}}$ = the rate or that rate × base = percentage. The student will recognize this as the old and well-known (R × B = P) and well-worn formula, "Base times rate equals percentage" which is usually written as B × R = P.

The student will recognize the familiar relationship that the product of two factors equals a third number; namely, that $a \times b = c$. If any two of these are known the third term is easily determined.

If c, the percentage, is missing, it is found by multiplication.

$$a \times b = \,?$$

If a, the rate, is unknown, it is found by division.

$$?\, \times b = c$$

If b, the base, is missing, it, too, is found by division.

$$a \times \,? = c$$

Thus there are three distinct types of percentage examples because there are three terms in the basic relationship.

1. When the percentage is unknown.
   Example: Find 35% of 700.   .35 × 700 = ?
2. When the rate is unknown.
   Example: What per cent of 8 is 6?   ?% × 8 = 6
3. When the base is unknown.
   Example: 45% of what number is 9?   .45 × ? = 9

The solution of percentage problems parallels the solution of the simple algebraic equation $a \times b = c$ and every simple one-step problem involving per cent can be and (according to the author) should be solved by the algebraic approach.

7.4 Solving Simple Percentage Problems by the Equation Method

The simplest problem involving per cent is the type which suggests multiplication. When one is asked to find 20% of 60, he is asked to find a part of 60 (to find the percentage). This can be done directly by multiplication.

What is 20% of 60? This problem should be expressed in the algebraic form of $a \times b = c$. The "is" represents the equality sign and separates the equation into its two parts. "What" represents the unknown. Then the equation becomes $N = .20 \times 60$. Solution: $N = 12$ (either $.20 \times 60$ or $\frac{1}{5} \times 60$).

Example: What is 61% of $2400?

Equation: $N = .61 \times \$2400$. Solving for N we find $N = \$1464$.
$N = \$1464$.

Example: Find 185% of 300. This is equivalent to "What is 185% of 300?"

Equation: $N = 1.85 \times 300$. Multiplying we find that $N = 555$.
$N = 555$.

The second type of percentage problem is the one in which the rate is the unknown. For instance, "What per cent of 80 is 4?" suggests a problem illustrating the missing multiplier. The rate is unknown, so we use r for per cent and write the equation $r \times 80 = 4$. This equation is in satisfactory form but students might have greater facility in handling it if they employ the commutative law as it affects multiplication and rewrite the equation as $80 \times r = 4$.

Solution: (divide both members by 80)
$r = \frac{4}{80}$ which is $\frac{1}{20}$ or 5%.

Hence the required per cent or rate is 5%.

Example: What per cent of 40 is 30?

Equation: $r \times 40 = 30$. Dividing both members by 40, $r = \frac{3}{4}$ or 75%.

Example: There were 50 items on a test. Joe has 43 right. What per cent of the number of items did he solve correctly?

Equation: $r \times 50 = 43$

Solution: Dividing both members of the equation by 50 we obtain $r = \frac{43}{50}$ or $\frac{86}{100}$ or .86 or 86%.

Therefore Joe solved 86% of the items correctly (check: $.86 \times 50 = 43$).

The third type of percentage problem is the least practical, for the solution usually implies knowledge of the answer beforehand. In this type we are looking for the base, or basis of comparison—we know the per cent and the percentage. For example: Mr. Smith saves $72 per month which is 12% of his monthly earnings. What are his monthly earnings?

Analysis   12% of the monthly income is $72.

Equation: .12 × N = 72 (when N represents the amount of monthly income).

Dividing both members by .12 we obtain N = 600.

Therefore Mr. Smith's monthly earnings are $600.

Example: How much money should Mr. Jones invest at 6% in order to realize an income of $1500 annually?

Analysis: 6% of what number is 1500.

Equation: .06 × N = 1500.

Dividing by .06 we have N = 25,000.

Therefore Mr. Jones should invest $25,000 at 6% in order to realize $1500 annually (.06 × $25,000 = $1500).

Every problem involving per cent can be translated into an algebraic sentence and solved as a simple equation.

Problem: 60% of 80 equals what number?

.60 × 80 = N   (use multiplication)   N = 48

Problem: What per cent of 20 is 5?

N × 20 = 5   (use division)   N = 25%

Problem: 12% of what number is 84?

.12 × N = 84   (use division)   N = 700

EXERCISES

SET 26

1. Express the following fractions as per cents:

$\dfrac{3}{5}$ $\dfrac{2}{9}$ $\dfrac{4}{11}$ $\dfrac{4}{3}$ $\dfrac{1}{200}$ $\dfrac{9}{50}$ $\dfrac{7}{250}$

.7   .23   .865   1.65   .007   2.1   .0065

2. Change these per cents to decimal fractions and then to simple common fractions.

90%   125%   425%   35%   5% $\frac{1}{2}$% $3\frac{1}{2}$%   5,000%

1,400%   850%   1.45% $13\frac{1}{4}$%   8%   19%   321%   .0005%

3. Solve for N:

$3N = 2$	$4N = .12$	$5N = 8$
$18N = 16$	$.02N = 42$	$1.25N = 6$
$9N = 9$	$.80 \times 425 = N$	$.02\frac{1}{4}N = 12$
$N = 37\frac{1}{2}\%$ of 6	$N = 1250\%$ of 9	$\frac{4}{5}N = 80$
$\frac{1}{4}\%$ of $N = 9$	$450N = 3$	$72N = 125$

4. Explain why $\frac{3}{5} = \frac{3}{5} \times 100\% = 60\%$.
5. Write all the common fractions whose values are less than 1 but greater than $\frac{1}{4}$ with denominators 2, 3, 4, 5, 6, 8, and 9 and find their equivalent per cents.
6. Compare these pairs of common fractions by first changing them to decimal fractions:

$$\frac{8}{11}, \frac{7}{9} \qquad \frac{3}{7}, \frac{9}{19} \qquad \frac{4}{21}, \frac{5}{26}$$

7. Rearrange the following beginning with the largest number.

(a)	0.125	25%	$\frac{1}{5}$	0.31	.062
(b)	.8809	.8909	.08899	.98980	.89909
(c)	1.717	1.707	1.077	1.770	1.0707
(d)	3 hundredths	$2\frac{1}{2}\%$	$\frac{1}{25}$	$.06\frac{1}{4}$	$\frac{1}{3}$

8. Do the following examples without the use of paper and pencil. Write only the answers.

75% of 400	$62\frac{1}{2}\%$ of 4	30% of 700	80% of 1200
2% of 10	3% of 15	4% of 35	150% of 6
25% of __?__ = 12		75% of __?__ = 36
60% of __?__ = 2400		1% of __?__ = 8
__?__ % of 40 is 20		__?__ % of 800 is 20
__?__ % of 2 is 3		__?__ % of 50 is 75

9. If Mr. Smith sells a house for $19,500 at a commission of $5\frac{1}{2}\%$, what is the amount of his commission?
10. Of the total enrollment of 1250 students in a school 750 are girls. What per cent of the entire enrollment are girls?
11. Find the annual interest on an investment of $450 at $4\frac{1}{2}\%$.
12. If a $40 watch is sold for $29.20, what is the rate of discount?
13. If a student wants to score 85% on a test of 250 items, how many questions should he answer correctly?
14. In a college the enrollments are as follows: Seniors, 450; Juniors, 650; Sophomores, 800: Freshmen, 900.
    (a) What per cent of the total enrollment are Juniors?
    (b) The size of the Freshman class is what per cent of the Senior class enrollment?
    (c) The enrollment of Juniors and Seniors combined represents what per cent of the total enrollment?
15. If one can allow 23% of his income for rent, what should a man's income be if he wants to live in a $120 (per month) apartment?
16. When a 5-inch square has been enlarged to a 6-inch square, find the per cent of increase in the area.

17. Mr. Grey is selling goods on a commission at 12%. What should his sales be in order for him to earn $9000 annually?
18. The normal rainfall for Teentown is 18.25 inches annually. One year the rainfall was 20.50 inches. This amount is what per cent more than the normal amount?
19. When the price of gasoline is raised from 31.5¢ per gallon to 32.5¢ per gallon, what is the per cent of increase?
20. (a) When a fly family of 20 multiplies so as to reach a family of 4800, what is the per cent of increase?
    (b) When a piece of metal .004 inches thick shrinks to a thickness of .0038 inches, what is the per cent of loss in thickness?

7.5 Problems in Per Cent Involving Gains or Losses

Many of the problems (percentage) met in daily life involve either a per cent of increase or per cent of decrease of a given number whose value we are required to find. Often a merchant knows the amount of money he must receive for an article but he wants to make the transaction appear attractive (a bargain) to the customer; he wants to offer a discount in per cent. His problem is one of finding the marked price. For instance, what price should a merchant mark a watch so as to offer a 25% discount and receive $36 for the watch?

An analysis of the problem suggests that we must find the marked price. This we represent by 100% (of the marked price) of N. Now we subtract 25% of this amount (which is 25%N or .25N) to obtain 75%N or .75N. Now this .75 of the marked price represents $36. Therefore .01 of the marked price is $36 ÷ 75 or $.48. Then 100% or the whole marked price is 100 × $.48 which is $48. The merchant should price the watch $48.

(Check: $48 less ¼ of $48 = $48 − $12 = $36 → the selling price.)

The solution of the above problem can be simplified greatly if the reasoning is expressed symbolically rather than in words. Witness the simpler solution when done algebraically.

$$\text{Let } n = \text{the marked price in dollars}$$
$$\text{Then } \tfrac{1}{4}n = \text{the amount of discount}$$
$$\text{Then } n - \tfrac{1}{4}n = 36 \text{ (marked price} - \text{discount} = \text{selling price)}$$
$$\text{So } \tfrac{3}{4}n = 36$$
$$\frac{\tfrac{3}{4}n}{\tfrac{3}{4}} = \frac{36}{\tfrac{3}{4}}$$
$$n = 36 \div \tfrac{3}{4}$$
$$n = 48$$

Dividing both members of the equation by ¾, $n = 48$. The marked price should be $48.

The problem can be and perhaps should also be solved pictorially. Let a whole rectangle represent the marked price; ¼ of it is discounted, then the remaining ¾ represents $36. Thus ¼ represents $12 and ⁴⁄₄ represents $48.

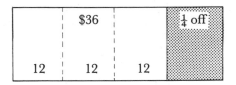

The whole then will represent $48.

At a sale a coat was marked as follows:

35% OFF
Now $78

What was the original marked price?

Solution: Let N = the original marked price (in dollars)
           .35N = the amount of discount

Therefore N − .35N = 78 (the present price)
Simplifying,   .65N = 78.
Dividing both members by .65, N = $120, the original marked price.

There are many problems of like nature which involve an increase rather than a decrease over a given amount.

Let us suppose that Mr. Jones received an increase of 10% in his salary and then made $9680 per year. What was his salary before the increase?

Algebraically: We let N = the old salary (in dollars)
           and .10N = the increase in his salary

Then   N + .10N = $9680
Simplifying   1.10N = 9680
Solving (÷1.10),   N = 8800
Then Mr. Jones' original salary was $8800.

Pictorially:

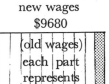

The attendance at the big game this year was 41,724 which was a 22% increase over the attendance last year. What was the attendance last year?

Algebraic solution: Let N = the number of people attending last year

Then   .22N = the increase in the attendance
Then   N + .22N = 41,724
Simplifying,   1.22N = 41,724
Solving (÷1.22), N = 34,200
The attendance last year was 34,200 people.
(Check: 34,200 + .22 × 34,200 = 34,200 + 7524 = 41,724.)

Problems involving successive rates of increase or decrease are usually treated in a course in business mathematics but an example or two should not be amiss here.

The census of a city showed an increase of 20% in 1955 over 1954 and an increase of 10% in 1956 over 1955. If the population in 1956 was 82,434, what was the population in 1954? In the analysis of the problem we discover that there are two successive increases, first one of 20% and then one of 10% but they are figured on different bases. Our problem is to find the number which when increased by $\frac{1}{5}$ of itself and then that amount increased by $\frac{1}{10}$ of that amount will be equal to 82,434.

Solution: Let N = the number of people in 1954
          then .20N represents the increase in population

Therefore N + .20N or 1.20N represents the population in 1955. The increase for 1956 is 10% of the 1955 population: .10 × 1.20N = .12N. This increase should be added to the 1955 population: 1.20N + .12N or 1.32N. Now this 1.32 N represents the population in 1956 which was 82,434. Since 1.32N = 82,434, then by dividing both terms by 1.32 we obtain N = 62,450, which was the population in 1954. Check: $\frac{1}{5}$ of 62,450 = 12,490. Add this to 62,450 to obtain 74,940. One-tenth of 74,940 = 7494, which must be added to 74,940 to obtain 82,434. It checks!

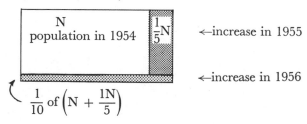

The solution can be effected in two successive (backward) steps. We can find the population for 1955 and then from this we can find the population for the previous year.

Let N = the population in 1955.
Then .10N = the increase.
Therefore N + .10N or 1.10N = 82,434 (the population in 1956).
Dividing both sides by 1.10, N = 74,940 (the population in 1955).

Now we find the population for the previous year.

Let Z = the population in 1954.
Then Z + .20Z = the population in 1955.
Therefore Z + .20Z or 1.20Z represents the population in 1955.
Since 1.20Z = 74,940.
Then Z = 62,450 the population in 1954.

Problems involving successive decreases would be similar in nature and would follow the same thought pattern in their solution except for the operations. The subtraction operation must replace the addition operation. One example will suffice. During its third year in a league a baseball team won 72 games, which was 10% fewer than it had won the year before. The second year it won 20% fewer games than it did the first year. Can you find the number of games it won the first year?

Solution: Let N = the number of games won the first year.

Then N − .20N or .80N represents the number of games won the second year.

Then .10 × .80N represents the number of games fewer that it won the third year.

Since .10 × .80N, then this represents the loss in number of games.

Then .80N − .08N or .72 N represents the number of games won the third year.

Therefore .72N = 72.

Dividing by .72, N = 100. The team won 100 games the first year.

There are also many problems representing alternating increases and decreases, some of which will be included in the set of exercises which follows.

EXERCISES

SET 27

1. Show the algebraic representation of a man's salary if he receives:
   (a) two successive 10% increases.
   (b) two successive 5% increases.
   (c) two successive 20% increases.
2. Set up the equation you would use to solve for the original salary if a man earned $10,000 after receiving:
   (a) increases of 10% and 20%.
   (b) increases of 30% and 10%.
   (c) increases of 10% and 2%.
3. Write the algebraic representation of a firm's business if it followed the following patterns:
   (a) up 20% down 4% up 5%
   (b) down 3% down 10% down 40%
   (c) up 5% up 5% down 10%
4. Write out problems which might fit the following equations:
   (a) N − .24N = 980   (b) N + .35N = 32,000
   (c) N − .10N + .11N = 4400 (d) N + 2N + 4N = $1,400,000
5. A, B, and C went into business and furnished capital as follows: A contributed $8000, B contributed $12,000, and C contributed $15,000.
   What per cent of the total capital did A contribute?
   What per cent of the annual profits should A receive?
   What per cent of the annual profits should B receive?
6. An employer deducts 4% for social security tax and 18% for withholding tax.   What is the take-home pay of an employee who earns $2.17½ per hour for a 40-hour week?   For one who earns $2.25 for a 44-hour week?
7. What one single discount is equivalent to the two successive discounts of 30% and 10%?
8. Mr. Smith gives a mortgage for $6000 on his new house with interest at 6% per year.   At the end of each yearly period he pays the interest and $1000 on the principal.   His last payment is $1060.   What is the total amount Mr. Smith has paid in interest?
9. Mr. Brown has a gross income for the year of $12,000.   His income tax is computed as follows: 22% on all gross income over $8000 and 7% on all gross income over $10,000.   What is the amount of Mr. Brown's income tax?
10. If the cost of food increases .3% from June to July, what would Mrs. Green pay for groceries in July which cost her $78 in June?

SET 28

1. An automobile listed at $1450 was sold at a discount of 15%. What was the selling price?
2. A man with a salary of $4000 was given a 10% raise. Later his salary was cut 10%. What was his salary after the cut?
3. A product loses 12% of its weight in processing. How many pounds of raw material are needed to produce 387.2 pounds of finished product?
4. Of an enrollment of 1250 students, 450 of them are male. What per cent of the total enrollment is female?
5. What should be the marked price of a watch in order to give a discount of 35% and still receive $60 for the watch?
6. Sirloin steak is listed at $1.80 per pound. If it is 25% bone or waste, what is the actual cost per pound for the lean meat?
7. After two successive 20% increases a man's salary is $6,480. What was his salary before the increases?
8. A house is insured for 80% of its assessed value of $8500. If the insurance rate is $\frac{1}{4}$% per year, what is the yearly premium?
9. A man sold two lots for $750 each. For one he received 25% more than it cost and for the other 25% less than it cost. How much did he gain or lose by the sale?
10. (a) 72 is 8% of what number?
    (b) 5% of what number is 315?
    (c) Rate is $7\frac{1}{2}$%, percentage is $12. Find the base.
    (d) Find a number which if decreased by $7\frac{1}{2}$% of itself is 323.75.
    (e) $.27 is $\frac{3}{7}$% of how many dollars?
11. Show *why* 48% of 75 is equivalent to 75% of 48.
12. Find the per cent of increase in the area of a circle if its diameter increases from 3 inches to 5 inches.
13. A manufacturer makes an article for $2.40. He sells it at a profit of 20% on sales to a wholesaler who in turn sells it at a profit of 20% on sales to a retailer. The retailer sells it for a profit of 25% on sales to a customer. What does the customer pay for the article?
14. Find the net cost of six chairs listed at $56.50 each with a discount of 15% and an extra $2\frac{1}{2}$% discount for paying cash.
15. After obtaining successive yearly raises of 20% and 10% Mr. Jones earned a salary of $11,088. What was his salary before the first increase?

CHAPTER 8

GEOMETRY OF SIZE AND FORM

8.1 Lines and Angles

The story of our civilization is the story of geometry—we live in a world of sizes and shapes, planes and solids, planets and outer space. Hardly a day passes without some personal reference to the size of things. Thus it is necessary to learn and understand a vocabulary of terms which describe lengths, distances, surfaces, contents, and space in general.

Mathematicians of long ago were precise in formulating definitions of terms and concepts which were in general use in their time, but today mathematicians allow the reader to formulate many of his own definitions in his own terms. Today's mathematicians begin by listing a set of assumptions. We formerly defined the straight line as the shortest distance between two points; the point formerly was defined as a geometric object having neither length, breadth, nor thickness (what a paradox, an object which has no dimensions). Today we assume a "point." Then the conglomeration of points, that is, a succession of points in ordered fashion.... You see, the writer is already in difficulty so we will also assume a straight line. Lines which are flat and parallel to the horizon are called *horizontal* lines while those which run straight up like a flag pole are *vertical* lines. Lines either intersect (meet) or they do not intersect. In the former case they are called *intersecting* lines and in the latter they are named *parallel* lines. Parallel lines are always the same distance apart. In the same plane two straight lines can intersect but once. Lines which are neither horizontal ——— nor vertical | are said to be oblique /. Lines can also be classified as broken or jagged ⌒⌄, dotted....., or curved (no part of which is straight) ⌒.

When two straight lines intersect, the space between them is called an *angle*. But more accurately, an angle is the amount of turning formed by rotating a line about one of its extremities as a fixed point. Then the rotation (the amount of turning) is referred to as the angle. When an angle has been formed by a line turning a complete revolution, the size of the angle is fixed as 360 degrees (1 degree is $\frac{1}{360}$ part of a complete revolution). If the line turns only half of a revolution, we have an angle of 180 degrees, which is called a *straight* angle; an angle of 90 degrees or ¼ of a complete revolution is a *right* angle. When two straight lines intersect so that four right angles are formed the lines are said to be *perpendicular*. An angle which is greater than 0 degrees but smaller than a right angle is called an *acute* angle; one which is greater than 90 degrees but less than 180 degrees is an *obtuse* angle; and one which is larger than 180 degrees but less than 360 degrees is a *reflex* angle.

Since an angle is an amount of turning there is no limit as to the maximum size of angles. If a line turns through two complete turns then an angle of 720 degrees has been generated, and if a wheel makes five revolutions then a point on its rim has passed through or has generated an angle of 1800 degrees. The reader should keep in mind that the lengths of the sides of the angles, the lengths of the generating lines have no bearing on the size of the angle.

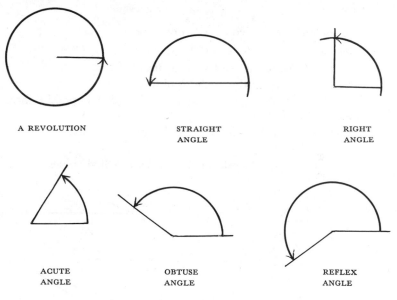

A REVOLUTION   STRAIGHT   RIGHT
ANGLE   ANGLE

ACUTE   OBTUSE   REFLEX
ANGLE   ANGLE   ANGLE

8.2 Polygons

Any plane figure bounded by straight lines is a *polygon* and the fewest number of straight lines needed to bound an area of space is three. A figure bounded by three straight lines is a *triangle*. Any figure bounded by four straight lines is a *quadrilateral*. There are concave and convex polygons depending on the size of the interior angles of the polygon.   If each interior angle of the polygon is less than 180 degrees, then the polygon is *convex*.   If one or more of the internal angles of the polygon are greater than a straight angle, then at least one of the sides, when produced, will intersect another side of the polygon.   Such a figure is called a *concave* polygon.   A concave polygon is one such that if one or more of its sides are extended it will intersect an opposite side.   If polygons have sides of equal length and angles of the same size then the polygons are called *regular*, otherwise they are irregular.

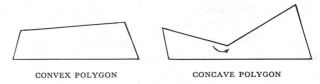

CONVEX POLYGON   CONCAVE POLYGON

Triangles can be classified into several types:

(*a*) *Right*: one of the angles is a right angle.

(*b*) *Acute angled*: All of the angles are acute.

(*c*) *Obtuse angled*: One of the angles is obtuse.

(*d*) *Isosceles*: Two of the sides are equal.   (The angles opposite these sides are also equal.)

(*e*) *Equilateral*: All of the sides are equal.   (The angles are all equal, too.)

(*f*) *Scalene*: Irregular, general, no equal sides or equal angles.

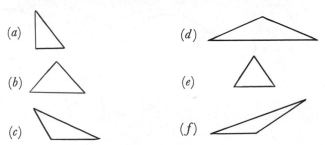

Quadrilaterals may take any one of several shapes:

(*a*) *Square*: All of the sides are equal and all of the angles are 90°.

(*b*) *Rectangle*: All of the angles are 90° but the sides are not necessarily equal.

(c) *Parallelogram*: The opposite pairs of sides are of equal length and parallel. (Opposite angles are also equal.)

(d) *Rhombus*: The sides are equal and opposite angles are equal.

(e) *Trapezoid*: Has only one pair of parallel sides.

(f) *Isosceles trapezoid*: One pair of sides is parallel and the other sides are equal.

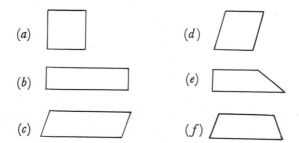

The most common of the regular polygons are the equilateral triangle, the square, the pentagon, the hexagon, and the octagon. The regular triangle (*equilateral triangle*) has three equal angles (each 60°) and sides of equal length. The regular quadrilateral is a *square*. It has four equal angles (each 90°) and four sides of equal length. The regular polygon of five equal angles (each 108°) and sides of equal length is a *pentagon*. The regular six-sided polygon is a *hexagon*. Each interior angle contains 120°. The regular eight-sided polygon is an *octagon*. It has eight sides of equal length and each of its interior angles contains 135°. A very special polygon of an infinite number of equal sides and equal angles (if we apply the principles known as the theory of limits) is the *circle*. The circle, which is usually defined as a closed curve all of whose points are the same distance from a point within called the center, can also be defined as a regular polygon of an infinite number of sides and equal angles.

 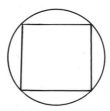 

EQUILATERAL TRIANGLE   SQUARE   REGULAR PENTAGON

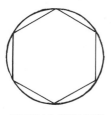

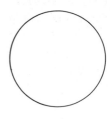

REGULAR HEXAGON   REGULAR OCTAGON   CIRCLE

8.3   Polyhedrons

Many objects encountered in our daily living are three-dimensional in form—they are solids.   The lump of sugar, the brick of ice cream, the stick of butter, the concrete pavement, the brick wall, the piece of pie, the inflated balloon, etc., are all objects, solid in form, which are common surroundings.   These solids, bounded or enclosed by plane surfaces, are called polyhedrons, the most common of which are:

(a) *The cube*: All of the bounding surfaces are squares.
(b) *The rectangular solid*: All of the bounding surfaces are rectangles or squares.
(c) *The right prism*: Some of the bounding surfaces are rectangles.
(d) *The pyramid*: Usually bounded by a many-sided base and tri-angular faces.

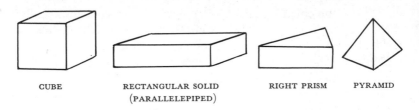

CUBE   RECTANGULAR SOLID   RIGHT PRISM   PYRAMID
              (PARALLELEPIPED)

There is a class of solids in which the circle plays an important role. A solid whose parallel bases are circles will have a *curved lateral surface* and is designated as a *cylinder*.   A solid with only one circular base and all the elements of the lateral surface meeting at a point is called a *cone*.   Hence a cone is bounded by one plane surface and one curved surface.   A solid which is bounded by one curved surface all points of which are equidistant from another point is a *sphere*.

Half of a sphere, that portion formed by passing a plane through the center of a sphere, is called a *hemisphere*. It, too, is bounded by one plane surface and one curved surface.

Solids which are bounded by regular polygons are called regular polyhedrons.

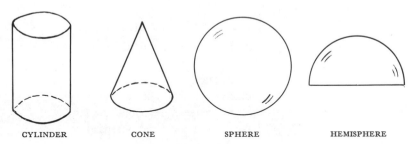

CYLINDER   CONE   SPHERE   HEMISPHERE

8.4 Other Lines and Angles

The longest straight line which one can draw in a circle must pass through the center and is called the *diameter*. One-half of a diameter is the *radius*. Any line through the circle terminated by the circumference is a *chord*. A line not terminated by the circumference is a *secant*. The curved line bounding the circle is the *circumference*. The side which a figure appears to rest on is called the *base*; a figure may have more than one base. The line drawn from a vertex perpendicular to the base is the *altitude* and a line drawn from a vertex of a triangle to the midpoint of the opposite side is a *median*. Therefore a triangle can have three different altitudes and three different medians.

If two or more angles have a sum of 90° they are said to be *complementary*. The complement of an angle is another angle which when combined with the given angle will produce a sum of 90°. The *supplement* of an angle is another angle which will produce a sum of 180° when added to the given angle. The complement of 70° is an angle of 20° while its supplement is 110°. An angle whose vertex is at the center of a circle and whose sides are radii of the circle is called a *central* angle. One whose vertex is on the circumference and whose sides are chords is an *inscribed* angle. Such angles are called interior because they lie inside the figure. Angles formed by one side of a polygon and another side produced are called *exterior* angles.

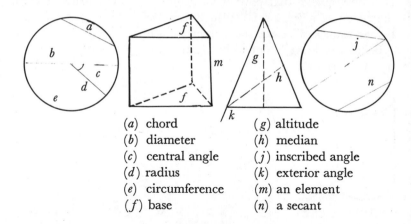

(a) chord   (g) altitude
(b) diameter   (h) median
(c) central angle   (j) inscribed angle
(d) radius   (k) exterior angle
(e) circumference   (m) an element
(f) base   (n) a secant

EXERCISES

SET 29

1. Name and define other lines than those illustrated in this chapter.
2. Define: ellipse   parabola   truncated prism
             rhombus   spheroid   truncated pyramid
3. Classify the following angles:
      130°   340°   16°   279°   189°   161°   3°   45°
4. Find the complements and/or supplements of the following angles:
      21° 16′   138° 30′   78° 34′   79° 50′   161° 56′   2° 21′ 23″
5. Draw two diagrams of different size for each of the following:
      regular hexagon   isosceles trapezoid   parallelepiped
      regular pentagonal prism   octagonal prism   right prism
6. Show that the sum of the interior angles of any triangle is equal to two right angles. Show that the sum of the interior angles of an octagon is equal to six straight angles.
7. How many degrees in the central angle of a regular inscribed pentagon? hexagon? octagon? How many degrees in each exterior angle of the regular polygons?
8. Draw three triangles of different size. In each triangle draw the three altitudes. Did you make any discovery?
9. Draw any three triangles of different size. In each triangle draw the three medians. Did you make any discovery?
10. How many degrees in the sum of the angles of a rectangle? a triangle? a parallelogram? of any pentagon?
11. How many acute angles can a triangle have? How many obtuse angles? How many right angles?

8.5 Perimeters of Plane Figures

The term *perimeter* refers to the outer boundary or rim of an object. When we speak of the perimeter of a square we refer to the entire distance measured along the bounding sides of the square. Since we are measuring the length of a line or finding the total length of several lines our result will be expressed in some form of linear measure such as inches, feet, yards, miles, etc. The perimeter should first be expressed in terms of the given units of measure and then can be converted to other units if desirable.

The perimeter of a square is the total distance around the square—its total boundary. Since the sides of a square are equal and since a square has four sides, the perimeter will be represented as the number of units of length in one side plus the number of units of length in the second side plus the length of the third side plus the length of the fourth side. In symbols, if we let P represent the number of units of length in the perimeter and s represent the number of units of length of one of the sides the formula for the perimeter will be $P = s + s + s + s$, or $P = 4 \times s$, or $P = 4s$. The perimeter of a triangle is equal to the combined lengths of the three sides. If the lengths of the sides are represented by a units, b units, and c units respectively, then $P = a + b + c$ units. If the three sides of the triangles are the same length (if the triangle is an equilateral triangle) the formula for the perimeter is expressed as $P = 3 \times a$ or $P = 3a$.

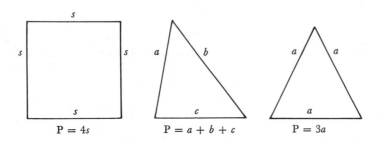

A rectangle has two sets of equal sides; the lengths or bases are equal and the widths or heights are equal. The perimeter of a rectangle can be expressed as the sum of the length plus the width plus the length plus the width (it is assumed that all dimensions are expressed in the same kind of units). Then $P = l + w + l + w$, or $P = 2l + 2w$. In words, the perimeter of a rectangle can be expressed as being equal to twice the number of units in the length increased by twice the number of units in the width. This is equivalent also to saying that the perimeter is twice the sum of the number of units of length and width combined. $P = 2(l + w)$.

A parallelogram is like a rectangle in that it, too, has two pairs of equal sides. The bases are of the same length and the ends are also equal. Then the perimeter of a parallelogram is equal to twice the sum of the length of the base and the length of one end. $P = 2(b + e)$.

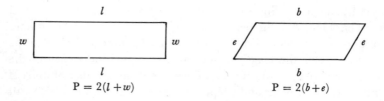

The perimeter of a circle is called its circumference. Mathematicians long ago determined that the circumference of a circle is approximately $3\frac{1}{7}$ times the length of its diameter. The $3\frac{1}{7}$ is an approximation for the inexact decimal number 3.14159+ and is designated as *pi* (the Greek symbol π). Thus $C = \pi d$ may also take the form of $C = 2\pi r$.

8.6 Areas of Plane Figures

Polygons are figures which inclose a plane or a flat surface. The amount of this surface is called its *area*. Before we measure this surface we need to decide upon a unit of surface or a unit of area. This can be a square 1 inch on each side—a square inch—or a square 1 foot on each side—a square foot—or any other convenient measure in the shape of a square because the measure of any area is always expressed in square units. The area of a book cover is a number of square inches, the area of a rug is a number of square feet or square yards, and the area of a large lake might be expressed in square miles. To find the area of a square or a rectangle we first express the given dimensions in the same kind of units and then select a unit of square measure with which we can conveniently measure the area. Suppose we have a square 4 feet on each edge. We will use 1 square foot as the unit of measure. We lay this measure off along the inside of the square to see how many square feet can be measured along the length of the square.

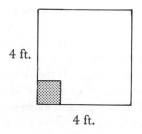 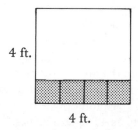

Now we find that we have one row with an area of 4 square feet. We ascertain that we can lay off another row of 4 square feet. In fact, we can do this 4 times. Thus the total area must be 4 × 4 square feet or 16 square feet.

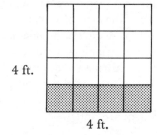

4 square feet   4 square feet

4 square feet $\times$ 4

4 square feet   16 square feet

4 square feet

To find the area of a rectangle we likewise select a convenient unit of square measure. We lay this off along the base. Then we make another row of square units, and another, and another until we have covered the entire surface or area. The total area will be the number of square units laid along the base multiplied by the number of rows of square units. If we have a rectangle whose base or length is 8 feet and whose height is 3 feet we will have 3 rows of 8 square feet or an area of 24 square feet.

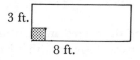 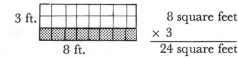

8 square feet

$\times$ 3

24 square feet

To find the area of a square or rectangle determine first the unit of measure to be used (square inches, square feet, etc.) and then multiply the number of units of measurement in the length by the number of units of measurement in the width. Express this product as square units. If the dimensions of a rectangle are 39 inches by 8 feet we determine first whether we want to express the area in square inches or square feet. The latter is more convenient and gives one a clearer concept of the size of the rectangle. Therefore, we express the width 39 inches as $3\frac{1}{4}$ feet. Now we multiply 8 by $3\frac{1}{4}$, which gives us a product of 26. This 26 should now be expressed as square feet— therefore the area of the rectangle is 26 square feet. If the side of a square is 7 inches we find it convenient to express its area in square inches. We multiply 7 by 7 (as abstract numbers) and express this quantity as 49 square inches. The reader should be impressed with the fact that one does not multiply "inches by inches" to get square inches nor "feet by feet" to obtain square feet. $A = L \times W$ (square units).

The area of a triangle with a given base and altitude is half the area of a rectangle having those same dimensions. If we have a triangle with base of 12 inches and altitude of 4 inches we can easily show that the surface of the triangle is one-half the area of a rectangle whose base is 12 inches and whose altitude is 4 inches, or one-half of 24 square inches. We can draw several triangles with given dimensions. Upon the base of each we can construct rectangles with altitudes of 4 inches. We can show that the area of the rectangle is twice the area of the given triangle. In other words, the formula for the area of a triangle is $A = \frac{1}{2}L \times W$ (square units).

  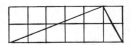

The area of a parallelogram is equal to the number of units of measure in its length multiplied by the number of units (of the same kind) in its altitude and this product expressed in square measure.

$$A = L \times H \text{ (square units)}$$

The derivation of this relationship can be discovered in the same manner as illustrated above. If we use a parallelogram with a base

equal to 8 inches and an altitude equal to 4 inches, we can discover
that this area is equal to 32 square inches.

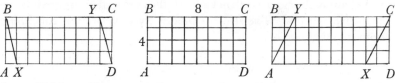

Area $ABCD$ = 36 square units	Area $ABCD$ = 40 square units
Area ABX = 2 square units	Area ABY = 4 square units
Area YCD = 2 square units	Area XDC = 4 square units
Area $BXDY$ = 32 square units	Area $AYCX$ = 32 square units

A trapezoid is a quadrilateral with only one pair of parallel sides
and has an area equal to half the sum of its parallel sides multiplied
by its altitude.   (It is assumed that the measurements will be of the
same kind of units and that the area will be expressed in square
measure.)   If the parallel bases of a trapezoid are 6 inches and
10 inches and the altitude is 4 inches, we can show that the area is
32 square inches.

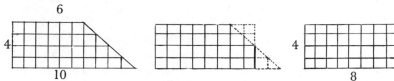

The area of the trapezoid is equivalent to the area of a rectangle whose
base or length is equal to the midsection of the trapezoid (half the
sum of the parallel sides) multiplied by the altitude.   Hence the
formula for the area of a trapezoid is A = $\frac{1}{2}(b_1 + b_2)$ × H.

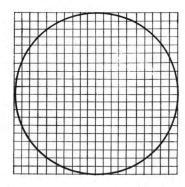

The area of a circle is always expressed in square measure and is equal to the square of the radius multiplied by pi. $A = \pi \times R^2$. If the radius of a circle is 10 inches then the area will be approximately 314 square inches. The student should try to verify this conclusion from the diagram.

8.7   Volumes of Familiar Solids

The unit of measure of volume is a cubic unit such as a cubic inch or a cubic foot. If we are given the dimensions of a familiar solid we want to know how much space or volume it occupies or we want to know its capacity. If we know the dimensions of a block of wood or block of steel we might be interested in knowing how many smaller blocks each 1 unit on an edge can be made from the given block. Or if our known dimensions are those of an empty box then we would be interested in knowing how many smaller boxes 1 unit on each edge (cubical in size and shape) we can pack inside. In this case we are finding capacity.

If we have a wooden box whose dimensions are 3 feet by 4 feet and 3 feet high we begin by covering the base (interior of the box) with small cubes each 1 foot on an edge. Since the base has an area of 12 square feet it can be covered with 12 cubic feet. Then we can put another layer of cubes for a total of 24 cubic feet. Now there is space for still another layer of little cubes. The box can be filled with 36 small cubes. There will be 3 layers of 12 cubic feet each. Thus the volume of the box will be expressed in cubic feet and will be equal in number to the product of the dimensions of the box.

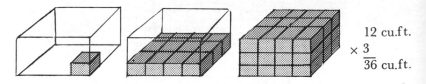

$$
\begin{array}{r}
12 \text{ cu.ft.} \\
\times\ 3 \\
\hline
36 \text{ cu.ft.}
\end{array}
$$

To find the volume of a rectangular solid we first express all the dimensions in the same kind of units. Then we multiply the number of units of measure in the length by the number of units of measure in the width. This product is multiplied by the number of units of measure in the height.   This will give the volume, which should be expressed in cubic units.   In other words, the volume of a rectangular solid is equal to the product of the three units of measure and that product expressed in cubic units.

$$V = L \times W \times H \text{ (cubic units)}$$

If the solid is a prism whose base is non-rectangular we proceed to find the number of square units of area in the base (there will be as many cubic units of volume in the bottom layer as there are square units of measure on the base) and multiply by the number of units of measure in the altitude.   If the base is a right triangle with legs 8 inches and 12 inches its area will be 48 square inches.   Then if the altitude of the prism is 10 inches its volume will be 480 cubic inches. $V = B \times H$ cubic inches.

The volume of a pyramid is one-third the volume of a prism having the same dimensions.   If the dimensions of the rectangular base of a pyramid are 12 feet by 6 feet and the altitude is 9 feet then the volume of the pyramid is $\frac{1}{3}$ of $12 \times 6 \times 9$ or 216 cubic feet. $V = \frac{1}{3}B \times H$ cubic units.

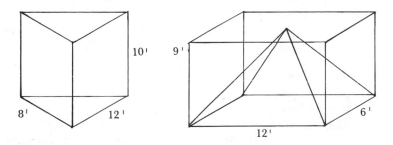

The volume of a cylinder is the product of the number of square units of measure which can be measured off on its base multiplied by the number of units in the altitude.   If the base of a cylinder has a diameter of 14 inches then the area of the base is πR^2 or 154 square inches.   On this base we can build a layer of 154 cubic inches.   Now if the altitude of the cylinder is 10 inches there will be 10 layers of 154 cubic inches for a total of 1540 cubic inches.   If the given dimensions are those of a cone the volume will be one-third the volume of the cylinder.   The volume of a sphere is equal to the cube of the radius multiplied by $\frac{4}{3}\pi$.

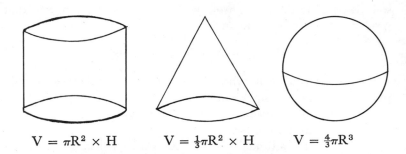

$$V = \pi R^2 \times H \qquad V = \tfrac{1}{3}\pi R^2 \times H \qquad V = \tfrac{4}{3}\pi R^3$$

8.8 The Pythagorean Theorem

One of the most valuable laws of mathematics was given us years ago by the Greek mathematician Pythagoras, who, it is said, discovered this important truth while playing with knotted rope. He was building or constructing right triangles and discovered that the number of square units of area in the square built upon the hypotenuse (longest side of a right triangle) is always equal to the sum of the areas of the squares built upon the other two sides. In other words, the square on the hypotenuse is equal to the sum of the squares on the other two sides. The law takes this form:

$$h^2 = a^2 + b^2$$

and through its proper use we can find any side of the right triangle if we know the other two.

If the legs of a right triangle are respectively 5 inches and 12 inches we can find the hypotenuse. First we square each of the given dimensions, then add them, and then find the square root of the sum: $5^2 = 25, 12^2 = 144, 25 + 144 = 169, \sqrt{169} = 13$. The hypotenuse will be 13 inches long.

$$h^2 = a^2 + b^2$$
$$h^2 = 5^2 + 12^2$$
$$h^2 = 25 + 144$$
$$h^2 = 169$$
$$h = \sqrt{169} \text{ or } 13$$

If the hypotenuse and one of the legs are known, we use the same formula to solve for the other leg. Suppose that the hypotenuse is

17 and one of the legs is 8. What is the length of the other leg? Substitution in the formula clearly reveals that the square of the units of measure of the leg is the difference between the other two squares, or in this case, 225. The square root of 225 is 15 which represents the dimension of the other leg.

$$a^2 + b^2 = 17^2$$
$$8^2 + b^2 = 17^2$$
$$64 + b^2 = 289$$
$$b^2 = 225$$
$$b = \sqrt{225} \text{ or } 15$$

The Pythagorean Theorem, as it is called, is of inestimable value in problems of triangulation. From its use we can find the lengths of diagonals of squares, cubes, and rectangular solids as well as other inaccessible distances; we can prove that the diagonal of a square is always the length of a side multiplied by $\sqrt{2}$ and that the diagonal of a cube is always the length of an edge multiplied by $\sqrt{3}$;—important generalizations which are useful to the mathematician. Let us show that the diagonal of a square is $\sqrt{2}$ times the length of one side.

If each side of a square is 5 inches then the diagonal is equal to the square root of the sum of $25 + 25$, or in other words the square root of 2×25. Therefore, the diagonal $d = \sqrt{2 \times 25}$ which is equivalent to the product of their respective square roots, $\sqrt{2} \times \sqrt{25}$ or $\sqrt{2} \times 5$ or $\sqrt{2}$ times the length of one side. In general terms we know that

$$d^2 = s^2 + s^2 \text{ or } d^2 = 2s^2 \quad \therefore d = \sqrt{2s^2}$$

$$\text{or } d = \sqrt{2} \times \sqrt{s^2} \text{ which is } \sqrt{2} \times s.$$

To find the diagonal of a rectangular solid, it is first necessary to find the diagonal of one face, preferably the base. If the dimensions of the base are L and W, and d is the diagonal of the base, then

$$d^2 = L^2 + W^2$$

If D is the diagonal of the solid

$$D^2 = d^2 + H^2$$

Substituting for d^2 we obtain

$$D^2 = L^2 + W^2 + H^2$$
$$\therefore D = \sqrt{L^2 + W^2 + H^2}$$

The diagonal of a rectangular solid is equal to the square root of the sum of the squares of the three dimensions.

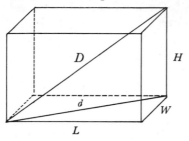 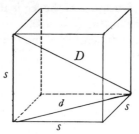

Since the dimensions of a cube are equal, then the diagonal is equal to the square root of $s^2 + s^2 + s^2$, or $D = \sqrt{3s^2}$. Since $\sqrt{3s^2} = \sqrt{3} \times \sqrt{s^2}$, then $D = \sqrt{3} \times s$. In other words, the diagonal of a cube is the product of one dimension times $\sqrt{3}$.

EXERCISES

SET 30

1. The side of a square is 5.6 inches. What is its perimeter and its area?
2. Find the perimeter and area of a rectangle whose base is 8.5 inches and whose altitude is 9.7 inches.
3. A trapezoid has parallel sides of 9 feet 3 inches and 11 feet 7 inches. Its altitude is 8 feet. What is its area?
4. If the diameter of a circle is 21 inches, find its circumference and its area.
5. A rectangular field is 60 rods wide and 100 rods long. How many acres of land does it contain? (160 square rods = 1 acre.)
6. Find the volume of a box whose inside dimensions are 2′ 5″, 3′ 7″, and 2′ 3″.
7. Which has the larger volume:
   (a) a sphere whose radius is 30 inches or
   .(b) a cube whose edge is 23 inches?
8. Compare the volume of a cone whose radius is 10″ and whose altitude is 10″ with the volume of a cube whose edge is 10″.
9. Find the total area of three circular flower beds whose diameters are 10 feet, 12 feet, and 15 feet.
10. If a circular sidewalk 4 feet wide surrounds each of the three flower beds (of exercise No. 9), find the total number of square feet of sidewalk surface.

11. The inner radius of a circular washer is .28 inches. The outer radius is .35 inches. What is the area of the washer?
12. A coal bin is 12 feet deep, 9 feet wide, and 4 feet deep. How many tons of coal will it hold if 1 ton of coal occupies 35 cubic feet?
13. A ball-bearing has a diameter of $\frac{4}{5}$ inch. How many cubic inches of material are needed to cast 700 ball-bearings?
14. A heavy roller is a hollow cylinder with an inside diameter of 8 inches and outside diameter of 15 inches. If the roller is 28 inches long, what is its volume in cubic inches?
15. How much material is wasted if a 12-inch circle is cut from a 12-inch square?
16. If the perimeter of a square is 160 feet, what is its area?
17. Find the area of a square whose side is equal to the base of a rectangle whose area is 75 square feet and whose altitude is 9 feet.
18. If the area of a triangle is 100 square inches and the altitude is 18 inches, what is the length of the base?
19. What are the dimensions of the biggest rectangle which can be drawn having a perimeter of 12 inches? (Use integers only.)
20. Find the diagonal of a square whose sides measure 30 inches.
21. Find the diagonal of the floor of a room whose width is 20 feet and whose length is 24 feet.
22. The dimensions of a box are 8″, 10″, and 12″. What is the diagonal of the box?

CHAPTER 9

DENOMINATE NUMBERS AND SIGNIFICANT FIGURES

9.1 Denominate Numbers

Numbers fall into many different classifications. There are numbers which answer the questions *which one* and *how many*; there are numbers which are integral or non-integral; there are numbers which are either prime or composite; and among other classifications there are numbers which are either discrete or continuous. In this chapter we will be concerned with the latter classifications.

Discrete numbers are exact numbers or counting numbers which answer the question *how many* and should be accepted irrevocably. When one says that there are 12 eggs in one dozen, that there are 10 tens in one hundred, that there are 34 students in the class, and that there are 154 games in a complete American League baseball schedule; these quantities are *exact* or *discrete* and there is no argument about them. A continuous number is a number of somewhat doubtful or uncertain magnitude and answers the question *how much* and always raises some question as to the degree of accuracy of the measurement. When one says that he is 34 years old, that he weighs 156 pounds, that he is 6 feet tall, and that he drinks two quarts of water daily; these quantities are not exact number quantities and their true measurements are questionable. This kind of number is called *continuous*. Measurements recorded as 34 years, 156 pounds, 6 feet, and 2 quarts are approximate measures (not exact measures) and are expressed in some specific denomination, hence are called *denominate* numbers.

What does the customer mean when he asks the butcher for a 12-pound turkey? Does the weight of the fowl have to be exactly 12 pounds? What does the motorist mean when he says that he averages a distance of 18 miles on each gallon of gasoline? Does he mean exactly 18 miles per gallon? What does the student mean when he says that he spent 3 hours studying an assignment? Does he mean exactly 3 hours?

Making a measurement of any kind involves making a comparison between the quantity measured and some recognized measuring standard. The weight of a fowl is compared with the standard unit of one pound, the distance traveled is compared with the standard linear unit of one mile, and the time spent in studying is compared with the unit one hour. Measurements are made with or compared with standards of measurement which are uniform in any one country and some of which are standard internationally.

Some of the more important standard units of measurement are:

Units	Class	Definition
inch, foot, yard, mile	Linear	Units of line measurement
pint, quart, gallon	Liquid	Units of capacity or contents
square inch, square foot, acre	Square	Units of surface or area
cubic inch, cubic foot	Cubic	Units of volume or contents
second, minute, hour, year	Time	Units of duration
peck, bushel, ton	Dry	Units of dry capacity or contents

Primitive people used parts of their bodies for measuring line distances. Some of the more common ones (a few of which are still in use) are:

span   The distance from the tip of the little finger to the tip of the thumb of an outspread hand.

digit   The width of a finger.

cubit   The distance from the elbow to the tip of the middle finger.

palm   The width of the hand measured at the base of the fingers.

fathom   The straight line distance from fingertip to fingertip of the arms outstretched to the side.

pace   The double step, about 5 feet.

ell   5 spans (used for measuring cloth).

furlong 125 paces or about 40 rods
           (one-eighth of a mile).

9.2 Our Standard Measures

Because of the great variability in the dimensions of the various parts of the human body and because of the need for greater accuracy in making and recording measurements, there developed, over the ages, a system of standard measures which we use today.

In the realm of measures of length we have the following standards:

(*a*) The *inch* originally was the length of three barley corns taken from the center of an ear and placed end to end.   Now the inch has been defined by the United States Bureau of Weights and Measures as one of the equal parts of the meter which has been divided into 39.37 equal parts.   1 meter = 39.37 inches.

(*b*) The *foot*, originally the average length of a man's foot and varied between $9\frac{3}{4}$ inches and 19 inches, now has been standardized to be equal to 12 inches.

(*c*) The *yard* as decreed by King Henry I was the distance from the point of his nose to the thumb of the outstretched hand but is now equal to a length of 3 feet.

(*d*) The *rod* was the combined length of the left feet of 16 men as they lined up after church on Sunday morning.   Now the rod is equal to $16\frac{1}{2}$ feet or $5\frac{1}{2}$ yards.

(*e*) The *mile* or mille was originally 1000 double steps or paces. A pace was equivalent to 5 feet so the first mile was established as 5000 feet.   Now the mile has been established as equivalent to 5280 feet.

The evolution of our present units for measuring contents (dry and liquid measure) has been complicated and haphazard and has seen the use and then the disuse of many measuring devices.   When primitive man first began to measure grains and liquids he resorted to crude devices such as hollowed gourds, egg shells, bowls, or the hollow horns of animals, and the like.   The first standard unit of liquid measure used in England was the wine gallon, which was defined as $\frac{1}{8}$ of a cubic foot, and since the first units of liquid measure were based on weight and because the different wines varied in density, we discover a great variation in the early standards. It was later discovered that a cubic foot of water weighs $62\frac{1}{2}$ pounds (about the same weight as light wine); therefore a gallon of water weighs approximately 8 pounds. In about 1830 the United States Treasury Department adopted as our standard unit of liquid measure the *gallon*, equal to 231 cubic inches. The *quart* (short form for quarter) is one-fourth the size of a gallon or is equal to 57.75 cubic inches. The *pint* is half the size of the quart, and the *cup* (now a standard household measurement) is half the size of one pint. Other smaller standard units of measure used by the pharmacist and the housekeeper are the tablespoon, the teaspoon, and the fluid ounce (about 1.8 cubic inches). A large unit of liquid measure which has advantages of packaging and delivery rather than as a measure of content is the *barrel*, which contains $31\frac{1}{2}$ gallons. Out-moded measures of capacity are the gill ($\frac{1}{2}$ cup) and the hogshead (2 barrels).

The standard unit of dry measure in the United States is the *bushel* and is defined as being equivalent to 2150.42 cubic inches. Thus we see definitely that the bushel is a measure of capacity and not one of weight. A bushel of potatoes should weigh 60 pounds, a bushel of apples 50 pounds, and a bushel of oats should weigh 32 pounds, but even these measurements might vary between the several states or even within the confines of any one state. Because there is no agreement between the number of pounds in a bushel of oats, a bushel of rye, a bushel of wheat, etc., certain farm organizations in the United States have recently recommended to the Department of Agriculture that the standard for contents should be changed from one of capacity to one of weight and have suggested as the standard unit of measure, the *hundredweight* (100 pounds). The adoption of this standard would make for uniformity and thus greatly facilitate comparisons and computations in the feed and grain industry. The *peck* is equal to one-fourth part of the bushel or 537.60 cubic inches. The *quart* (dry measure) is $\frac{1}{8}$ the contents of the peck or $\frac{1}{32}$ the size of the bushel. One quart equals 67.2 cubic inches.

The standard unit of weight in the United States is the *pound*. Originally the pound was defined as the weight of 7000 grains of wheat but today it is defined in connection with the weight of distilled water. A cubic inch of distilled water is said to weigh about 252.46 grains or, conversely, 1 *grain* is about $\frac{1}{250}$ of the weight of 1 cubic inch of water. At various times in the long ago the pound was divided into 12, 14, 16, and 20 equal parts but the standard division of the pound today is $\frac{1}{16}$ part of the pound, the *ounce*. A total of 100 pounds is referred to as a *hundredweight* and 2000 pounds is officially a *ton* though a long ton of 2240 pounds is still recognized in marketing heavy goods.

Time is a measure of duration, the name given to "how long it takes" to do something. In olden times man reckoned happenings by the position of the sun by day or the moon by night. He ate when he was hungry and went to bed when it became dark. Today time plays a very important role in the affairs of our lives; it helps us to keep a record of events transpired or yet to come in their proper place. Today time is also used to express distance, not in linear units, but in length of time it takes one to get from place to place. A business man might live 40 minutes from his office, the airline distance from Chicago to New York is often expressed as 3 hours, and the athlete runs a 4-minute mile—these are all examples of time being used to represent distance. However, when we say that the man of the house still likes his 3-minute eggs and his instant coffee for breakfast we use time to represent duration.

Time, like our number system, has two aspects or interpretations. First, it has the quantitative aspect—it represents duration or amount, such as 3 hours. Secondly, it has the positional aspect—it represents a point on a number line, such as 3 o'clock (3 hours past noon or midnight).

There is no single unit of measure for time. The *year* is the length of time required for the revolution of the earth about the sun, the *month* is the period of one revolution of the moon, and the *day* is one revolution of the moon around the earth, all three of these having variations in their durations. The day is a unit quite easy to comprehend, for it is the duration from one dawn to another, or from sundown to sundown. It has been divided into 24 equal portions called *hours*. The hour in turn has been divided into 60 equal parts designated as *minutes*. Each minute is divided into 60 *seconds*. The second is subdivided further into tenths, hundredths, and thousandths of a second.

9.3 The Metric System of Measures

The metric system of weights and measures is a decimal system adopted by the government of France in the late 1700's. It is not a haphazard system of individually determined standards but is based on logic and is used by all the major countries of the world except the United States and Great Britain. Efforts have been expended to have the metric system adopted as our standard system of measurement but to no avail. Strangely enough, however, many of our units or standards of measure are defined in terms of units in the metric system. Where our system follows the cumbersome and irregular pattern of equivalents, the metric system is a decimal system just like the Hindu-Arabic number system—each new unit is 10 times the value of the preceding unit. The value of each successive unit, counting or naming from right to left (in order of size), is 10 times the value of the unit immediately to the right. The ratio is always 10 to 1.

The standard unit of length is the *meter* and is based on the quarter meridian running through Paris. Officially the meter is one tenmillionth part of the length of the meridian between the North Pole and the Equator and is equal to 39.37 inches. This distance is delineated on a platinum bar which is kept as the standard in the International Bureau of Weights and Measures near Paris, France.

The standard unit of capacity is the *liter*, which is $\frac{21}{20}$ the volume of a quart. Conversely, the volume of a quart is about $\frac{20}{21}$ the volume of a liter.

The standard unit of weight is the *gram*, which is equal to the weight of one cubic centimeter of water at near freezing temperature and is equal to $\frac{1}{28}$ the value of the ounce. Conversely, the ounce is equal to about 28 grams.

Other useful units of measure inherent in the metric system are the *are*, a unit of land measuring 10 meters on each side; the *hectare*, equal to 100 ares; the *stere*, which is equivalent to a cubic meter; and a *metric ton*, which is equal to a thousand kilograms.

As we have said before, the metric system is a decimal system of measurement. Each new order of greater magnitude is an integral multiple of its immediate neighbor to the right, and each new order to the right is a non-integral multiple of its immediate neighbor to the left. In other words, as the new units increase in size, their values are 10 times the values of the units adjacent to the right, and when the new units are smaller than a given unit, the new unit is .1 the size of the value immediately adjacent to the left. In other words, the units of measure increase or decrease by powers of 10 just as the orders of our decimal number system.

Because of its use in scientific literature as well as for purposes of general information, children in the upper elementary classes should be encouraged to learn the basic aspects of the metric system.

KILO	HECTO	DECA	METERS LITERS GRAMS	DECI	CENTI	MILLI
10^3	10^2	10^1	10^0	10^{-1}	10^{-2}	10^{-3}
1000	100	10	1	.1	.01	.001

LINEAR

12 inches	= 1 foot
3 feet	= 1 yard
5½ yards } 16½ feet }	= 1 rod
5280 feet } 1760 yards }	= 1 mile

LIQUID MEASURE

2 gills	= 1 cup
2 cups	= 1 pint
2 pints	= 1 quart
4 quarts	= 1 gallon
31½ gallons	= 1 barrel
2 barrels	= 1 hogshead
231 cubic inches	= 1 gallon

DRY MEASURE

2 pints	= 1 quart
8 quarts	= 1 peck
4 pecks	= 1 bushel

SQUARE MEASURE

144 square inches	= 1 square foot
9 square feet	= 1 square yard
30¼ square yards	= 1 square rod
160 square rods	= 1 acre
640 acres	= 1 section

CUBIC MEASURE

1728 cubic inches	= 1 cubic foot
27 cubic feet	= 1 cubic yard
128 cubic feet	= 1 cord
1¼ cubic feet	= 1 bushel

MEASURES OF WEIGHT

16 ounces	= 1 pound
100 pounds	= 1 hundredweight
2000 pounds	= 1 ton
2240 pounds	= 1 long ton

TIME

60 seconds	= 1 minute	12 months	= 1 year
60 minutes	= 1 hour	365 days	= 1 year
24 hours	= 1 day	366 days	= 1 leap year
7 days	= 1 week	360 days	= 1 business year
4⅓ weeks	= 1 month	52 weeks	= 1 year

CONVERSION EQUIVALENTS

1 meter	= 39.37 inches	1 square inch	= 6.45 square centimeters
1 hectare	= 2.47 acres	1 pound	= .454 kilograms
1 inch	= 2.54 centimeters	1 kilometer	= .62 miles
1 mile	= 1609 meters	1 kilogram	= 2.20 pounds
1 quart	= .95 liters	1 cubic inch	= 16.39 cubic centimeters
		1 gallon	= 3.79 liters

EXERCISES

SET 31

1. Define or illustrate the following units of measurement:

   cord   furlong   board foot   chain

   ell   hogshead   baker's dozen   iota

2. In recent years the following units of measure have come into prominent usage. Define or illustrate their meaning.

   erg   light-year   man-hour   decibel

   foot-pound   trillion   horsepower

   kilowatt hour   foot-per-second   .22 rifle

3. Can you suggest other modern units of measure?

4. Find a map of the United States showing the time belts or time zones. How much and in what direction would you change your watch in going from:

Chicago to Denver	Detroit to Norfolk
El Paso to Dayton	St. Louis to Baltimore
Washington to St. Paul	Louisville to Reno
Seattle to Boston	Walla Walla to Miami
Tampa to Cheyenne	New Orleans to New York
Atlanta to Cleveland	Madison to Pasadena

5. What does a child mean when he says it is five minutes after half past four? Can you express this time in two other ways?

6. Show that the table of liquid measure from gills to quarts follows a binary system.

7. Discuss the significance of "The International Date Line."

8. How much time has elapsed from 10:34 A.M. on Monday to 5:13 P.M. on Friday of the same week?

9. Draw a number line which begins with the birth of Christ and extends to the present. Show the following on the line:

   Discovery of America

   The close of the Civil War

   The signing of the Declaration of Independence

   The middle of the Fourth Century A.D.

   Your birthday

10. Estimate the size (in some other unit of measure) of one pound of each of the following:

potato chips	writing paper	wood	water
bread	sawdust	sponge	pennies
light bulbs	cotton	pencils	iron

11. Draw several straight lines on the margin of your worksheet and then estimate their lengths in inches. Measure them to determine your ability to estimate distance.

12. How many days have elapsed from March 11, 1955, to July 3, 1957?

13. Find the length of a line (in meters) if it measures 2 hectometers, 7 decameters, 9 meters. Find the length of a line in meters if it measures 2 decimeters, 7 centimeters, 8 millimeters. Find the combined lengths of the two lines.

14. Change the following units to grams:

3 kilograms	17 centigrams	3.4 decigrams
4 decagrams	300 milligrams	100.2 hectograms

15. The length of a chain is 7.38 meters. Express this measurement in decameters, in millimeters, and then in decimeters.

16. The measurements of a room are 12 feet by 15 feet. Express these measurements in meters. The measurements of another room are 7 meters by 8 meters. Express these measurements in feet.

17. Select the larger of the two measurements:

3 yards or 3 meters	1 kilogram or $2\frac{1}{4}$ pounds
5 feet or 2 meters	3 quarts or 4 liters
5 meters or 200 inches	5 miles or 7 kilometers

18. Express your age in total number of days.

9.4 Addition and Subtraction with Denominate Numbers

When measurements of the same kind are added, the sum should represent the same kind of measurement. When hours are added to hours the sum should be hours, and when minutes are added to minutes the sum should be expressed in minutes. However, after the sum has been obtained, or before, for that matter, the measurement can be expressed in some other form. If the sum of two addends is 48 hours this can be expressed conveniently as days or as minutes. The sum of two or more addends expressed as inches could be expressed in feet, yards, rods, or metric units as one's fancy dictates. Usually when measurements are given in unlike units (of the same kind of measurement) they are all equated to the same unit. Thus the sum of three measurements given as 2 yards, 2 feet, and 9 inches can be expressed in one of several ways. The sum is 2 yd. + 2 ft. + 9 in. or 2 × 36 in. + 2 × 12 in. + 9 in. for a total of 93 inches or expressed in feet as 2 × 3 ft. + 2 ft. + ¾ ft. for a total 8¾ ft. or expressed in yards as 2 yd. + ⅔ yd. + ¼ yd. for a total of 2¹¹⁄₁₂ yards. Custom dictates that we change all the given denominations or measurements to the smallest given unit unless the demands of the problem situation suggest differently.

When two or more measurements are combined they can be added by changing them to common units of measure or they can be added as they stand and the necessary conversions made and the principle of carrying in addition applied.

Example: Combine: 2 feet 3 inches
                        1 foot 5 inches
                        1 foot 2 inches

         Solution: 2 feet 3 inches = 27 inches
                        1 foot 5 inches = 17 inches
                        1 foot 2 inches = 14 inches
                        4 feet 10 inches = 58 inches

Example: Add: 3 days 11 hr. 40 min. 40 sec.
                1 day 15 hr. 30 min. 30 sec.

Solution: (1)← ‒ ┐ (1)← ┐ (1)← ‒ ┐
          3 days 11 hr. 40 min. 40 sec.
          1 day 15 hr. 30 min. 30 sec.
                              7̸0̸ sec.
                        7̸1̸ min. 10 sec.
                  2̸7̸ hr. 11 min.
          5 days 3 hr.
          5 days 3 hr. 11 min. 10 sec.

The student will note that the conversions are made as the additions are performed, moving from right to left (from the lower denomination to the higher denomination). From the 70 seconds we subtract 60 seconds and convert this to 1 minute and carry it to the next higher denomination. From the 71 minutes we take 60 minutes and convert this to 1 hour and carry it to the next denomination and continue in this manner. However, it is possible to perform all the additions first and then make the necessary conversions.

Example: Add: 2 ft. 3 in.   Solution: 2 ft. 3 in.
                  1 ft. 8 in.   1 ft. 8 in.
                  1 ft. 1 in.   1 ft. 2 in.
                  _____   _____
                                                   4 ft. 13 in.

Now we change the 13 inches to 1 foot and 1 inch and combine the 1 foot with the 4 feet to make 5 feet. Now we convert the 5 feet to 1 yard and 2 feet, giving us the sum: 1 yard 2 feet 1 inch.

The process of changing all of the denominations to one common denomination might be useful in the subtraction operation. Let us subtract 2 yd. 2 ft. 11 in. from 7 yd. 1 ft. 3 in. If we change the minuend to inches we will have a total of 267 inches and if we express the subtrahend in inches we will have a total of 107 inches. The difference is 160 inches. When this amount in converted to higher units of measurement we obtain 4 yd. 1 ft. 4 in.

Perhaps the most desirable algorism is the one which makes use of the decomposition (commonly called "borrowing") method. If solved in this manner the algorism would look like this:

$$\begin{array}{r} 7 \text{ yd. } 1 \text{ ft. } \quad 3 \text{ in.} \\ - \; 2 \text{ yd. } 2 \text{ ft. } 11 \text{ in.} \\ \hline \end{array}$$

$$\begin{array}{r} \quad\quad\quad 0 \quad\quad 15 \\ 7 \text{ yd. } \cancel{1} \text{ ft. } \quad \cancel{3} \text{ in.} \\ - \; 2 \text{ yd. } 2 \text{ ft. } 11 \text{ in.} \\ \hline 4 \text{ in.} \end{array}$$

$$\begin{array}{r} \quad\quad\quad\; 3 \\ 6 \quad\;\; \cancel{0} \quad\quad 15 \\ \cancel{7} \text{ yd. } \cancel{1} \text{ ft. } \quad \cancel{3} \text{ in.} \\ - \; 2 \text{ yd. } 2 \text{ ft. } 11 \text{ in.} \\ \hline 4 \text{ yd. } 1 \text{ ft. } \quad 4 \text{ in.} \end{array}$$

The same example could also be solved by the equal-additions method, in which case the algorism would look like this:

| Add 12 inches to the minuend | 7 yd. 1 ft. 15 in. |
| and 1 foot to the subtrahend | 2 yd. 3 ft. 11 in. |

Subtract 11 in. from 15 in.

| | 4 in. |

Add 3 feet to the minuend	7 yd. 4 ft. 15 in.
and 1 yard to the subtrahend	3 yd. 3 ft. 11 in.
Subtract:	4 yd. 1 ft. 4 in.

As an exercise the student should perform this subtraction in three different ways:

$$5 \text{ lb.}$$
$$- 2 \text{ lb. } 10 \text{ oz.}$$

One of the more common everyday problems involving subtraction of denominate numbers concerns finding the difference between two given times. This problem often presents itself in the interpretation of a timetable. Should one leave a station at 2:15 and arrive at his desired destination at 5:45 he is concerned with the total amount of time which has elapsed. He wants to know how long it took for the trip. The analysis of the problem suggests that one must find the difference between the two times—one must subtract. However, it is possible to find the answer to our question through the additive approach; we might count ahead or add.

From 2:15 to 3:00 is 45 minutes
From 3:00 to 5:00 is 2 hours
From 5:00 to 5:45 is 45 minutes

By the operation of addition we determine that the amount of elapsed time is equal to the sum of 45 minutes, 2 hours, and 45 minutes for a total of 3 hours and 30 minutes. The use of a clock face or a number line will clearly reveal the thinking process of the solver in finding the answer and the use of the line and this additive process will bring out many different thought patterns of analysis.

| 45 minutes | 2 hours | 45 minutes |
| 2:15 | | 5:45 |

| 2:00 | 3:00 | 4:00 | 5:00 | 6:00 |

9.5 Multiplication and Division with Denominate Numbers

Multiplications involving denominate numbers can be performed directly or the multiplicand can be changed to a single unit of measure and then the multiplications performed.   The amount of mechanical manipulations involved will govern the selection of the procedure. Here is a problem whose solution is obtained by the use of multiplication.   Mr. Jones worked 8 hours and 15 minutes every day for 5 days. Find the total working time for the week.

Solution: 8 hr. 15 min.
                              × 5
                          ——————————
                        40 hr. 75 min. = 41 hr. 15 min.

Alternate solution: 8 hr. 15 min. = 495 minutes (8 × 60 + 15)
                                     × 5
                                  ——————————
                                 2475 minutes or 41 hr. 15 min.

In the last step of the latter solution the student is performing measurement division when he finds the number of groups of 60 minutes there are in the entire group of 2475 minutes.

Suppose a steel chain is 2 yards 1 foot and 6 inches long.   What would be the combined length of 12 steel chains?

Direct multiplication: 2 yards 1 foot 6 inches
                                   × 12
                       ——————————————————————
                        24 yards 12 feet 72 inches
Make the first conversion: 24 yards 4 yards 6 feet
Second conversion: 24 yards 4 yards 2 yards = 30 yards

Alternate solution: 2 yards 1 foot 6 inches = 90 inches
                               × 12   × 12
                    ———————————————   ——————————
                                            1080 inches = 30 yards

(Since there are 36 inches in 1 yard we divide 1080 inches by 36 inches.)

The student will probably conclude that the direct method, which might not necessitate inversion, is usually superior or at least is the more advantageous one to use.

The conversions or changes to the larger denominations can be made as one "carries" in addition or they can be made after the multiplications are completed.

Example: 1 week   4 days   9 hours
                              × 3
_____

Solution: (1)   (1)
              1 week   4 days   9 hours
                              × 3
_____
              4 weeks 13 days 27 hours
                      6 days   3 hours

Example: 2 gal.   3 qt.   1 pt.
                              × 5
_____
              10 gal. 15 qt.   5 pt.
              10 gal. 17 qt.   1 pt.   (5 pt. = 2 qt. 1 pt.)
              14 gal.   1 qt.   1 pt. (17 qt. = 4 gal. 1 qt.)

The division operation with denominate numbers can also be performed by converting the measurements to a single denomination. When the divisor is a composite denominate number it is more feasible to convert both the dividend and the divisor to the same single denomination. The reader has perhaps concluded by this time that such a division must surely represent the "measurement" aspect of division. For our illustration let us determine how many jars, each containing 1 gallon 1 quart, can be filled from a larger jar of liquid containing 8 gallons.

If both the dividend and divisor are expressed in quarts, they become 32 and 5 respectively. Then the integral quotient will be 6 (representing full jars) with 2 quarts remaining. The complete quotient is $6\frac{2}{5}$ jars.

The procedure just suggested is commonly used in ordinary business practice. When one desires to know how many neckties, at $1.25 each, he can buy with $10, he converts both number expressions to cents and divides 1000 cents by 125 cents. The quotient is 8 (ties).

If the problem represents "partitioning" division it is usually simpler to perform the operation directly. Let us find the length of each piece of ribbon if a piece 5 yards 2 feet long is divided into three pieces of the same length.

$$3 \overline{) \; 5 \text{ yards 2 feet}}$$

$$
\begin{array}{l}
\phantom{3) 5 \text{ yards }} 2 \text{ yards} \\
3 \;) \; \underline{5 \text{ yards } 2 \text{ feet}} \\
 1 \text{ yard}
\end{array}
$$
The 2 yards remaining are changed to feet (6 feet) and added to the 2 feet of the dividend.

$$
\begin{array}{l}
3 \;) \; \underline{3 \text{ yards } 8 \text{ feet}} \\
 1 \text{ yard } 2 \text{ feet}
\end{array}
$$
with 2 feet remaining.
The 2 feet remaining are changed to 24 inches.

$$
\begin{array}{l}
3 \;) \; \underline{3 \text{ yards } 6 \text{ feet } 24 \text{ inches}} \\
 1 \text{ yard } 2 \text{ feet } 8 \text{ inches}
\end{array}
$$

The length of each piece will be 1 yard 2 feet 8 inches.

The same problem can be solved by first converting all the units to inches and then performing the division. Then the conversions can be made back again to higher denominations.

$$5 \text{ yards 2 feet} = 5 \times 36 \text{ inches} + 2 \times 12 \text{ inches}$$
$$= 180 \text{ inches} + 24 \text{ inches} = 204 \text{ inches.}$$

$$204 \text{ inches} \div 3 = 68 \text{ inches}$$
$$68 \text{ inches} = 5 \text{ feet 8 inches}$$
$$5 \text{ feet 8 inches} = 1 \text{ yard 2 feet 8 inches.}$$

9.6   Errors in Measurement

Measured numbers represent a class of numbers by themselves for they are or represent approximations. The written numbers are exact but the measurements they represent are only approximate. If the distance between two points is expressed as 8 inches the mathematician assumes that the unit of measurement is 1 inch, and that the total distance is nearer 8 inches than 6, 7, 9, or 10 inches. The true measurement is a value equal to or greater than 7.5 inches but less than 8.5 inches.

```
 .     .     .     .     .     .     .     . ↓  . ↓   .     .
 0     1     2     3     4     5     6     7    8     9     10
```

Measured numbers are always expressed in some specific unit of measure and are always expressed to the nearest integral number of those units.   If the unit is feet, then a measurement of 13 feet means a value nearer to 13 feet than to 12 feet or 14 feet.   If the unit is 100 rods then a measurement of 700 rods means a value nearer to 700 rods than to 600 or 800 rods.   If the unit is hundredths of an inch, then a measurement of .41 inches is nearer to .41 inches than to .40 inches or .42 inches—the unit one-hundredth has been measured off either 40 or 41 times.

Since the measurement is given to the nearest unit there can be no error in the measurement greater than one half-unit in either direction—one half-unit greater than the recorded numeral or one half-unit less then the recorded numeral.   Since 17 inches means a value nearer 17 than 18 inches and nearer 17 than 16 inches, its limiting values are $16\frac{1}{2}$ and $17\frac{1}{2}$.   Then a line AB which is 17 inches long has its terminating point anywhere between $16\frac{1}{2}$ and $17\frac{1}{2}$.

```
 0 1 2 3 4 5 6 7 8 9 10 11 12 13 14 15 16 17 18 19 20
───────────────────────────────────────────╫────────
 A                                           B
```

If the distance between two points A and B is recorded as 17 inches when the unit of measure is *an inch*, then the amount of allowable variability from this measure is one-half inch.   This variation is called *error* or *tolerance*.   The amount of tolerance or error should not exceed one-half of the unit of measurement in either direction.   Thus 7 tens means $6\frac{1}{2}$ up to $7\frac{1}{2}$ tens, 13 thousand means $12\frac{1}{2}$ up to $13\frac{1}{2}$ thousand, and 6 tenths means $5\frac{1}{2}$ up to $6\frac{1}{2}$ tenths.

Elsewhere in the text we have discussed the equivalence of fractions.   We showed that $\frac{2}{4}$ was equivalent to $\frac{1}{2}$ but that $\frac{2}{4}$ represents 2 units of size $\frac{1}{4}$ while $\frac{1}{2}$ represents only 1 unit of size $\frac{1}{2}$.   The former number when used as a measurement is said to be more precise.   The former has a tolerance or error no greater than $\frac{1}{2}$ the unit of measurement ($\frac{1}{2}$ of $\frac{1}{4}$) which is $\frac{1}{8}$ inch; the latter also has an error no greater than $\frac{1}{2}$ the unit of measurement ($\frac{1}{2}$ of $\frac{1}{2}$ inch) which is $\frac{1}{4}$ inch. The measurement obtained by the use of the smaller of two or more units of measurement is said to be more *precise*. Measurements in industry which must be obtained to thousandths or even ten-thousandths of a unit are made by *precision* instruments. We conclude that the finer (or smaller) the unit of measurement, the more precise will be the actual measurement. Any man whose height is recorded as 6 feet, 6 feet 0 inches, or 72 inches is a man of unknown stature. If he is a "six-footer" then his height can be assumed to be anywhere between $5\frac{1}{2}$ and $6\frac{1}{2}$ feet. If he is 6 feet 0 inches tall, his true height is assumed to be between 5 feet $11\frac{1}{2}$ inches and 6 feet $\frac{1}{2}$ inch. The latter measurement is more precise than the first, for it more nearly approaches the true value; it is the better approximation of the real height.

Civilization owes its progress to the invention of precision instruments and the most notable of these are the vernier caliper which was invented by Joseph Brown in 1851 and the gauge blocks invented by Carl Johansson in 1896. These two inventions are in a large measure responsible for the great strides made in industry, especially the automobile industry in the last half-century. In 1923 Henry Ford acquired the manufacturing rights of the Johansson Blocks and made them accessible to the whole scientific world. These blocks make it possible to perform measurements in millionths of an inch.

9.7   Relative Errors

The amount of error or tolerance in a measurement is called "absolute error," and the ratio of the apparent error to the approximate measurement is known as the *relative error*. The relative error can be expressed either in common or decimal fraction form or in per cent. When the latter form is used we speak of "per cent of error."

If the weight of a metal block is recorded as 25 pounds, we know that:
    25 pounds is an approximation of the true weight.
    The unit of measurement is 1 pound.
    The amount of tolerance or absolute error is $\frac{1}{2}$ pound.
    The true weight varies between $25 - \frac{1}{2}$ lb. and $25 + \frac{1}{2}$ lb.
    The relative error is the ratio of $\frac{1}{2}$ to 25 or 1 to 50.
    The per cent of error is 2%.

If the airline distance between 2 cities is recorded as 800 miles, then:
800 miles is an approximation of the true mileage.
The unit of measurement is 100 miles.
The amount of tolerance or absolute error is 50 miles.
The true mileage is more than 750 miles but is less than 850 miles.
The relative error is $\frac{50}{800}$ or 1 to 16.
The per cent of error is $6\frac{1}{4}\%$.

If the distance between the same 2 cities is expressed as 820 miles, then:
820 miles is an approximation of the true mileage.
The unit of measurement is 10 miles.
The amount of tolerance or absolute error is 5 miles.
The true mileage is more than 815 miles but less than 825 miles.
The relative error is $\frac{5}{820}$ or 1 to 164.
The per cent of error is $.6\%$.

Since the latter measurement is expressed in a smaller unit of measurement (10 miles versus 100 miles) it is more precise, and since its per cent of error is smaller the measurement is also more accurate.

Measurement	Unit of measurement	Equal to or greater than	Less than	Tolerance or error
46 lb.	1 lb.	$45\frac{1}{2}$	$46\frac{1}{2}$	$\pm \frac{1}{2}$ lb.
.17 ft.	.01 ft.	.165	.175	$\pm$ .005 ft.
72.3 yd.	.1 yd.	72.25	72.35	$\pm$ .05 yd.
9000 ft.	1000 ft.	8500	9500	$\pm$ 500 ft.
730 mi.	10 mi.	725	735	$\pm$ 5 mi.
.004 in.	.001 in.	.0035	.0045	$\pm$ .0005 in.
2600 rods	100 rods	2550	2650	$\pm$ 50 rods

If there should be any doubt as to the degree of precision in a measured number it can be dispelled by the use of a verbal explanation. If one wished to show that the length of AB is 70 inches correct to the nearest whole inch then it could be so indicated in writing. Length of $AB = 70$ inches (to the nearest inch) or length of $AB = 70$ inches (unit of measurement is 1 inch).

In the same manner we show that a weight of 150 pounds means a value between $149\frac{1}{2}$ and $150\frac{1}{2}$ pounds. To do this we represent the approximate values as 150 pounds (to the nearest pound) or 150 pounds (unit of measurement is 1 pound).

A second way of expressing precision is to append the amount of tolerance to the recorded measurement. Should the length of *BC* be recorded as 80 inches when measured to the nearest inch the error would be $\frac{1}{2}$ inch. We would write the length of *BC* as 80 inches $\pm \frac{1}{2}$ inch. If we meant that the true value lies somewhere between 70 and 90 inches but nearer to 80 inches than to either of these other two measurements, then the unit of measurement is 10 inches and the absolute error is 5 inches ($\frac{1}{2}$ of 10). Then the length of *BC* = 80 inches $\pm$ 5 inches.

When the amount of tolerance is stated we are able to determine the unit of measurement and the accuracy. A measured value of 5000 $\pm$ 50 miles is expressed to the nearest hundred miles (the unit of measurement is twice the absolute error) and a value of .6 feet $\pm$ .005 feet is expressed to the nearest hundredth of a foot. A distance of 70,000 feet $\pm$ 500 feet is expressed to the nearest 1000 feet—the real value lies between 69,500 feet and 71,500 feet. How precise is a measurement expressed as 5000° $\pm$ 5°? Though very little work of this kind will be presented to children of the elementary schools, teachers should be cognizant of this concept and gradually make children aware of the fact that measured numbers (measurements) are indefinite or inexact. Any attention given to this topic will truly serve as readiness for the topic in later classes.

9.8   Significance

The preceding discussion leads us to an understanding of *significant digits*. We have seen in the number 700, if the unit is hundred, that the 7 is the only measured or counted number, but if the measurement represents 70 tens then the zero is a measured number and has some significance. If the 700 represents exactly 700 ones or units then both of the zeros are significant. If a number (a digit) is a measured or a counted number, then that number is said to be significant. If the number of units counted can be represented by all non-zero numerals, then every one of them is a measured number and is significant. The number expressions 41 units, 2.3 units, .67 units, .081 units, and .0056 units all contain two significant figures. They represent 41 ones, 23 tenths, 67 hundredths, 81 thousandths, and 56 ten-thousandths respectively. Likewise, the number expressions (all representing inches) 234, 24.1, 3.62, .578, and .0823 all contain three significant digits—all the non-zero numerals are significant.

The zero plays a very interesting and yet confusing role in the realm of significant numbers. It can be treated both as a number (a counting number representing quantity) or it can be interpreted as a place holder indicating that the number of units in that place was not determined.   In the numbers above in which the zero appears it is definitely a place holder and is not significant.   It indicates that there are no whole tenths in the number .073 and at the same time fills the tenths place.   The unit of measurement is one-thousandth and was measured off 73 times.   Then we conclude that when zeros appear between the decimal point and the first non-zero number in a pure decimal number, then those zeros are not significant.   In the numerals .003, .05886, .0004, and .000456 the zeros which prefix the non-zero digits are not significant.

Zeros written internally are significant digits for they represent counted numbers.   The number expression 405 indicates that there are 4 groups of 100, 0 groups of 10, and 5 single items.   In the number 6009 there are 4 significant digits, the internal zeros indicating the number of hundreds and tens respectively.   In the number .904 the internal zero is significant for it tells us that there are no complete hundredths in the composition of the given number.   The unit of measurement is one-thousandth, and we counted 9 hundreds, 0 tens, and 4 ones of them.   Internal zeros are significant.

Terminal zeros of integral numbers may or may not be significant depending upon the degree of measurement.   At first glance the terminal zeros in the number 6000 are not significant, but if we learn that the unit of measurement is 10 then the first two zeros are significant—there are zero hundreds and zero tens in the number which has a total of three significant places.   The accuracy of integral numerals governs the number of significant places in such numbers.

If a decimal number ends in zero, then this terminal zero (or terminal zeros) indicates that the measurement has been taken to that place and is significant.   In the number expression, 8.0 feet, we know that the number of tenths of a foot has been determined, hence the 0 is significant.   In the measurement .600 we know that the measurement was taken to the thousandths place and that the two zeros are significant.   There are (6 hundreds + 0 tens + 0 ones) exactly 600 one-thousandths.   Thus terminal zeros in decimal numerals are significant.

The numerals 405   5.00   113 .00567 have 3 significant places
The numerals   45   .37   .10   91000 have 2 significant places
The numerals 2349 203400 16.04 .01610 have 4 significant places
The numerals 5000   .0001   .7   700000 have 1 significant place.

9.9 Computations with Approximate Numbers

Pupils in the elementary grades are being asked to perform the addition of long columns of irregular decimal fractions (or *ragged decimals* as they are called) with little or no attention having been given to the mathematical accuracy of such a performance. The justification for such examples lies in the practice they provide for copying addends so as to align properly the respective place values. Addition examples of this type seldom occur in real life situations. Since decimal fractions usually represent measurements, then the addends should all be of the same kind. If a measurement of a line is ascertained to be 5.6 inches long, then measurements of other lines should be made with the same instrument. It's foolish to measure the next one in hundredths of inches, such as 6.74 inches, for if it can be measured with this precision then the former measurement should have been made to the same degree. Thus all measurements should be made to the same number of decimal places; then it will be unnecessary for students to resort to the unsound practice of inserting zeros or annexing zeros to the right of the non-zero digits in decimal fractions.

Before decimal fractions are added, subtracted, or compared, they should first all be expressed in the same kind of measurement. If some measurements have been made which are more precise than others, these should be rounded off so as to agree with the least precise of the given measurements. Thus, if we were to add the two lengths above, we would round off the 6.74 inches to 6.7 inches before we combine it with 5.6 inches. Now both measurements are expressed in tenths and the sum is correct to tenths.

The example:	Correct solution:	Incorrect solution:
5.6 in.	5.6 in.	5.60 in.
+ 6.74 in.	+ 6.7 in.	+ 6.74 in.
	12.3 in.	12.34 in.

The sum of two or more measured numbers cannot be of greater precision than the least precise of the addends. If one of several addends is expressed correct only to tenths, then one should not attempt to express a sum, including that addend, in thousandths.

Let us elaborate on this principle. Let us suppose one measurement is 4.2 inches and another is 3.36 inches. We remember that the absolute error of the first one is ± .05 inches while the absolute error of the second measurement is ± .005. From this information we conclude that the 2 in 4.2 is an uncertain numeral. When these two values are added we are sure that all values obtained for places to the right of the tenths place will also be uncertain.

$$\begin{array}{r} 4.2 \text{ in.} \\ + \ 3.36 \text{ in.} \\ \hline 7.56 \text{ in.} \end{array}$$

└─is an uncertain number; therefore all values
to the right of this place will also be uncertain.

4.2 in. represents a value between 4.15 in. and 4.25 in.
3.36 in. represents a value between 3.355 in. and 3.365 in.
Then the sum must represent a value between 7.505 in. and 7.605 in.

If we round off all measurements to tenths the solution becomes

$$\begin{array}{r} 4.2 \text{ in.} \\ + \ 3.4 \text{ in.} \\ \hline 7.6 \text{ in.} \end{array}$$

Thus it appears that 7.6 in. is the best estimate for the sum of the two values and we find that this amount is a value between 7.505 inches and 7.604 inches.

If we wish to combine a measurement of 17.28 feet with 14.171 feet we round off all measurements to the same place value.

$$\begin{array}{r} 17.28 \text{ feet} \\ + \ 14.17 \text{ feet} \\ \hline 34.45 \text{ feet} \end{array}$$

Now if we find the minimum and maximum values for this sum we find

$$\begin{array}{r} 17.275 \\ + \ 14.1705 \\ \hline 31.4455 \end{array}$$

for the minimum and

$$\begin{array}{r} 17.284 \\ + \ 14.1714 \\ \hline 31.4554 \end{array}$$

for the maximum with the true value 31.45 somewhere between these.

There is an alternate practice, highly recommended, which suggests the rounded-off numbers should carry one more digit than the addend which is the least precise.   Then when the additions and subtractions have been performed, the results should be rounded off so as to have the same number of decimal places as the number which is least precise.

Example: 4.6   in.   Solution: 4.6   in.
               3.72 in.   3.72 in.
            + 5.374 in.   + 5.37 in.
            _____   _____
                                           13.69 in. or 13.7 in.

General principles:

1. When adding or subtracting approximate numbers, round off all numbers to the same place value or retain one more place than the numeral which is least precise.

2. The result can be no more precise than the least precise measure used.

3. The absolute error is at least as great as the greatest error among the measures used.

When adding or subtracting approximate numbers we are concerned with the precision of each measure involved.   In multiplication and division we are concerned with the accuracy or the relative errors of the numbers used.   The relative error of any product or quotient is at least as great as the greatest relative error in any one of the measures used in the operation.   In other words, it is safe to say that computations involving multiplication and division are concerned with the number of significant digits contained in the separate measures.   If we multiply a number of two significant digits by another containing two significant digits we can expect a product correct only to two significant digits.   The product of $2.1 \times 2.3 = 4.8$.

If we multiply a number containing two significant digits by a number containing three significant digits, the product is not correct beyond two significant figures. Thus $3.3 \times 70.2 = 230$. (The product 231.66 is rounded off to two significant figures.) The product of two or more approximate numbers never contains more significant figures than the measure which has the least number of significant figures.

Thus 2.1 × .36 × .1136 will have only two significant figures in the product.

Multiply: 4.2 (correct to tenths)
          × 3.2 (correct to tenths)
          ──────
           8 4
         1 2 6
          ──────
         1 3.4 4 If corrected to tenths becomes 13.4.
                  If corrected to two significant places becomes 13.
                  If expressed one place beyond degree of accuracy becomes 13.4.

Multiply: .1 2 (2 significant figures)
          × .1 3 (2 significant figures)
          ──────
           3 6
         1 2
          ──────
         .0 1 5 6 If corrected to hundredths becomes .02.
                   If corrected to two significant figures becomes .016.
                   If corrected one place beyond degree of accuracy becomes .0156.

Multiply: .2 4 6°   (Numbers marked ° are uncertain
          × .3 1 5° numbers)
          ──────────
         1 2°3°0°   All numerals to the right of the thousandths
         2 4°6°   place in the product are uncertain numer-
         7 3 8°   als. Hence the product cannot be correct
          ──────────
         .0 7 7 4°9°0° beyond the thousandths place though
         .0 7 7 5   common practice permits one place
                        beyond the degree of accuracy.

The student should perform the following multiplication according to the above pattern and suggestions:

          .784
        × .523
        ────────

A quotient of two approximate numbers does not contain more significant figures than the measure in the example which has the least number of significant figures. If a number of three significant figures is divided by a number containing two significant figures, the quotient should contain no more than two significant figures. The quotient cannot be more correct that the least correct measure involved in the operation. Another way to express this principle is to say that the relative error in the quotient is at least as great as the greatest relative error in the measures involved. Thus $16.16 \div 8.11$ should have only three significant figures in the quotient and $.8456 \div .24$ should have only two significant figures in the quotient.

Sometimes the computer rounds off one number so that it has no more than one extra significant figure than the factor having the least accuracy. Then the division is performed so as to obtain a quotient having as many significant digits as contained in the term having the least accuracy.

When dividing .793 by .61 we can either round off the dividend to hundredths (so as to conform in accuracy with the least accurate measure) or we can perform the division directly carrying the operation until we obtain a number of two significant figures in the quotient.

$$
\begin{array}{r}
1.3 \\
.61 \overline{\smash{)}\ .793} \\
61 \\
\hline
183 \\
183
\end{array}
$$
The quotient will not be correct beyond two significant figures.

If we round off the dividend to two significant figures before performing the division we will obtain a quotient of $1.29+$ and when this is expressed to two significant figures it becomes 1.3.

In the division example, $1.4864 \div 4.5$, there will be no accuracy beyond two significant figures; the quotient will be .33. The following division examples would have quotients correct only to two significant figures:

$$3200 \div .15 \qquad .48 \div .1235 \qquad .755 \div .81$$

EXERCISES

SET 32

1. What is the total weight of two dozen candy bars if each bar weighs $1\frac{3}{4}$ oz?
2. Find the combined weight of three packages of frozen meat if they weigh respectively 8 lb. 7 oz., 6 lb. 5 oz., and 9 lb. 11 oz.

3. A roll of wire is 20 rods long. If I cut off 8 pieces, each 10 yards 2 feet 8 inches long, how much wire will be left on the roll?

4. Combine: 5 gal. 2 qt. 1 pt.
           2 gal. 1 qt. 1 pt.
           2 gal. 3 qt. 1 pt.

5. From twice the sum of 3 months 2 weeks 3 days subtract one-half of 2 months 3 weeks 4 days.

6. Subtract (a) 5 yd. 3 ft. 8 in.   (b) 2 miles
            2 yd. 2 ft. 10 in.   1 mile 400 yd. 2 ft.

7. Convert the following to square inches:
    (a) 21 sq. yd.   (b) 1 sq. rd.   (c) 2 sq. yd. + 2 sq. ft.

8. Divide a rope 25 yards long into 4 pieces of the same length. What would be the combined length of 3 of those pieces? Would 7 pieces of rope be longer than 50 yards?

9. How many packages of black pepper each containing $2\frac{3}{4}$ oz. can be packaged from one pound of pepper?

10. Copy and complete this table:

Measurement	error	maximum value	relative error	% of error
.45 in. 12 ft. 5000 lb.				

11. Perform the indicated operations paying special attention to significant digits.
    (a) .62 ft. + .381 ft. + .766 ft.   (e) 15.1 oz. + 16.1 oz. + 17.1 oz.
    (b) 23 yd. − 16.8 yd.   + 18 oz.
    (c) 43.2 gal. − 18.92 gal.   (f) 260 ft. + 380 ft. + 146.8 ft.
    (d) (2800 lb. ± 5 lb.) − 1762 lb.

12. Find the areas of the following rectangles:
    (a) 14.6 in. × 12.22 in.   (d) 1.003 in. × 1.2 in.
    (b) 48.25 in. × 40.3 in.   (e) 30.5 in. × 40.5 in.
    (c) .027 in. × .037 in.   (f) .355 in. × .25 in.

13. If the area of a rectangle is 42 sq. in. and its length is 7.8 in., find the width.
    If A = 167.8 sq. in. and L = 11.8 in., find width.
    If A = 75.40 sq. in. and L = 15.20 in., find width.
    If A = 96.4 sq. in. and L = 9.2 in., find width.

14. Write a story problem to fit this algorism: 29.6 feet ÷ 4.3 feet.

15. Show that the sum of .4 + .3 + 1.2 can vary between 1.75 and 2.05.

16. Multiply .346 by .239 and put a circle around every uncertain number in the partial products and the final product.

17. Explain the difference in meaning between 4.1 inches and 4.100 inches.
    Explain the difference in meaning between .3½ feet and .35 feet.
    Explain the difference in meaning between ¼ yard and .25 yards.
18. Divide (*a*) .827 by .17 (*b*) .40 by .12
19. Multiply .68 by .44 and then divide the product by .15.
20. Explain why .82 ÷ .82 = 1.0

CHAPTER 10

AN INTRODUCTION TO STATISTICS

10.1 Constants and Variables

There are numerous classifications of number, many of which have already been mentioned in this text. There is a kind of number which is always the same and another kind of number which has or takes on different values. Numbers whose values are always the same are called *constants* and those which change are referred to as *variables*. Numbers which are always the same, like the number of stars in the Big Dipper, the number of eggs in a dozen, the number of miles in a kilometer, the square root of 25, etc., are constants, while numbers which represent changing amounts, such as the cost of sending parcel-post packages, the volume of a metal ball-bearing which changes with temperature changes, the total distance traveled in one day by automobile, and the number of calories needed by a working man, are illustrations of variables.

If two numbers are so related that a value assigned to one of them produces only one value for the other, then the second number is a function of the first. In other words, a function suggests a correspondence between two variables x and y. For every value of x there is one value of y. Both x and y are variables for they are quantities which change. The first value, because it depends on the second number, is called the dependent variable, while the second number, which may take on an unrestricted set of values, is the independent value. Since the area of a square is equal in square units to the square of the linear dimensions, the number of units of area represents a dependent variable. The number of units in the side of the square is an independent variable. Likewise, the perimeter of a square is equal to the length of one side multiplied by 4. Thus the perimeter equals 4 times the side. The number 4 is a constant and the number of units in the perimeter and the side are variables and the perimeter is a function of the side.

$$p = 4s$$

If any change in the independent variable results in the same kind of change in the dependent variable, we say that the relationship is a direct one or that the dependent variable is directly proportional to the other variable.   In the foregoing illustrations we know that if the side of the square increases then the perimeter and the area will both increase and if the side decreases then the perimeter and area will both decrease.   These are examples of direct variation.   However, if one variable of a relationship increases while the other decreases, or vice versa, then we have an illustration of indirect or inverse variation. In driving a given distance to school each morning a student increases his driving speed in miles per hour.   This will automatically decrease the time necessary for the trip.   We know that the volume of a gas depends upon the pressure exerted upon it.   If we increase the pressure then we automatically decrease the volume.   The intensity of light on the printed page is increased if we reduce the distance from the source of the light.   Students will probably agree that their academic success in college is inversely proportional to the number of hours spent in the Student Center.   A decrease in the latter variable should show an increase in one's academic achievement, though not necessarily.

10.2   Four Ways to Show Relationships

There are four ways to show the relationship between two variables, namely, (1) by word statement, (2) by formula, (3) by table, and (4) by graph.   Quite frequently the representations in the table and the graphical form are more illuminating and more dramatic and are to be preferred over the other two.   To illustrate these four presentations we will use the relationship which exists between the three variables, distance, rate, and time.

Mr. Jones is driving his automobile at the constant speed of 45 miles per hour.

1. The total distance traveled at the rate of 45 miles per hour is equal to 45 miles multiplied by the number of hours.

2. $D = 45t$ (distance is in miles, time is in hours)

3.

If $t =$	1	2	3	5		10		30	
then $D =$	45	90	135	225		450		1350	

4.

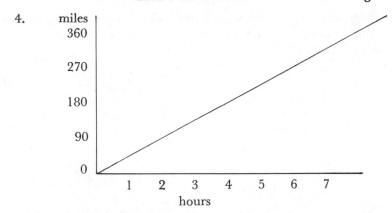

Any problem involving the given information can be solved through either of the four approaches. Suppose we want to find the total distance traveled in 5 hours. From (1) and (2) we multiply 45 miles by 5 to obtain 225 miles. From (3) we read the total distance from the pair of ordered values $t = 5$, $D = 225$ and from (4) we read to the 5 on the base line, then up to the line graph and across to the corresponding number on the miles scale, 225 miles. Should we want to know the distance covered in $3\frac{1}{2}$ hours we read to the $3\frac{1}{2}$ on the base line, up to the graph line, then across to the vertical miles scale. Here we find a total of $157\frac{1}{2}$ miles (if the scale is graduated for such accurate readings).

10.3 Kinds of Graphs

The simplest type of graph to make and to understand is the circle or pie graph. This type of picture represents the whole of anything (100%) with one whole circle. Then if we want to show parts of the whole we divide it accordingly. Should we want to show that in the 24-hour day we sleep 8 hours, work 8 hours, and use 8 hours for miscellaneous activities, we draw a circle and divide it into three equal parts. Since there are 360 degrees in the circle, we can easily, by the use of the protractor, divide the circle into three equal parts, each part containing 120 degrees of arc. Should we wish to show that one's yearly income is divided into 25% for rent, 30% for food, 15% for clothing, 10% for education, and 20% for savings and miscellaneous items we can show this with the help of a circle graph. We take the respective per cents of 360 degrees and ascertain the size of the arc or the central angle to represent that portion of the circle. Thus 10% of one's income is represented by an arc or a central angle of 36 degrees.

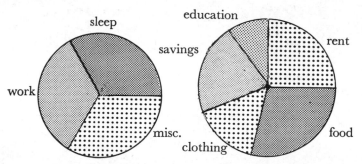

DIVISIONS OF THE 24-HOUR DAY   HOW THE YEARLY INCOME IS SPENT

The bar graph is made up of a series of bars whose lengths should be proportional to the given data. Thus if we wish to show enrollments in classes in mathematics as 20, 30, 25, 40, and 40 students we will draw bars representing that many units of length. The last two bars will be twice the length of the short one and $1\frac{1}{3}$ times the length of the second bar. The bars can be drawn either horizontally or vertically, and for an attractive appearance there should be a space separating them equal in width to the bars themselves.

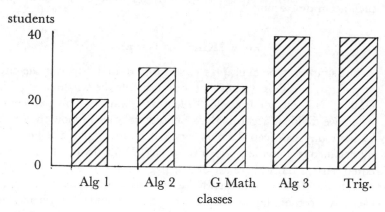

ENROLLMENTS IN MATHEMATICS CLASSES AT CENTRAL HIGH SCHOOL

If the bars of a graph are drawn only in the imagination and dots are used to represent the highest point of the bars and then joined together with a set of straight lines, the bar graph becomes a broken line graph.

The straight line graph is used to show the constant or proportional relationship between two variables such as the total cost of a number of items at a given price per unit. A typical problem might concern the cost of bread at 22 cents per loaf. The price is directly proportional to the cost of the bread, and this relationship will be expressed graphically in the form of a straight line, one with a constant steepness or slope or inclination. The heights of the successive bars, if the cost of the bread is represented in bars, have the ratio of 1 to 2 to 3 to 4, etc. Now when there is a problem or relationship in which the heights are not in this ratio, the straight line becomes a broken line. The several marks a student receives in his examinations should be represented in the form of a broken line graph, for the heights probably do not form a constant ratio. If one received the following marks in his examinations: History 88%, English 82%, Biology 78%, Spanish 86%, and Mathematics 90%, the picture representation might take the following form:

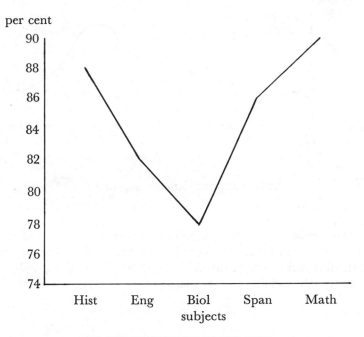

EXAMINATION MARKS IN PER CENT

The curved line is used to represent data which make gradual rather than abrupt changes in passing from one value to another. One of the best illustrations of this type of information is that of the temperature readings for various times of the day. When the temperature falls from 56 to 55 we know that it must pass through all possible values between 56 and 55, so we represent this type of continuous data with a curved line to distinguish it from the exact data. When one's weight changes from 178 pounds on January 1 to 182 pounds on February 1, we know that it is absolutely necessary that the weight pass all values between these given values. The use of the curve suggests fluctuations or changes between these two points It is conceivable that the individual might weigh 176 pounds or even 184 pounds at some time between the two given dates. The curved line is used to depict continuous or flowing data. The graph below shows the temperature readings for June 17 taken every two hours beginning at midnight.

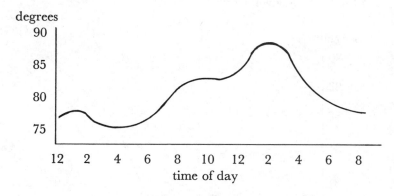

TEMPERATURE READINGS ON JUNE 17

There are several other types of graphs with which the student of the social sciences has an acquaintance but which deserve only mentioning here; namely, the belt graph, the distribution graph, the picture graph, and the weather map.

EXERCISES

SET 33

1. Draw a broken line graph to show the number of square miles in the areas of the five Great Lakes.

2. Draw a bar graph showing the number of games won (for any one season) by the baseball teams of the two major leagues. Put these data in the same graph showing the number of games won by the first-place team, second-place team, and so on. Use different colors to represent two different leagues.

3. Make a circle graph showing costs of your various textbooks purchased this semester, with respect to the total cost of textbooks.

4. Select from the daily newspaper the morning temperature readings in 10 different cities in the United States and show this information by means of a broken line graph.

5. Select four different (and perhaps unusual) graphs from the daily newspaper or from current magazines and mount them collectively.

6. Graph the following data:

   Time of day   5   6   7   8   9 10 11 12   1   2   3   4   5   6   7   8   9
   Temperature   31 33 36 37 40 45 46 46 49 50 53 47 43 41 41 40 38

   Determine the following from the graph:
   - (a) What was the temperature at 10:30?
   - (b) What was the temperature at 5:30?
   - (c) When was the temperature 42 degrees?
   - (d) When was the temperature 45 degrees?
   - (e) At what time did the temperature change the fastest?

7. Make a table of squares for the integers from 0 to 10.
   Graph these values plotting the integers along the base line.
   From the graph determine the square of 7.5 and the square root of 75.

8. The reading on a Fahrenheit thermometer is 32 degrees more than $\frac{9}{5}$ of the corresponding temperature on the Centigrade scale. Express this relationship as a formula, by a table, and by a graph.

9. The cost (C) in dollars of publishing a small booklet will depend upon the number (N) to be printed, as shown in the table:

N	1000	2000	3000	4000
C	160	180	200	220

   Express this relationship both in words and by formula.

10. The table below shows the enrollment and the number of faculty at the leading Presbyterian theological seminaries in the United States. Make a bar graph to show these data using only a single bar for each school.

Seminary	Total enrollment	Number of faculty
Princeton	480	40
Western	128	16
McCormick	278	34
Dubuque	114	10
Louisville	167	13
San Francisco	292	27

10.4 Classification of Data

It has been pointed out elsewhere in this text that there are two kinds of numbers, namely, approximate and exact. In the field of statistics these classifications are often referred to as continuous and discontinuous. Most of the traits which we measure in the scientific field are thought of as forming a continuous series. Even though the measures are given as integral values we shall assume that all values within the neighborhood are possible values. Thus when a man says that he weighs something in the neighborhood of 175 pounds, perhaps his true weight is between 174.5 pounds and 175.5 pounds. Though one's score on a test is given as 47 points we assume that scores of 46.5 and 47.5 are just as likely. The statistician assumes that all data are continuous.

Data which are not classified but are listed in the order of their occurrence are referred to as *ungrouped* data but when classified in some way either in table or graphical form they are said to be *grouped* data. Since the science of statistics deals with the collection, organization, and interpretation of data, one can readily see the advantages of grouping measures when the number of items reaches 20 or more.

Whenever there is a large number of observations to be considered it is convenient to group the data in a frequency table or a frequency distribution table as it is frequently called. Let us assume for illustrative purposes the following IQ scores of 41 sixth-grade children.

```
111  116  118  123  104  113   98  131  117  115
114  120  120  116  119  106  100  106  109  117
127  125  134  108  112  121  123  124  104  108
115  118  101  129  113  115  107  117  126  114  103
```

Our first problem is to determine the number of classes or groups into which the scores should be classified. One should not use too many nor too few groups; the general pattern of the distribution should not be obscured. There ought to be approximately 9 or 10 classes in order to give some degree of soundness to the computations which are to be based thereon. An examination of the given scores reveals that the lowest one is 98 and the highest one is 134; then the range is from 98 to 134 for a total of 36 points. If we organize these scores into about 10 classes, each class will have a range of 4 points. Let us begin by selecting for our lowest class the group of scores including 97, 98, 99, and 100. Thus the width of the class is 4 and the limits of the class are 96.5 and 100.5 with a mid-mark (the average of the limits) of 98.5. The second class will contain all the scores from 101 to 104 inclusive with limits of 100.5 and 104.5, or a middle score of 102.5, the average of the limits. If the width of a class had been chosen as an odd number, then the mid-mark would have been an integer. A class of scores containing 97, 98, 99, 100 and 101 would have a mid-mark of 99. Now the next step is to determine the number of scores which fall into the various classes or intervals. This is done by tallying the scores, one at a time, from the original set of scores in the order in which they have been listed. The 111 is tallied first, then 116, and so on. When the tallying has been completed then the totals for each class are determined and entered in the frequency column. It is then that the scores have been grouped into a frequency distribution table.

Class scores	Real limits	Mid-mark	Tally	Frequency
133–136	132.5–136.5	134.5	1	1
129–132	128.5–132.5	130.5	11	2
125–128	124.5–128.5	126.5	111	3
121–124	120.5–124.5	122.5	1111	4
117–120	116.5–120.5	118.5	1H1 111	8
113–116	112.5–116.5	114.5	1H1 1111	9
109–112	108.5–112.5	110.5	111	3
105–108	104.5–108.5	106.5	1H1	5
101–104	100.5–104.5	102.5	1111	4
97–100	96.5–100.5	98.5	11	2

$$N = 41$$

10.5 Measures of Central Tendency

Usually the first step in the analysis of a set of scores is to find some one score which is representative of all the scores. This number is called the average or mean score.   Such a number is the score which, if assigned to every member of the group, would result in the same total score.   The average score of 80 made on three tests is the score which, if obtained on each of the tests, would give a total of 240 points (maybe 70, 80, and 90) which is equivalent to an average score of 80. The golfer who scores a 72 total for 18 holes averages 4 strokes per hole but the chances are pretty high that he didn't shoot all fours. The average is obtained by dividing the sum of the scores by the number of scores.

$$\text{Average} = \frac{\text{sum of scores}}{\text{number of scores}}$$

When the raw data have been classified and grouped in a table the identity of the individual scores has been lost.   If there are several scores grouped within the interval (or even if there is but one score) the statistician assumes that all the scores lie either at the mid-point of the interval or are evenly spaced within the interval.   It is more convenient to assume the former.   Thus the single score in the upper bracket of the previous table has a value of 134.5, the two scores in the next interval are assumed to be 130.5, the next three scores are each 126.5, etc.   Then to find the total of all the scores, from the frequency table, we proceed as follows:

1 × 134.5	134.5
2 × 130.5	261.0
3 × 126.5	379.5
4 × 122.5	490.0
8 × 118.5	948.0
9 × 114.5	1030.5
3 × 110.5	331.5
5 × 106.5	532.5
4 × 102.5	410.0
2 × 98.5	197.0
Sum	4714.5

The mid-score is multiplied by the number of frequencies and then these products are added.   This grand total is then divided by the number of scores, (4714.5 ÷ 41).   This computation produces a value of 115.0, called the *mean*, which is a measure representative of the entire group.   It is referred to as a measure of central tendency.

There are many short cuts for finding the mean or average.   One of the most common methods is to assume some number for the mean and then average the differences from the assumed mean. This average is added to the mean. If we wish to find the mean of three scores: 80, 84, and 85, we assume a mean of 80. The differences from the assumed mean (0, 4, and 5) give an average of 3. Thus the true mean is 80 + 3 or 83. Should we have assumed a mean of 84, then the average of the differences (-4, 0, and 1) would result in a value of -1 (we assumed a mean greater than the true mean) which when combined with the assumed mean of 84 would result in the true mean of 83. We usually assume a mean somewhere near the true mean so as to simplify the computations knowing full well that such a choice will introduce negative numbers into the computations. The application of this method to a frequency distribution of scores is left to the student of statistics.

The *median* is another useful measure of central tendency. It represents a score which is a middle score, or a score such that half of the elements are equal to or greater than it and half of the elements are equal to or less than it. In common practice we say that the median is the mid-score of the entire group. In a set of 41 scores we arrange them from the highest to the lowest (we rank them) and find the twenty-first score. This score represents the median of the group, for half of the scores will be equal to or greater than this number and the other half will be equal to or less than the number. If we examine the preceding distribution table for its median we find that there are 14 scores whose values are less than 112.5. To find the twenty-first score we must count ahead 7 more scores. There are 9 scores in the next interval. We assume that these 9 scores are evenly spaced throughout the interval and we count to the seventh score in the interval. We want the seventh of the 9 scores—we move into the interval $\frac{7}{9}$ of the total distance. Since the total distance is 4, then $\frac{7}{9}$ of 4 is approximately 3. Therefore if we move 3 units into the interval whose lower limit is 112.5 we find that the seventh score in the interval is 115.5 which, since it is the twenty-first score, represents the middle score of the entire group, hence is the median.

The interval		113	114	115	116	
The scores in the interval	x	x x	x x	x x	x x	x
14 scores up to the interval:				(x)		
Count ahead 7 more scores				115.5		
This gives 115.5						

Thus the median of 115.5 represents a point or value such that 50 per cent of the class have scores above that point and 50 per cent have scores below that value.

A third measure which is a representative score for the entire group is called the *mode* and from a distribution table is found by inspection. The mode is simply that value or score which appears more often than any other. From the previous distribution the interval 113–116 has the greatest number of frequencies, so we select its midpoint 114.5 as the mode of the distribution. The mode is not a very useful statistic but since it can be found without computation, it is often used to state a characteristic of the group. A set of data may have one real mode, two real modes (in which case it is called bi-modal), or no mode at all.

10.6 Measures of Variation

The average measures, which are extremely valuable, do not reveal the differences within the group. Since several sets of scores might have the same mean but be different in their distributions, measures have been devised to exploit these differences and characterize the scores within the group.

The simplest of these measures of variability is the *range*, which has already been defined as the difference between the high and the low scores of a distribution. It is possible for two or more sets of scores to have the same mean but have considerably different ranges. The range of the scores merely tells us the maximum and minimum scores of the set.

A second measure of variability is the *average deviation* or the average of the deviations (without regard to direction or quality of deviation) of all the scores from the mean. Three scores of 78, 88, and 89 have a mean of 85 and deviations from the mean of -7, 3, and 4, for a total of 14 points, or an average deviation of $4\frac{2}{3}$ points. (The student might observe that the algebraic sum of the deviations from the mean is zero.)

$$\text{Average deviation} = \frac{\text{Sum of the absolute values of the deviations*}}{\text{Number of scores}}$$

The most useful and the most descriptive measure of variation is the *standard deviation* (sigma, σ). To find σ from a set of ungrouped

*The absolute value of a signed number is the number without its sign.

data we first find the mean of the group; then we find the deviations
of each score from the mean; then we square the deviations (to
eliminate the negative numbers) and find the sum of the squares.
The sum of the squares is divided by the number of scores and then the
square root of this quotient is determined. This number is the
standard deviation, σ, and represents a distance or an amount of score
such that if it is added to the mean and subtracted from the mean we
obtain two scores (or points on the scale) between which 68 per cent
of the given scores will fall. Thus if the mean of a distribution is
47 and the standard deviation is 8 then we know that 68 per cent of
the scores will lie between 39 and 55. The statisticians also tell us
that between the limits of mean $- 2\sigma$ and mean $+ 2\sigma$ about 95 per
cent of the scores will lie and that practically all the scores of a given
distribution will lie within the limits of mean $- 3\sigma$ and mean $+ 3\sigma$.
Therefore in the above example we would expect the scores to range
from 23 to 71 ($M - 3\sigma$ to $M + 3\sigma$).

TO FIND σ FROM UNGROUPED DATA

1. Find the mean of the scores.
2. Find the difference between the mean and each score.
3. Square these differences.
4. Find the sum of the squares.
5. Divide this sum by the number of scores.
6. Find the square root of this quotient.
7. This number is the standard deviation.

$$\text{Standard deviation} = \sqrt{\frac{(\text{Sum of deviations})^2}{\text{Number of scores}}}$$

Other measures of variability are the percentile points, quartile
and decile points, the semi-interquartile range—a discussion of which
can be found in a modern book on Statistics.

10.7 Graphs of Distributions

A picture representation of a set of scores can be shown either as a
broken line graph (frequency polygon), a bar graph (histogram),
or a curve. If a frequency polygon is used to present the information

it is usually closed at the upper and lower extremities, and if a histogram is used to depict the data the bars are immediately adjacent to one another resembling the skyline of any modern city.

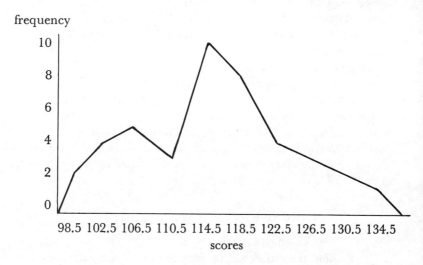

FREQUENCY POLYGON

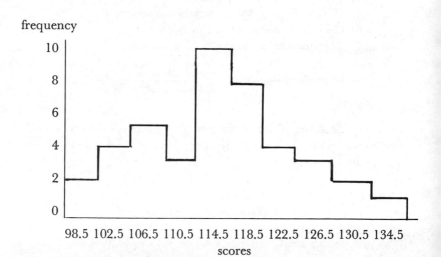

HISTOGRAM

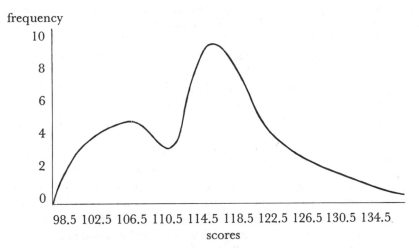

frequency

CURVE OF DISTRIBUTION

10.8 The Normal Curve

A curve of distribution can assume almost any shape, the most common of which is bell-shaped (also called humpbacked, parabolic, or convex). This curve has the greatest number of frequencies at the center of the curve and the smallest number of frequencies appearing at the extremities of the curve. When the left-hand half of the curve is a mirror reflection of the right-hand half, the curve is said to be symmetrical; if not, then the curve is asymmetrical or skewed. If the curve is symmetrical, then the mean, median, and the mode coincide—they all have the same value.

Data from the physical or social sciences when plotted in a curve of distribution quite frequently form the bell-shaped pattern with symmetry about the mean. This special type of curve is useful in studying the aspects of a large group of things (whose actual properties cannot be determined by actual counting or observation) and is called the *normal curve*, or the curve of a normal distribution. There is a very special and complicated formula from which the height of the curve (the ordinate y) is found in terms of the horizontal distance (the abscissa x) but this will not be discussed here. However, the student of algebra might be interested in plotting, as ordinates on successive units along the base line, the coefficients of the expansion $(a + b)^n$ for $n = 1, 2, 3, \ldots, 8$ or beyond. When these points are joined successively they will form a curve which will resemble the normal curve. For $n = 8$, the coefficients are 1, 8, 28, 56, 70, 56, 28, 8, and 1.

The normal curve serves many purposes, the chief of which is to enable us, by studying the characteristics of a small sample group, to predict the properties of a large universe or population whose elements are impossible to collect. For instance, if we wanted to know the average life (in terms of miles) of automobile tires in general, we would need to know the mileage of all automobile tires at the time of discard. Since it is impossible to gather this information, we select and study a small sample of this information. If we want to know the average length of service given by all secondary school teachers now employed, we could not possibly contact all teachers; we would study only a small sample of this group. If a shirt manufacturer wants to know how many shirts of various sizes he should manufacture, he would determine these figures from the study of a sample of the entire male population. The attributes of the normal curve are invaluable today in such fields as economics, education, agriculture, and industry.

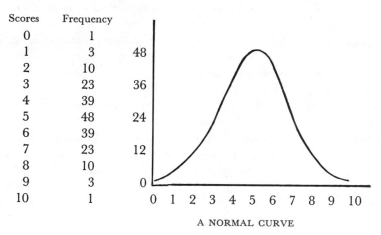

Scores	Frequency
0	1
1	3
2	10
3	23
4	39
5	48
6	39
7	23
8	10
9	3
10	1

A NORMAL CURVE

EXERCISES

SET 34

1. Find the average of the following scores made by students on a history test:

78 87 98 76 85 89 91 90 80 91 84 83 89 89 90 79 78 74 88 81

2. Find the median and the mode for the above set of scores.
3. Find the average deviation from the mean for all the scores above.
4. The following table represents the distribution of scores made by 200 students on a test in general mathematics:

Scores	Frequencies
80–84	9
75–79	11
70–74	19
65–69	33
60–64	50
55–59	34
50–54	24
45–49	12
40–44	8

Assuming that all the scores have the value of the mid-point of their respective interval, find the mean of the distribution.
5. Construct a frequency polygon and a histogram for the distribution.
6. Construct the curve for the above distribution.
7. If the standard deviation of the set of scores is 9.5, what inferences can you make regarding the set of scores?
8. I threw 7 pennies 128 times with the following results:

Number of heads	0	1	2	3	4	5	6	7
Frequency of occurrence	1	6	20	38	34	19	9	1

The frequencies which I expected are respectively: 1, 7, 21, 35, 35, 21, 7, and 1. Plot both the observed frequencies and the expected frequencies on the same set of axes.

SUPPLEMENTARY EXERCISES

SET A

1. Mrs. Brown's recreation room has dimensions of 10 feet by $15\frac{1}{2}$ feet. What will be the cost to cover the floor with linoleum at $3.60 per square yard?
2. Mrs. Smith wants to buy drapery material for the three windows in her living room. The finished curtains are to be $2\frac{3}{4}$ yards long and will require an extra $\frac{1}{8}$ yard at each end for the hem. If there are to be two drapes to each window, what will the material cost at $2.65 per yard?
3. A 15-pound turkey required 20 minutes per pound for roasting. If I want to serve the turkey at 2:30, at what time should I place it in the oven?
4. Billy receives carfare of 10 cents each way, 35 cents for his lunch, and 15 cents spending money each day. What is his allowance per day and per week? How much money will he need if he attends school for 180 days in the year?

5. A plane leaves New York at 10:14 A.M. Eastern Standard Time and arrives in St. Louis at 3:05 Central Daylight Time. It leaves St. Louis the same night at 8:43 and arrives in New York at 11 minutes after midnight. How long did it take the plane to make the round trip?

6. A basic recipe for oatmeal cookies calls for

$\frac{1}{2}$ c. lard	$\frac{1}{2}$ c. butter	1 c. raisins
$\frac{1}{4}$ c. milk	3 eggs	$\frac{1}{4}$ c. nutmeats
$2\frac{1}{2}$ c. flour	$\frac{1}{2}$ t. salt	
$\frac{2}{3}$ t. soda	2 c. oatmeal	

Find the quantities of ingredients needed to make 5 times the recipe.

7. Find the total cost of Mrs. Gray's laundry for the week if she sent out 5 sheets at 19¢, 8 shirts at 27¢, 12 towels at 9¢, 4 pillow cases at 17¢, 3 small rugs at 59¢, and 3 white uniforms at 47¢ each.

8. Mr. Green has a weekly take-home pay of $86.95. If he spends 23% of this for clothes, 27% for food, and 20% for rent, how much does he spend for each of these items and how much money will he have left?

9. I bought a typewriter listed at $95.50 with a discount of 15%. I received a second discount of 2% for paying cash. What was the net cost of the typewriter? (The discounts are figured successively.)

10. A merchant lists a rug for $315 with successive discounts of 20%, 5%, and 1%. What is the net price of the rug?

11. Which is the better offer?
    (a) 6 chairs at $19.50 less 30%, 10%, and 2%.
    (b) $\frac{1}{2}$ dozen chairs at $237.50 (per dozen) less 25%, 15%, and 2%.

12. Mr. Black's weekly salary is $145. The following deductions are made: withholding tax $28.85, social security $3.50, hospitalization $6, and insurance $4.80. What is the amount of his take-home pay? What per cent of his weekly salary is deducted for each of these items?

13. Sara bought 25 yards of ribbon at $.13 per yard. The arm bands which she made out of the ribbon required $\frac{2}{3}$ of a yard of ribbon. How many arm bands did she make? What was the cost of each arm band? What should the selling price be per arm band if she wants to realize a profit of 25 per cent?

14. Estimate the total cost of the following items if purchased at your favorite grocery store: 2 pounds of Chase and Sanborn coffee, 1 pound of butter, 10 pounds of potatoes, 1 dozen oranges, $2\frac{1}{2}$ pounds of green beans, 5 pounds of roast beef, 3 pounds of bacon, 25 pounds of flour, 8 packages of jello, and $\frac{1}{2}$ gallon of ice cream?

SET B

1 Find the interest on
   (a) $500 at 7% for 90 days
   (b) $360 at 5% for 100 days
   (c) $480 at 4% for 21 days
   (d) $1200 at 4% for 89 days
   (e) $6000 at 5% for 10 days

2. Which airplane has the faster speed: A which makes 1250 miles in $5\frac{1}{2}$ hours, or B which makes 1100 miles in $4\frac{3}{4}$ hours?

3. What is the yearly premium on each of the following policies?
   (a) A life insurance policy for \$5000 at \$46.70 per \$1000.
   (b) A fire insurance policy for \$7400 at 65¢ per \$100.
   (c) A windstorm policy for \$7200 at \$6.84 per \$1000.

4. Which of the following throw rugs will cover the largest area?
   (a) $27'' \times 4'\ 3''$ (c) $3'\ 2'' \times 3'\ 3''$
   (b) $30'' \times 4'$ (d) $3' \quad \times 3'\ 6''$

5. Find the cost of a sidewalk 4 feet wide and 22 feet long at \$.35 per cubic foot if the cement is to be 6 inches thick.

6. Find the cost of a sidewalk around a swimming pool 40 feet by 60 feet if the walk is 6 feet wide and the cost is 54 cents per square foot.

7. An airplane flew 500 miles at 120 miles per hour and then flew 700 miles in $4\frac{2}{3}$ hours. What was the airplane's average speed per hour for the trip?

8. I drove an automobile 120 miles in 4 hours and then made another trip of 160 miles in 3 hours. What was my average speed per hour for each trip?

9. What is the capacity of an ice-cream freezer whose diameter is 11 inches and whose depth is 28 inches?

10. How many little ball bearings $\frac{1}{2}$ inch in diameter can be made from the material of a larger metal ball 3 inches in diameter?

11. Find one single discount which is equivalent to the two successive discounts of 40% and 10%.

SET C

1. Write seven and one-quarter million. Divide the number by 2.
2. Write 17 tenths as a decimal fraction.
3. Write 232.5 and .00037 in scientific notation.
4. Write the base of any number system, expressed in terms of that system.
5. Is a set of odd numbers closed with respect to division?
6. List all prime numbers between 70 and 80.
7. Is a common fraction always smaller than one?
8. What is the difference between 1 lb. 5 oz. and 3 lb. 12 oz.?
9. Which is larger, .7654 or .800?
10. How many significant digits are in 326.0?
11. Which number is twice as big as $\frac{7}{7}$? $\frac{7}{14}$, $\frac{18}{9}$, $\frac{14}{14}$, $\frac{1}{2}$.
12. In what base does $4 \times 5 = 13$?
13. Is 34,568 divisible by 4? by 6? by 8? by 9?
14. What are all the prime factors of 98?
15. Add $777 + 999$ in base thirteen and then double your sum.
16. Multiply 23 by 99 in base twelve. Then add TEE to the product.
17. Multiply 33 by 44 by the lattice method.
18. Subtract in base twelve: $22,458 - 10,969$.
19. What is the lowest common multiple of 125 and 225?
20. Show by use of a number line that the L.C.M. of 3 and 5 is 15.

21. Is 323 a composite number?   Is 93 a prime number?
22. What is the excess of elevens in 433,567?
23. What is the test for divisibility by 6?
24. Replace Y in 202,34Y with a numeral so that it is divisible by 2 and by 3.
25. Show 98 × 94 by the complementary method.
26. What is the G.C.D. of 16 and 24?   What is the L.C.M. of 16 and 24?
27. Define (a) multiplicand (b) algorism (c) proper fraction.
28. Write 1,764 is factored form.
29. Without multiplying write the product of 25 × 644840816.
30. One-fourth of 80 tens is how many hundredths?
31. What is the remainder when $3\frac{1}{2}$ is divided by $\frac{3}{4}$?
32. What is one-half per cent of $80?
33. Add these approximate numbers: 23.45; 345.100; 32.8897.
34. Change 2.15 to a common fraction.
35. Estimate the square root of 14568.
36. What is $\frac{1}{4}$% of $800?
37. Find 127% of $80 increased by $3\frac{1}{2}$% of $9.
38. Multiply $3\frac{1}{4}$ by $5\frac{1}{2}$ directly.
39. Locate the following numbers on a number line: .01 .001 1.01.
40. How many $\frac{1}{4}$'s are there in 8?
41. Change IT2E from the duodecimal scale to the decimal scale.
42. Find the excess of nines in 583,628.
43. What law is illustrated here?   3 × 8 = 8 × 3.
44. What is the least common multiple of 12, 18, and 32.
45. Give two illustrations of number used in the ordinal sense.
46. In what base does 3 × 4 = 22?
47. What is the formula for the area of a trapezoid?
48. If the area of a square is 900 square units, what is its perimeter?
49. If the perimeter of a square is 900 units, what is its area?
50. If you divide $31\frac{1}{2}$ by 10, what is the complete quotient?

SET D

FUN WITH FIGURES

1. At the bottom of a well 15 feet deep is a snail which starts crawling toward the top in a vertical line.   The snail climbs 3 feet each day and slides back 2 feet each night.   In how many days will it get out of the well?
2. Find two numbers which contain only ones, whose sum is equal to their product.
3. Arrange 6 coins so that there will be 4 coins in each of two rows.
4. Construct a magic square so that the sum of the numbers in the rows is equal to the sum of the numbers in the columns.   (Use numbers 1 to 9.)
5. Insert 2 plus signs and 2 minus signs to make this statement read correctly:

$$1 \quad 2 \quad 3 \quad 4 \quad 5 \quad 6 \quad 7 \quad 8 \quad 9 = 100$$

6. Mr. Gardener wishes to build a fence around a field which is 20 rods square.   How many posts are needed to enclose the land if the posts are set exactly one rod apart?

7. Can you re-arrange the numbers in these two rows so that the sum of the numbers in the top row will be the same as the sum of the numbers in the bottom row?

3   2   7   9

6   4   5   8

8. An army officer decided to form his men in a solid square.   When he did this he found that he had 27 men left over.   When he increased the number of men by one on each side he found that he needed 30 additional men to complete the square.   How many men did the officer have?

9. I sold my car for $400 and bought it back again for $350.   Then I sold it for $450.   How much did I gain?

10. Nip and Tuck were walking through a park and they came to a square pond.   Within the pond was a square island 10 feet from each bank.   There was a tree with ripe apples on the island and there were two 10-foot planks on the bank.   They got the apples without getting wet.   How?

11. All the coins in my pocket are dimes except two; all are nickels but two; all are quarters but two.   How much money have I?

12. A girl goes to the dairy with two pitchers, one of which holds 3 pints and the other 5 pints.   How can she measure out and bring back 2 pints of milk?

13. Draw an equilateral triangle 3 inches on each side.   Mark off segments one inch long and draw lines connecting all points.   How many equilateral triangles are there in the diagram?

14. Write the largest number you can think of using only 3 fours.

ANSWERS

SET 1 (p. 4)

2. 52,300.

4. 30.

8. 460; 1826; 110,029; 1,001,103.

SET 2 (p. 9)

1. LXXIII; CDVI; MMMMDCD; MMMDCCCXXXVIII; $\overline{\text{XIX}}$; $\overline{\text{CLXXVIL}}$.

2. 19; 1009; 76; 200,044; 813; 278.

4. V; L.

12. 12; 10; 3; 11.

SET 3 (p. 20)

2. 3027; 1212; 202,006; 40,040,004; 2,002,020,020; 6,066,606,006.

6. 7,250,000; 500,000; 750,000; 999,900; 650; 50,000; 250,000,000; 1250; 9988; 350,000; 3,500,000,000.

7. 2^{22}; $4\frac{4}{4}$.

SET 4 (p. 27)

1. $1\frac{5}{16}$; $1\frac{11}{36}$.

2. 4; 17; 325; 190; 3700; 54,000; $\frac{1}{2}$.

4. 9 hundred; 11 hundred; 321 hundred; $5\frac{1}{2}$ hundred; 8000 hundred; 9270 hundred.

7. Eight thousand one hundred tens = 8100 tens.
Fifty-two thousand thousand = 52,000 thousand.

8. 8×10^3; 2.1×10^3; 7.65×10^6; 3.8×10; 7.2×10^0; 8.25×10.

SET 5 (p. 39)

4. 216; 2E1; 144; 143; 509; 341.

5. 21; 171; 42; 2942; 62; 8864; 1486; 390,756.

6. 4334.

10. No.

SET 7 (p. 51)

1. 120.

2. 1003.

5. $123.68.

7. Sum is increased by 450.

8. Sum is increased by 140.
9. Sum is increased by X + Y.
11. Sum is increased by $r - s$.

SET 8 (p. 69)

5. 103; 107; 102; 101; 101; 105.
6. 1003; 1133; 1231; 1220; 2331.
9. nine; seven; four or higher; twelve; six.

SET 9 (p. 83)

6. 3 mi. 143 rd. 4 yd. 2 ft. 4 in.
9. d.

SET 10 (p. 89)

2. Eleven; nine; ten; seven.
3. 22224; 176T8; E667; ITETE.
6. (b) 3; 778; 492; 55,497; 48,977; 7,440,000.

SET 11 (p. 102)

9. 249,774; 623,152; 173,332; 548,188; 567,545; 124,352.
10. 194,094; 257,625; 303,376; 861,184; 186,558; 435,360.
11. 8,737,248; 210,261,042; 6,596,052,048; 23,078,245,153,000.
12. 8100.

SET 12 (p. 114)

4. 18 + 36 + 144 = 198; 63 + 1008 = 1071; 79 + 316 + 1264 = 1659; 43 + 172 + 1376 = 1591.
8. 197,028; 290,184; 318,932; 1,398,720.
10. 3; 4; 4; 4; 5; 4; 5; 6; 6; 400; 3600; 4000; 1000; 32,000; 6000; 40,000; 420,000; 120,000.
11. (a) It is multiplied by 16. (b) It is multiplied by 25. (c) It is increased 100 times the multiplier. (d) It is increased 100 times the multiplicand. (f) It is unchanged. (g) It becomes zero.

SET 13 (p. 125)

5. 157154; 212117; 514361; 130030.
6. 115130; T65T7; 526998; 1909E1.
10. 21400; 15,700; 331,500; 800,000; 456,000; 33,600; 66,400; 600,000.
13. 275; 990; 2596; 68,794; 1078; 737; 33,143; 97,878.
17. Eleven; thirteen; fifteen; sixty-two; eleven.
18. No; yes (sixteen); no; no.

SET 14 (p. 141)

1. c; c; c.
5. Integral quotient is 6, remainder 11.

9. 169 is divided into 17 parts or groups.
10. 1; N; 0; no solution.

SET 15 (p. 147)

3. Hundreds, 7.
4. Hundreds, 3; ones, 4; hundreds, 1; tens, 3; hundreds, 8.
5. 75; 506; 7; 277; 900; 16.
7. 1000; $21\frac{3}{7}$; $87\frac{1}{2}$; 1000; $16\frac{2}{3}$; 120.

SET 16 (p. 148)

6. Integral quotient is 11, remainder is 27.
7. $(5 + 3)$tens $+ 5 + 2$.
9. 80,000; 40; 44; 46,844.
13. 5,867; 210,043; 22,121; 20,208; 72,002; 5008; 56,839; 100,201; 36,047; 74,271.

SET 17 (p. 163)

1. $13+$; $23+$; $29+$; $39+$; $103+$.
2. 5; 72; 4; 8; 4; 198; 12; 8; 1536.
6. 74,988.
8. 2244 (seven) and 3333 (nine).
11. 1, 3; 3, 5; 5, 7; 11, 13; 17, 19; 29, 31; 41, 43; 59, 61; 71, 73.

SET 18 (p. 177)

3. a, b, c, d, e.
5. Simple, proper; simple, improper; simple, improper; simple, proper; complex, proper; compound, proper; complex, proper; simple, improper; simple, proper; compound, proper.
6. $\frac{2}{5}$ hr., $\frac{3}{7}$ wk., $\frac{43}{144}$ sq. ft., $\frac{5}{12}$ yr.; $\frac{73}{100}$ dollars, $\frac{3}{4}$ gal., $\frac{4}{5}$ hand, $\frac{1}{2}$ pair, $\frac{3}{4}$ ton, $\frac{7}{12}$ doz., $\frac{3}{16}$ lb., $\frac{91}{100}$ century.
10. $\frac{7}{18}$, $\frac{5}{7}$, $\frac{29}{33}$, 1, $\frac{17}{176}$, $\frac{19}{17}$, 2.
11. $\frac{12}{35}$, $\frac{8}{8}$, $\frac{13}{15}$, $\frac{5}{9}$.

SET 19 (p. 191)

1. $1\frac{1}{2}$; $3\frac{2}{5}$; $1\frac{1}{12}$; $6\frac{3}{4}$; $1\frac{3}{8}$; 5; $1\frac{3}{4}$; $3\frac{1}{3}$; $1\frac{1}{16}$.
4. $\frac{2}{3}$; $\frac{2}{3}$; $\frac{3}{11}$; $\frac{15}{17}$; $\frac{7}{12}$; $\frac{7}{191}$.
5. Twenty-fourths; forty-fifths; one-hundred-eightieths; thirtieths; ninety-sixths.
7. $1\frac{15}{16}$; $\frac{35}{48}$; $1\frac{7}{16}$; $\frac{17}{30}$; $1\frac{1}{40}$; 0.
9. Yes. $\dfrac{42}{180} = \dfrac{4\frac{2}{3}}{20}$.
11. $3\frac{1}{7}$; $3\frac{1}{15}$; $2\frac{8}{59}$; $1\frac{10}{33}$.

SET 20 (p. 199)

1. $4\frac{2}{3}$; $2\frac{2}{3}$; 12; $10\frac{2}{7}$; $18\frac{3}{4}$; $12\frac{4}{11}$; $\frac{12}{13}$.
2. $29\frac{1}{3}$; $50\frac{2}{5}$; $6\frac{2}{3}$; $15\frac{1}{3}$; 90; 91.

3. 48; 216; 33; 62; 153; 108.

8. $\frac{32}{105}$; $\frac{1}{2}$; $\frac{1}{8}$; $\frac{1}{2}$.

10. $42\frac{1}{2}$; $\frac{1}{7}$; $15\frac{7}{15}$; $13\frac{11}{13}$.

SET 21 (p. 211)

1. $2\frac{1}{2}$; $1\frac{3}{4}$; $\frac{5}{16}$; $5\frac{1}{2}$; $1\frac{3}{5}$; $1\frac{1}{13}$; $\frac{5}{6}$.

3. $1\frac{19}{44}$; $6\frac{14}{27}$; $6\frac{1}{4}$; $2\frac{17}{20}$; 3; $1\frac{38}{145}$.

8. $6\frac{13}{20}$; $7\frac{7}{12}$; $\frac{16}{21}$; $12\frac{1}{4}$; $1\frac{1}{8}$; $2\frac{3}{10}$; $202\frac{1}{2}$.

10. $1\frac{1}{2}$.

11. There are $7\frac{3}{4}$ twos in $15\frac{1}{2}$ or when $15\frac{1}{2}$ is divided into 2 parts, each part contains $7\frac{3}{4}$.

12. Yes.

SET 22 (p. 230)

2. Two hundred thousandths; four hundred one thousandths; four hundred thousandths; two hundred-thousandths; four hundred four thousandths; four hundred and four thousandths; nine hundred ten thousandths; three thousand three millionths.

3. .610; .0600; .0610; 610.010; .700; $.00\frac{1}{4}$; .00005; 31.0.

4. Three tenths; three and one-half tenths; 3.50 tenths; 3.05 tenths; 35 tenths; 350 tenths; 35 tenths; 30.5 tenths; 3500 tenths.

7. 1 (five); 1.1 (four); .5 (six).

12. 1.08; .04; .4; .0160; $\frac{3}{8}$; $\frac{3}{17}$; $1\frac{1}{2}$.

SET 23 (p. 239)

1. $53\frac{23}{30}$; .6; 11.375;.

2. $16 \div 27$; $\frac{1}{3}$ of .92; $8 - 1.35$; same value.

5. .13; .02; .10; .05.

6. $\dfrac{2\frac{1}{2}}{10}$.

8. .10; .23; .41; .41; 3.21; 12.21; 1.400; 110.30.

10. Six, five, nine, eight, ten.

11. 105; 3; 35; 3.

SET 24 (p. 247)

1. .19; .39; .67; .16; .54; 9.35; 20.04; 443.94.

2. 60.95.

3. 34.275.

4. 53.64.

5. 74.803.

6. 2656.25.

10. 60; 150.

SET 25 (p. 257)

1. 5.88; .24; 6.51; .74; 15.08; 2.20; .74; 11.90.

3. 102; 30; 35; 1.6; 40.

4. Smith.

7. $\frac{1}{6}$; $\frac{1}{7}$; $\frac{1}{9}$; $\frac{1}{11}$; $\frac{1}{12}$; $\frac{1}{15}$.
9. First car.

SET 26 (p. 266)

3. $\frac{2}{3}$; .03; $1\frac{3}{5}$; $\frac{8}{9}$; 2100; 4.8; 1; 340; 480; $2\frac{1}{4}$; 112.5; 100; 2700; $\frac{1}{150}$; $\frac{125}{72}$.
6. $\frac{7}{9} > \frac{8}{11}$; $\frac{9}{19} > \frac{3}{7}$; $\frac{5}{26} > \frac{4}{21}$.
9. $1072.50.
10. 60%.
12. 27%.
13. 213.
15. $521.74 monthly.
16. 44%.
17. $75,000.

SET 27 (p. 272)

1. 1.21N; 1.1025N; 1.44N.
2. 1.32N = 10,000; 1.43N = 10,000; 1.122N = 10,000.
3. 1.2096N; .5238N; .99225N.
7. 37%.
8. $1260.
10. $78.23.

SET 28 (p. 273)

1. $1232.50.
2. $3960.
3. 440 lb.
4. 64%.
5. $92.31.
6. $2.40.
7. $4500.
8. $17.00.
9. Lost $100.
10. 900; 6300; $160; 350; $63.
12. 178%.
13. $5.00.
14. 280.95.

SET 29 (p. 280)

3. Obtuse, reflex, acute, reflex, reflex, obtuse, acute, acute.
4. 68° 44′; 158° 44′; 41° 30′; 11° 26′; 101° 26′; 10° 10′; 100° 10′; 18° 4′; 87° 38′ 37″; 177° 38′ 37″.
10. 360°, 180°, 360°, 540°.
11. 3; 1; 1.

SET 30 (p. 290)

1. 22.4, 31.36.
3. $83\frac{1}{3}$.

5. $37\frac{1}{2}$.
7. Sphere.
9. 368.5.
11. .1386.
13. $187\frac{11}{15}$.
15. $30\frac{6}{7}$.
17. $69\frac{4}{9}$.

SET 31 (p. 299)

8. 102 hr. 39 min.
12. 844.
13. 279.
15. .738;   7380;   73.8.
16. 3.65 by 4.5;   22.96 by 26.24.
17. 3 meters;   2 meters;   200 inches; $2\frac{1}{2}$ lb.;   4 liters;   7 kilos.

SET 32 (p. 316)

1. 2 lb. 10 oz.
3. 22 yd. 2 ft. 8 in.
5. 5 mo. 3 wk. $\frac{1}{2}$ day.
9. 5.
11. (a) 1.77.
12. (a) 178.
13. 5.4
18. 4.9;   3.3.
19. 2.0.

SET 34 (p. 334)

1. 85.
2. 85;   89.
3. 5.2.

INDEX

347

CATALOG OF DOVER BOOKS

The more difficult books are indicated by an asterisk (*)

Books Explaining Science and Mathematics

WHAT IS SCIENCE?, N. Campbell. The role of experiment and measurement, the function of mathematics, the nature of scientific laws, the difference between laws and theories, the limitations of science, and many similarly provocative topics are treated clearly and without technicalities by an eminent scientist. "Still an excellent introduction to scientific philosophy," H. Margenau in PHYSICS TODAY. "A first-rate primer . . . deserves a wide audience," SCIENTIFIC AMERICAN. 192pp. 5⅜ x 8.   S43 Paperbound **$1.25**

THE NATURE OF PHYSICAL THEORY, P. W. Bridgman. A Nobel Laureate's clear, non-technical lectures on difficulties and paradoxes connected with frontier research on the physical sciences. Concerned with such central concepts as thought, logic, mathematics, relativity, probability, wave mechanics, etc. he analyzes the contributions of such men as Newton, Einstein, Bohr, Heisenberg, and many others. "Lucid and entertaining . . . recommended to anyone who wants to get some insight into current philosophies of science," THE NEW PHILOSOPHY. Index. xi + 138pp. 5⅜ x 8.   S33 Paperbound **$1.25**

EXPERIMENT AND THEORY IN PHYSICS, Max Born. A Nobel Laureate examines the nature of experiment and theory in theoretical physics and analyzes the advances made by the great physicists of our day: Heisenberg, Einstein, Bohr, Planck, Dirac, and others. The actual process of creation is detailed step-by-step by one who participated. A fine examination of the scientific method at work. 44pp. 5⅜ x 8.   S308 Paperbound **75¢**

THE PSYCHOLOGY OF INVENTION IN THE MATHEMATICAL FIELD, J. Hadamard. The reports of such men as Descartes, Pascal, Einstein, Poincaré, and others are considered in this investigation of the method of idea-creation in mathematics and other sciences and the thinking process in general. How do ideas originate? What is the role of the unconscious? What is Poincaré's forgetting hypothesis? are some of the fascinating questions treated. A penetrating analysis of Einstein's thought processes concludes the book. xiii + 145pp. 5⅜ x 8.   T107 Paperbound **$1.25**

THE NATURE OF LIGHT AND COLOUR IN THE OPEN AIR, M. Minnaert. Why are shadows sometimes blue, sometimes green, or other colors depending on the light and surroundings? What causes mirages? Why do multiple suns and moons appear in the sky? Professor Minnaert explains these unusual phenomena and hundreds of others in simple, easy-to-understand terms based on optical laws and the properties of light and color. No mathematics is required but artists, scientists, students, and everyone fascinated by these "tricks" of nature will find thousands of useful and amazing pieces of information. Hundreds of observational experiments are suggested which require no special equipment. 200 illustrations; 42 photos. xvi + 362pp. 5⅜ x 8.   T196 Paperbound **$1.95**

THE UNIVERSE OF LIGHT, W. Bragg. Sir William Bragg, Nobel Laureate and great modern physicist, is also well known for his powers of clear exposition. Here he analyzes all aspects of light for the layman: lenses, reflection, refraction, the optics of vision, x-rays, the photoelectric effect, etc. He tells you what causes the color of spectra, rainbows, and soap bubbles, how magic mirrors work, and much more. Dozens of simple experiments are described. Preface. Index. 199 line drawings and photographs, including 2 full-page color plates. x + 283pp. 5⅜ x 8.   T538 Paperbound **$1.85**

SOAP-BUBBLES: THEIR COLOURS AND THE FORCES THAT MOULD THEM, C. V. Boys. For continuing popularity and validity as scientific primer, few books can match this volume of easily-followed experiments, explanations. Lucid exposition of complexities of liquid films, surface tension and related phenomena, bubbles' reaction to heat, motion, music, magnetic fields. Experiments with capillary attraction, soap bubbles on frames, composite bubbles, liquid cylinders and jets, bubbles other than soap, etc. Wonderful introduction to scientific method, natural laws that have many ramifications in areas of modern physics. Only complete edition in print. New Introduction by S. Z. Lewin, New York University. 83 illustrations; 1 full-page color plate. xii + 190pp. 5⅜ x 8½.   T542 Paperbound **95¢**

CATALOGUE OF DOVER BOOKS

THE STORY OF X-RAYS FROM RONTGEN TO ISOTOPES, A. R. Bleich, M.D. This book, by a member of the American College of Radiology, gives the scientific explanation of x-rays, their applications in medicine, industry and art, and their danger (and that of atmospheric radiation) to the individual and the species. You learn how radiation therapy is applied against cancer, how x-rays diagnose heart disease and other ailments, how they are used to examine mummies for information on diseases of early societies, and industrial materials for hidden weaknesses. 54 illustrations show x-rays of flowers, bones, stomach, gears with flaws, etc. 1st publication. Index. xix + 186pp. 5⅜ x 8. **T622 Paperbound $1.35**

SPINNING TOPS AND GYROSCOPIC MOTION, John Perry. A classic elementary text of the dynamics of rotation — the behavior and use of rotating bodies such as gyroscopes and tops. In simple, everyday English you are shown how quasi-rigidity is induced in discs of paper, smoke rings, chains, etc., by rapid motions; why a gyrostat falls and why a top rises; precession; how the earth's motion affects climate; and many other phenomena. Appendix on practical use of gyroscopes. 62 figures. 128pp. 5⅜ x 8. **T416 Paperbound $1.00**

SNOW CRYSTALS, W. A. Bentley, M. J. Humphreys. For almost 50 years W. A. Bentley photographed snow flakes in his laboratory in Jericho, Vermont; in 1931 the American Meteorological Society gathered together the best of his work, some 2400 photographs of snow flakes, plus a few ice flowers, windowpane frosts, dew, frozen rain, and other ice formations. Pictures were selected for beauty and scientific value. A very valuable work to anyone in meteorology, cryology; most interesting to layman; extremely useful for artist who wants beautiful, crystalline designs. All copyright free. Unabridged reprint of 1931 edition. 2453 illustrations. 227pp. 8 x 10½. **T287 Paperbound $3.00**

A DOVER SCIENCE SAMPLER, edited by George Barkin. A collection of brief, non-technical passages from 44 Dover Books Explaining Science for the enjoyment of the science-minded browser. Includes work of Bertrand Russell, Poincaré, Laplace, Max Born, Galileo, Newton; material on physics, mathematics, metallurgy, anatomy, astronomy, chemistry, etc. You will be fascinated by Martin Gardner's analysis of the sincere pseudo-scientist, Moritz's account of Newton's absentmindedness, Bernard's examples of human vivisection, etc. Illustrations from the Diderot Pictorial Encyclopedia and De Re Metallica. 64 pages. **FREE**

THE STORY OF ATOMIC THEORY AND ATOMIC ENERGY, J. G. Feinberg. A broader approach to subject of nuclear energy and its cultural implications than any other similar source. Very readable, informal, completely non-technical text. Begins with first atomic theory, 600 B.C. and carries you through the work of Mendelejeff, Röntgen, Madame Curie, to Einstein's equation and the A-bomb. New chapter goes through thermonuclear fission, binding energy, other events up to 1959. Radioactive decay and radiation hazards, future benefits, work of Bohr, moderns, hundreds more topics. "Deserves special mention . . . not only authoritative but thoroughly popular in the best sense of the word," Saturday Review. Formerly, "The Atom Story." Expanded with new chapter. Three appendixes. Index. 34 illustrations. vii + 243pp. 5⅜ x 8. **T625 Paperbound $1.45**

THE STRANGE STORY OF THE QUANTUM, AN ACCOUNT FOR THE GENERAL READER OF THE GROWTH OF IDEAS UNDERLYING OUR PRESENT ATOMIC KNOWLEDGE, B. Hoffmann. Presents lucidly and expertly, with barest amount of mathematics, the problems and theories which led to modern quantum physics. Dr. Hoffmann begins with the closing years of the 19th century, when certain trifling discrepancies were noticed, and with illuminating analogies and examples takes you through the brilliant concepts of Planck, Einstein, Pauli, Broglie, Bohr, Schroedinger, Heisenberg, Dirac, Sommerfeld, Feynman, etc. This edition includes a new, long postscript carrying the story through 1958. "Of the books attempting an account of the history and contents of our modern atomic physics which have come to my attention, this is the best," H. Margenau, Yale University, in "American Journal of Physics." 32 tables and line illustrations. Index. 275pp. 5⅜ x 8. **T518 Paperbound $1.50**

SPACE AND TIME, E. Borel. Written by a versatile mathematician of world renown with his customary lucidity and precision, this introduction to relativity for the layman presents scores of examples, analogies, and illustrations that open up new ways of thinking about space and time. It covers abstract geometry and geographical maps, continuity and topology, the propagation of light, the special theory of relativity, the general theory of relativity, theoretical researches, and much more. Mathematical notes. 2 Indexes. 4 Appendices. 15 figures. xvi + 243pp. 5⅜ x 8. **T592 Paperbound $1.45**

FROM EUCLID TO EDDINGTON: A STUDY OF THE CONCEPTIONS OF THE EXTERNAL WORLD, Sir Edmund Whittaker. A foremost British scientist traces the development of theories of natural philosophy from the western rediscovery of Euclid to Eddington, Einstein, Dirac, etc. The inadequacy of classical physics is contrasted with present day attempts to understand the physical world through relativity, non-Euclidean geometry, space curvature, wave mechanics, etc. 5 major divisions of examination: Space; Time and Movement; the Concepts of Classical Physics; the Concepts of Quantum Mechanics; the Eddington Universe. 212pp. 5⅜ x 8. **T491 Paperbound $1.35**

CATALOGUE OF DOVER BOOKS

*THE EVOLUTION OF SCIENTIFIC THOUGHT FROM NEWTON TO EINSTEIN, A. d'Abro. A detailed account of the evolution of classical physics into modern relativistic theory and the concomitant changes in scientific methodology. The breakdown of classical physics in the face of non-Euclidean geometry and the electromagnetic equations is carefully discussed and then an exhaustive analysis of Einstein's special and general theories of relativity and their implications is given. Newton, Riemann, Weyl, Lorentz, Planck, Maxwell, and many others are considered. A non-technical explanation of space, time, electromagnetic waves, etc. as understood today. "Model of semi-popular exposition," NEW REPUBLIC. 21 diagrams. 482pp. 5⅜ x 8.

T2 Paperbound **$2.00**

EINSTEIN'S THEORY OF RELATIVITY, Max Born. Nobel Laureate explains Einstein's special and general theories of relativity, beginning with a thorough review of classical physics in simple, non-technical language. Exposition of Einstein's work discusses concept of simultaneity, kinematics, relativity of arbitrary motions, the space-time continuum, geometry of curved surfaces, etc., steering middle course between vague popularizations and complex scientific presentations. 1962 edition revised by author takes into account latest findings, predictions of theory and implications for cosmology, indicates what is being sought in unified field theory. Mathematics very elementary, illustrative diagrams and experiments informative but simple. Revised 1962 edition. Revised by Max Born, assisted by Gunther Leibfried and Walter Biem. Index. 143 illustrations. vii + 376pp. 5⅜ x 8.

S769 Paperbound **$2.00**

PHILOSOPHY AND THE PHYSICISTS, L. Susan Stebbing. A philosopher examines the philosophical aspects of modern science, in terms of a lively critical attack on the ideas of Jeans and Eddington. Such basic questions are treated as the task of science, causality, determinism, probability, consciousness, the relation of the world of physics to the world of everyday experience. The author probes the concepts of man's smallness before an inscrutable universe, the tendency to idealize mathematical construction, unpredictability theorems and human freedom, the supposed opposition between 19th century determinism and modern science, and many others. Introduces many thought-stimulating ideas about the implications of modern physical concepts. xvi + 295pp. 5⅜ x 8. T480 Paperbound **$1.65**

THE RESTLESS UNIVERSE, Max Born. A remarkably lucid account by a Nobel Laureate of recent theories of wave mechanics, behavior of gases, electrons and ions, waves and particles, electronic structure of the atom, nuclear physics, and similar topics. "Much more thorough and deeper than most attempts . . . easy and delightful," CHEMICAL AND ENGINEERING NEWS. Special feature: 7 animated sequences of 60 figures each showing such phenomena as gas molecules in motion, the scattering of alpha particles, etc. 11 full-page plates of photographs. Total of nearly 600 illustrations. 351pp. 6⅛ x 9¼. T412 Paperbound **$2.00**

THE COMMON SENSE OF THE EXACT SCIENCES, W. K. Clifford. For 70 years a guide to the basic concepts of scientific and mathematical thought. Acclaimed by scientists and laymen alike, it offers a wonderful insight into concepts such as the extension of meaning of symbols, characteristics of surface boundaries, properties of plane figures, measurement of quantities, vectors, the nature of position, bending of space, motion, mass and force, and many others. Prefaces by Bertrand Russell and Karl Pearson. Critical introduction by James Newman. 130 figures. 249pp. 5⅜ x 8. T61 Paperbound **$1.60**

MATTER AND LIGHT, THE NEW PHYSICS, Louis de Broglie. Non-technical explanations by a Nobel Laureate of electro-magnetic theory, relativity, matter, light and radiation, wave mechanics, quantum physics, philosophy of science, and similar topics. This is one of the simplest yet most accurate introductions to the work of men like Planck, Einstein, Bohr, and others. Only 2 of the 21 chapters require a knowledge of mathematics. 300pp. 5⅜ x 8.

T35 Paperbound **$1.75**

SCIENCE, THEORY AND MAN, Erwin Schrödinger. This is a complete and unabridged reissue of SCIENCE AND THE HUMAN TEMPERAMENT plus an additional essay: "What Is an Elementary Particle?" Nobel Laureate Schrödinger discusses such topics as nature of scientific method, the nature of science, chance and determinism, science and society, conceptual models for physical entities, elementary particles and wave mechanics. Presentation is popular and may be followed by most people with little or no scientific training. "Fine practical preparation for a time when laws of nature, human institutions . . . are undergoing a critical examination without parallel," Waldemar Kaempffert, N. Y. TIMES. 192pp. 5⅜ x 8.

T428 Paperbound **$1.35**

CONCERNING THE NATURE OF THINGS, Sir William Bragg. The Nobel Laureate physicist in his Royal Institute Christmas Lectures explains such diverse phenomena as the formation of crystals, how uranium is transmuted to lead, the way X-rays work, why a spinning ball travels in a curved path, the reason why bubbles bounce from each other, and many other scientific topics that are seldom explained in simple terms. No scientific background needed—book is easy enough that any intelligent adult or youngster can understand it. Unabridged. 32pp. of photos; 57 figures. xii + 232pp. 5⅜ x 8. T31 Paperbound **$1.35**

*THE RISE OF THE NEW PHYSICS (formerly THE DECLINE OF MECHANISM), A. d'Abro. This authoritative and comprehensive 2 volume exposition is unique in scientific publishing. Written for intelligent readers not familiar with higher mathematics, it is the only thorough explanation in non-technical language of modern mathematical-physical theory. Combining both history and exposition, it ranges from classical Newtonian concepts up through the electronic theories of Dirac and Heisenberg, the statistical mechanics of Fermi, and Einstein's relativity theories. "A must for anyone doing serious study in the physical sciences," J. OF FRANKLIN INST. 97 illustrations. 991pp. 2 volumes. T3 Vol. 1, Paperbound **$2.00**
T4 Vol. 2, Paperbound **$2.00**

SCIENCE AND HYPOTHESIS, Henri Poincaré. Creative psychology in science. How such concepts as number, magnitude, space, force, classical mechanics were developed and how the modern scientist uses them in his thought. Hypothesis in physics, theories of modern physics. Introduction by Sir James Larmor. "Few mathematicians have had the breadth of vision of Poincaré, and none is his superior in the gift of clear exposition," E. T. Bell. Index. 272pp. 5⅜ x 8.
S221 Paperbound **$1.35**

THE VALUE OF SCIENCE, Henri Poincaré. Many of the most mature ideas of the "last scientific universalist" conveyed with charm and vigor for both the beginning student and the advanced worker. Discusses the nature of scientific truth, whether order is innate in the universe or imposed upon it by man, logical thought versus intuition (relating to mathematics through the works of Weierstrass, Lie, Klein, Riemann), time and space (relativity, psychological time, simultaneity), Hertz's concept of force, interrelationship of mathematical physics to pure math, values within disciplines of Maxwell, Carnot, Mayer, Newton, Lorentz, etc. Index. iii + 147pp. 5⅜ x 8.
S469 Paperbound **$1.35**

THE SKY AND ITS MYSTERIES, E. A. Beet. One of the most lucid books on the mysteries of the universe; covers history of astronomy from earliest observations to modern theories of expanding universe, source of stellar energy, birth of planets, origin of moon craters, possibilities of life on other planets. Discusses effects of sunspots on weather; distance, age of stars; methods and tools of astronomers; much more. Expert and fascinating. "Eminently readable book," London Times. Bibliography. Over 50 diagrams, 12 full-page plates. Fold-out star map. Introduction. Index. 238pp. 5¼ x 7½.
T627 Clothbound **$3.50**

OUT OF THE SKY: AN INTRODUCTION TO METEORITES, H. H. Nininger. A non-technical yet comprehensive introduction to the young science of meteoritics: all aspects of the arrival of cosmic matter on our planet from outer space and the reaction and alteration of this matter in the terrestrial environment. Essential facts and major theories presented by one of the world's leading experts. Covers ancient reports of meteors; modern systematic investigations; fireball clusters; meteorite showers; tektites; planetoidal encounters; etc. 52 full-page plates with over 175 photographs. 22 figures. Bibliography and references. Index. viii + 336pp. 5⅜ x 8.
T519 Paperbound **$1.85**

THE REALM OF THE NEBULAE, E. Hubble. One of great astronomers of our day records his formulation of concept of "island universes." Covers velocity-distance relationship; classification, nature, distances, general types of nebulae; cosmological theories. A fine introduction to modern theories for layman. No math needed. New introduction by A. Sandage. 55 illustrations, photos. Index. iv + 201pp. 5⅜ x 8.
S455 Paperbound **$1.50**

AN ELEMENTARY SURVEY OF CELESTIAL MECHANICS, Y. Ryabov. Elementary exposition of gravitational theory and celestial mechanics. Historical introduction and coverage of basic principles, including: the ecliptic, the orbital plane, the 2- and 3-body problems, the discovery of Neptune, planetary rotation, the length of the day, the shapes of galaxies, satellites (detailed treatment of Sputnik I), etc. First American reprinting of successful Russian popular exposition. Follow actual methods of astrophysicists with only high school math! Appendix. 58 figures. 165pp. 5⅜ x 8.
T756 Paperbound **$1.25**

GREAT IDEAS AND THEORIES OF MODERN COSMOLOGY, Jagjit Singh. Companion volume to author's popular "Great Ideas of Modern Mathematics" (Dover, $1.55). The best non-technical survey of post-Einstein attempts to answer perhaps unanswerable questions of origin, age of Universe, possibility of life on other worlds, etc. Fundamental theories of cosmology and cosmogony recounted, explained, evaluated in light of most recent data: Einstein's concepts of relativity, space-time; Milne's a priori world-system; astrophysical theories of Jeans, Eddington; Hoyle's "continuous creation;" contributions of dozens more scientists. A faithful, comprehensive critical summary of complex material presented in an extremely well-written text intended for laymen. Original publication. Index. xii + 276pp. 5⅜ x 8½.
T925 Paperbound **$1.85**

BASIC ELECTRICITY, Bureau of Naval Personnel. Very thorough, easily followed course in basic electricity for beginner, layman, or intermediate student. Begins with simplest definitions, presents coordinated, systematic coverage of basic theory and application: conductors, insulators, static electricity, magnetism, production of voltage, Ohm's law, direct current series and parallel circuits, wiring techniques, electromagnetism, alternating current, capacitance and inductance, measuring instruments, etc.; application to electrical machines such as alternating and direct current generators, motors, transformers, magnetic magnifiers, etc. Each chapter contains problems to test progress; answers at rear. No math needed beyond algebra. Appendices on signs, formulas, etc. 345 illustrations. 448pp. 7½ x 10.
S973 Paperbound **$2.95**

ELEMENTARY METALLURGY AND METALLOGRAPHY, A. M. Shrager. An introduction to common metals and alloys; stress is upon steel and iron, but other metals and alloys also covered. All aspects of production, processing, working of metals. Designed for student who wishes to enter metallurgy, for bright high school or college beginner, layman who wants background on extremely important industry. Questions, at ends of chapters, many microphotographs, glossary. Greatly revised 1961 edition. 195 illustrations, tables. ix + 389pp. 5⅜ x 8.
S138 Paperbound **$2.25**

CATALOGUE OF DOVER BOOKS

BRIDGES AND THEIR BUILDERS, D. B. Steinman & S. R. Watson. Engineers, historians, and every person who has ever been fascinated by great spans will find this book an endless source of information and interest. Greek and Roman structures, Medieval bridges, modern classics such as the Brooklyn Bridge, and the latest developments in the science are retold by one of the world's leading authorities on bridge design and construction. BRIDGES AND THEIR BUILDERS is the only comprehensive and accurate semi-popular history of these important measures of progress in print. New, greatly revised, enlarged edition. 23 photos; 26 line-drawings. Index. xvii + 401pp. 5⅜ x 8.   T431 Paperbound **$2.00**

FAMOUS BRIDGES OF THE WORLD, D. B. Steinman. An up-to-the-minute new edition of a book that explains the fascinating drama of how the world's great bridges came to be built. The author, designer of the famed Mackinac bridge, discusses bridges from all periods and all parts of the world, explaining their various types of construction, and describing the problems their builders faced. Although primarily for youngsters, this cannot fail to interest readers of all ages. 48 illustrations in the text. 23 photographs. 99pp. 6⅛ x 9¼.   T161 Paperbound **$1.00**

HOW DO YOU USE A SLIDE RULE? by A. A. Merrill. A step-by-step explanation of the slide rule that presents the fundamental rules clearly enough for the non-mathematician to understand. Unlike most instruction manuals, this work concentrates on the two most important operations: multiplication and division. 10 easy lessons, each with a clear drawing, for the reader who has difficulty following other expositions. 1st publication. Index. 2 Appendices. 10 illustrations. 78 problems, all with answers. vi + 36 pp. 6⅛ x 9¼.   T62 Paperbound **60¢**

HOW TO CALCULATE QUICKLY, H. Sticker. A tried and true method for increasing your "number sense" — the ability to see relationships between numbers and groups of numbers. Addition, subtraction, multiplication, division, fractions, and other topics are treated through techniques not generally taught in schools: left to right multiplication, division by inspection, etc. This is not a collection of tricks which work only on special numbers, but a detailed well-planned course, consisting of over 9,000 problems that you can work in spare moments. It is excellent for anyone who is inconvenienced by slow computational skills. 5 or 10 minutes of this book daily will double or triple your calculation speed. 9,000 problems, answers. 256pp. 5⅜ x 8.   T295 Paperbound **$1.00**

MATHEMATICAL FUN, GAMES AND PUZZLES, Jack Frohlichstein. A valuable service for parents of children who have trouble with math, for teachers in need of a supplement to regular upper elementary and junior high math texts (each section is graded—easy, average, difficult —for ready adaptation to different levels of ability), and for just anyone who would like to develop basic skills in an informal and entertaining manner. The author combines ten years of experience as a junior high school math teacher with a method that uses puzzles and games to introduce the basic ideas and operations of arithmetic. Stress on everyday uses of math: banking, stock market, personal budgets, insurance, taxes. Intellectually stimulating and practical, too. 418 problems and diversions with answers. Bibliography. 120 illustrations. xix + 306pp. 5⅝ x 8½.   T789 Paperbound **$1.75**

GREAT IDEAS OF MODERN MATHEMATICS: THEIR NATURE AND USE, Jagjit Singh. Reader with only high school math will understand main mathematical ideas of modern physics, astronomy, genetics, psychology, evolution, etc. better than many who use them as tools, but comprehend little of their basic structure. Author uses his wide knowledge of non-mathematical fields in brilliant exposition of differential equations, matrices, group theory, logic, statistics, problems of mathematical foundations, imaginary numbers, vectors, etc. Original publication. 2 appendixes. 2 indexes. 65 illustr. 322pp. 5⅜ x 8.   S587 Paperbound **$1.75**

*MATHEMATICS IN ACTION, O. G. Sutton. Everyone with a command of high school algebra will find this book one of the finest possible introductions to the application of mathematics to physical theory. Ballistics, numerical analysis, waves and wavelike phenomena, Fourier series, group concepts, fluid flow and aerodynamics, statistical measures, and meteorology are discussed with unusual clarity. Some calculus and differential equations theory is developed by the author for the reader's help in the more difficult sections. 88 figures. Index. viii + 236pp. 5⅜ x 8.   T440 Clothbound **$3.50**

*INTRODUCTION TO SYMBOLIC LOGIC AND ITS APPLICATIONS, Rudolph Carnap. One of the clearest, most comprehensive, and rigorous introductions to modern symbolic logic, by perhaps its greatest living master. Not merely elementary theory, but demonstrated applications in mathematics, physics, and biology. Symbolic languages of various degrees of complexity are analyzed, and one constructed. "A creation of the rank of a masterpiece," Zentralblatt für Mathematik und Ihre Grenzgebiete. Over 300 exercises. 5 figures. Bibliography. Index. xvi + 241pp. 5⅜ x 8.   S453 Paperbound **$1.85**

*HIGHER MATHEMATICS FOR STUDENTS OF CHEMISTRY AND PHYSICS, J. W. Mellor. Not abstract, but practical, drawing its problems from familiar laboratory material, this book covers theory and application of differential calculus, analytic geometry, functions with singularities, integral calculus, infinite series, solution of numerical equations, differential equations, Fourier's theorem and extensions, probability and the theory of errors, calculus of variations, determinants, etc. "If the reader is not familiar with this book, it will repay him to examine it," CHEM. & ENGINEERING NEWS. 800 problems. 189 figures. 2 appendices; 30 tables of integrals, probability functions, etc. Bibliography. xxi + 641pp. 5⅜ x 8.
                                                                                S193 Paperbound **$2.25**

CATALOGUE OF DOVER BOOKS

THE FOURTH DIMENSION SIMPLY EXPLAINED, edited by Henry P. Manning. Originally written as entries in contest sponsored by "Scientific American," then published in book form, these 22 essays present easily understood explanations of how the fourth dimension may be studied, the relationship of non-Euclidean geometry to the fourth dimension, analogies to three-dimensional space, some fourth-dimensional absurdities and curiosities, possible measurements and forms in the fourth dimension. In general, a thorough coverage of many of the simpler properties of fourth-dimensional space. Multi-points of view on many of the most important aspects are valuable aid to comprehension. Introduction by Dr. Henry P. Manning gives proper emphasis to points in essays, more advanced account of fourth-dimensional geometry. 82 figures. 251pp. 5⅜ x 8. **T711 Paperbound $1.35**

TRIGONOMETRY REFRESHER FOR TECHNICAL MEN, A. A. Klaf. A modern question and answer text on plane and spherical trigonometry. Part I covers plane trigonometry: angles, quadrants, trigonometrical functions, graphical representation, interpolation, equations, logarithms, solution of triangles, slide rules, etc. Part II discusses applications to navigation, surveying, elasticity, architecture, and engineering. Small angles, periodic functions, vectors, polar coordinates, De Moivre's theorem, fully covered. Part III is devoted to spherical trigonometry and the solution of spherical triangles, with applications to terrestrial and astronomical problems. Special time-savers for numerical calculation. 913 questions answered for you! 1738 problems; answers to odd numbers. 494 figures. 14 pages of functions, formulae. Index. x + 629pp. 5⅜ x 8. **T371 Paperbound $2.00**

CALCULUS REFRESHER FOR TECHNICAL MEN. A. A. Klaf. Not an ordinary textbook but a unique refresher for engineers, technicians, and students. An examination of the most important aspects of differential and integral calculus by means of 756 key questions. Part I covers simple differential calculus: constants, variables, functions, increments, derivatives, logarithms, curvature, etc. Part II treats fundamental concepts of integration: inspection, substitution, transformation, reduction, areas and volumes, mean value, successive and partial integration, double and triple integration. Stresses practical aspects! A 50 page section gives applications to civil and nautical engineering, electricity, stress and strain, elasticity, industrial engineering, and similar fields. 756 questions answered. 556 problems; solutions to odd numbers. 36 pages of constants, formulae. Index. v + 431pp. 5⅜ x 8. **T370 Paperbound $2.00**

PROBABILITIES AND LIFE, Emile Borel. One of the leading French mathematicians of the last 100 years makes use of certain results of mathematics of probabilities and explains a number of problems that for the most part, are related to everyday living or to illness and death: computation of life expectancy tables, chances of recovery from various diseases, probabilities of job accidents, weather predictions, games of chance, and so on. Emphasis on results not processes, though some indication is made of mathematical proofs. Simple in style, free of technical terminology, limited in scope to everyday situations, it is comprehensible to laymen, fine reading for beginning students of probability. New English translation. Index. Appendix. vi + 87pp. 5⅜ x 8½. **T121 Paperbound $1.00**

POPULAR SCIENTIFIC LECTURES, Hermann von Helmholtz. 7 lucid expositions by a pre-eminent scientific mind: "The Physiological Causes of Harmony in Music," "On the Relation of Optics to Painting," "On the Conservation of Force," "On the Interaction of Natural Forces," "On Goethe's Scientific Researches" into theory of color, "On the Origin and Significance of Geometric Axioms," "On Recent Progress in the Theory of Vision." Written with simplicity of expression, stripped of technicalities, these are easy to understand and delightful reading for anyone interested in science or looking for an introduction to serious study of acoustics or optics. Introduction by Professor Morris Kline, Director, Division of Electromagnetic Research, New York University, contains astute, impartial evaluations. Selected from "Popular Lectures on Scientific Subjects," 1st and 2nd series. xii + 286pp. 5⅜ x 8½. **T799 Paperbound $1.45**

SCIENCE AND METHOD, Henri Poincaré. Procedure of scientific discovery, methodology, experiment, idea-germination—the intellectual processes by which discoveries come into being. Most significant and most interesting aspects of development, application of ideas. Chapters cover selection of facts, chance, mathematical reasoning, mathematics, and logic; Whitehead, Russell, Cantor; the new mechanics, etc. 288pp. 5⅜ x 8. **S222 Paperbound $1.35**

HEAT AND ITS WORKINGS, Morton Mott-Smith, Ph.D. An unusual book; to our knowledge the only middle-level survey of this important area of science. Explains clearly such important concepts as physiological sensation of heat and Weber's law, measurement of heat, evolution of thermometer, nature of heat, expansion and contraction of solids, Boyle's law, specific heat. BTU's and calories, evaporation, Andrews's isothermals, radiation, the relation of heat to light, many more topics inseparable from other aspects of physics. A wide, non-mathematical yet thorough explanation of basic ideas, theories, phenomena for laymen and beginning scientists illustrated by experiences of daily life. Bibliography. 50 illustrations. x + 165pp. 5⅜ x 8½. **T978 Paperbound $1.00**

Classics of Science

THE DIDEROT PICTORIAL ENCYCLOPEDIA OF TRADES AND INDUSTRY, MANUFACTURING AND THE TECHNICAL ARTS IN PLATES SELECTED FROM "L'ENCYCLOPEDIE OU DICTIONNAIRE RAISONNE DES SCIENCES, DES ARTS, ET DES METIERS" OF DENIS DIDEROT, edited with text by C. Gillispie. The first modern selection of plates from the high point of 18th century French engraving, Diderot's famous Encyclopedia. Over 2000 illustrations on 485 full page plates, most of them original size, illustrating the trades and industries of one of the most fascinating periods of modern history, 18th century France. These magnificent engravings provide an invaluable glimpse into the past for the student of early technology, a lively and accurate social document to students of cultures, an outstanding find to the lover of fine engravings. The plates teem with life, with men, women, and children performing all of the thousands of operations necessary to the trades before and during the early stages of the industrial revolution. Plates are in sequence, and show general operations, closeups of difficult operations, and details of complex machinery. Such important and interesting trades and industries are illustrated as sowing, harvesting, beekeeping, cheesemaking, operating windmills, milling flour, charcoal burning, tobacco processing, indigo, fishing, arts of war, salt extraction, mining, smelting iron, casting iron, steel, extracting mercury, zinc, sulphur, copper, etc., slating, tinning, silverplating, gilding, making gunpowder, cannons, bells, shoeing horses, tanning, papermaking, printing, dying, and more than 40 other categories. 920pp. 9 x 12. Heavy library cloth.   T421 Two volume set **$18.50**

THE PRINCIPLES OF SCIENCE, A TREATISE ON LOGIC AND THE SCIENTIFIC METHOD, W. Stanley Jevons. Treating such topics as Inductive and Deductive Logic, the Theory of Number, Probability, and the Limits of Scientific Method, this milestone in the development of symbolic logic remains a stimulating contribution to the investigation of inferential validity in the natural and social sciences. It significantly advances Boole's logic, and describes a machine which is a foundation of modern electronic calculators. In his introduction, Ernest Nagel of Columbia University says, "(Jevons) . . . continues to be of interest as an attempt to articulate the logic of scientific inquiry." Index. liii + 786pp. 5⅜ x 8.
S446 Paperbound **$2.98**

*DIALOGUES CONCERNING TWO NEW SCIENCES, Galileo Galilei. A classic of experimental science which has had a profound and enduring influence on the entire history of mechanics and engineering. Galileo based this, his finest work, on 30 years of experimentation. It offers a fascinating and vivid exposition of dynamics, elasticity, sound, ballistics, strength of materials, and the scientific method. Translated by H. Crew and A. de Salvio. 126 diagrams. Index. xxi + 288pp. 5⅜ x 8.   S99 Paperbound **$1.75**

DE MAGNETE, William Gilbert. This classic work on magnetism founded a new science. Gilbert was the first to use the word "electricity," to recognize mass as distinct from weight, to discover the effect of heat on magnetic bodies; invented an electroscope, differentiated between static electricity and magnetism, conceived of the earth as a magnet. Written by the first great experimental scientist, this lively work is valuable not only as an historical landmark, but as the delightfully easy-to-follow record of a perpetually searching, ingenious mind. Translated by P. F. Mottelay. 25 page biographical memoir. 90 fix. lix + 368pp. 5⅜ x 8.   S470 Paperbound **$2.00**

*OPTICKS, Sir Isaac Newton. An enormous storehouse of insights and discoveries on light, reflection, color, refraction, theories of wave and corpuscular propagation of light, optical apparatus, and mathematical devices which have recently been reevaluated in terms of modern physics and placed in the top-most ranks of Newton's work! Foreword by Albert Einstein. Preface by I. B. Cohen of Harvard U. 7 pages of portraits, facsimile pages, letters, etc. cxvi + 412pp. 5⅜ x 8.   S205 Paperbound **$2.25**

A SURVEY OF PHYSICAL THEORY, M. Planck. Lucid essays on modern physics for the general reader by the Nobel Laureate and creator of the quantum revolution. Planck explains how the new concepts came into being; explores the clash between theories of mechanics, electrodynamics, and thermodynamics; and traces the evolution of the concept of light through Newton, Huygens, Maxwell, and his own quantum theory, providing unparalleled insights into his development of this momentous modern concept. Bibliography. Index. vii + 121pp. 5⅜ x 8.
S650 Paperbound **$1.15**

A SOURCE BOOK IN MATHEMATICS, D. E. Smith. English translations of the original papers that announced the great discoveries in mathematics from the Renaissance to the end of the 19th century: succinct selections from 125 different treatises and articles, most of them unavailable elsewhere in English—Newton, Leibniz, Pascal, Riemann, Bernoulli, etc. 24 articles trace developments in the field of number, 18 cover algebra, 36 are on geometry, and 13 on calculus. Biographical-historical introductions to each article. Two volume set. Index in each. Total of 115 illustrations. Total of xxviii + 742pp. 5⅜ x 8.   S552 Vol I Paperbound **$1.85**
S553 Vol II Paperbound **$1.85**
The set, boxed **$3.50**

CATALOGUE OF DOVER BOOKS

*THE THIRTEEN BOOKS OF EUCLID'S ELEMENTS, edited by T. L. Heath. This is the complete EUCLID — the definitive edition of one of the greatest classics of the western world. Complete English translation of the Heiberg text with spurious Book XIV. Detailed 150-page introduction discusses aspects of Greek and medieval mathematics: Euclid, texts, commentators, etc. Paralleling the text is an elaborate critical exposition analyzing each definition, proposition, postulate, etc., and covering textual matters, mathematical analyses, refutations, extensions, etc. Unabridged reproduction of the Cambridge 2nd edition. 3 volumes. Total of 995 figures, 1426pp. 5⅜ x 8. S88, 89, 90 — 3 vol. set, Paperbound **$6.75**

*THE GEOMETRY OF RENE DESCARTES. The great work which founded analytic geometry. The renowned Smith-Latham translation faced with the original French text containing all of Descartes' own diagrams! Contains: Problems the Construction of Which Requires Only Straight Lines and Circles; On the Nature of Curved Lines; On the Construction of Solid or Supersolid Problems. Notes. Diagrams. 258pp. S68 Paperbound **$1.60**

*A PHILOSOPHICAL ESSAY ON PROBABILITIES, P. Laplace. Without recourse to any mathematics above grammar school, Laplace develops a philosophically, mathematically and historically classical exposition of the nature of probability: its functions and limitations, operations in practical affairs, calculations in games of chance, insurance, government, astronomy, and countless other fields. New introduction by E. T. Bell. viii + 196pp. S166 Paperbound **$1.35**

DE RE METALLICA, Georgius Agricola. Written over 400 years ago, for 200 years the most authoritative first-hand account of the production of metals, translated in 1912 by former President Herbert Hoover and his wife, and today still one of the most beautiful and fascinating volumes ever produced in the history of science! 12 books, exhaustively annotated, give a wonderfully lucid and vivid picture of the history of mining, selection of sites, types of deposits, excavating pits, sinking shafts, ventilating, pumps, crushing machinery, assaying, smelting, refining metals, making salt, alum, nitre, glass, and many other topics. This definitive edition contains all 289 of the 16th century woodcuts which made the original an artistic masterpiece. It makes a superb gift for geologists, engineers, libraries, artists, historians, and everyone interested in science and early illustrative art. Biographical, historical introductions. Bibliography, survey of ancient authors. Indices. 289 illustrations. 672pp. 6¾ x 10¾. Deluxe library edition. S6 Clothbound **$10.00**

GEOGRAPHICAL ESSAYS, W. M. Davis. Modern geography and geomorphology rest on the fundamental work of this scientist. His new concepts of earth-processes revolutionized science and his broad interpretation of the scope of geography created a deeper understanding of the interrelation of the landscape and the forces that mold it. This first inexpensive unabridged edition covers theory of geography, methods of advanced geographic teaching, descriptions of geographic areas, analyses of land-shaping processes, and much besides. Not only a factual and historical classic, it is still widely read for its reflections of modern scientific thought. Introduction. 130 figures. Index. vi + 777pp. 5⅜ x 8.
S383 Paperbound **$2.95**

CHARLES BABBAGE AND HIS CALCULATING ENGINES, edited by P. Morrison and E. Morrison. Friend of Darwin, Humboldt, and Laplace, Babbage was a leading pioneer in large-scale mathematical machines and a prophetic herald of modern operational research—true father of Harvard's relay computer Mark I. His Difference Engine and Analytical Engine were the first successful machines in the field. This volume contains a valuable introduction on his life and work; major excerpts from his fascinating autobiography, revealing his eccentric and unusual personality; and extensive selections from "Babbage's Calculating Engines," a compilation of hard-to-find journal articles, both by Babbage and by such eminent contributors as the Countess of Lovelace, L. F. Menabrea, and Dionysius Lardner. 11 illustrations. Appendix of miscellaneous papers. Index. Bibliography. xxxviii + 400pp. 5⅜ x 8. T12 Paperbound **$2.00**

*THE WORKS OF ARCHIMEDES WITH THE METHOD OF ARCHIMEDES, edited by T. L. Heath. All the known works of the greatest mathematician of antiquity including the recently discovered METHOD OF ARCHIMEDES. This last is the only work we have which shows exactly how early mathematicians discovered their proofs before setting them down in their final perfection. A 186 page study by the eminent scholar Heath discusses Archimedes and the history of Greek mathematics. Bibliography. 563pp. 5⅜ x 8. S9 Paperbound **$2.25**

Psychology

YOGA: A SCIENTIFIC EVALUATION, Kovoor T. Behanan. A complete reprinting of the book that for the first time gave Western readers a sane, scientific explanation and analysis of yoga. The author draws on controlled laboratory experiments and personal records of a year as a disciple of a yoga, to investigate yoga psychology, concepts of knowledge, physiology, "supernatural" phenomena, and the ability to tap the deepest human powers. In this study under the auspices of Yale University Institute of Human Relations, the strictest principles of physiological and psychological inquiry are followed throughout. Foreword by W. A. Miles, Yale University. 17 photographs. Glossary. Index. xx + 270pp. 5⅜ x 8. T505 Paperbound **$1.75**

CONDITIONED REFLEXES: AN INVESTIGATION OF THE PHYSIOLOGICAL ACTIVITIES OF THE CEREBRAL CORTEX, I. P. Pavlov. Full, authorized translation of Pavlov's own survey of his work in experimental psychology reviews entire course of experiments, summarizes conclusions, outlines psychological system based on famous "conditioned reflex" concept. Details of technical means used in experiments, observations on formation of conditioned reflexes, function of cerebral hemispheres, results of damage, nature of sleep, typology of nervous system, significance of experiments for human psychology. Trans. by Dr. G. V. Anrep, Cambridge Univ. 235-item bibliography. 18 figures. 445pp. 5⅜ x 8. S614 Paperbound **$2.25**

EXPLANATION OF HUMAN BEHAVIOUR, F. V. Smith. A major intermediate-level introduction to and criticism of 8 complete systems of the psychology of human behavior, with unusual emphasis on theory of investigation and methodology. Part I is an illuminating analysis of the problems involved in the explanation of observed phenomena, and the differing viewpoints on the nature of causality. Parts II and III are a closely detailed survey of the systems of McDougall, Gordon Allport, Lewin, the Gestalt group, Freud, Watson, Hull, and Tolman. Biographical notes. Bibliography of over 800 items. 2 Indexes. 38 figures. xii + 460pp. 5½ x 8¾.
T253 Clothbound **$6.00**

SEX IN PSYCHO-ANALYSIS (formerly CONTRIBUTIONS TO PSYCHO-ANALYSIS), S. Ferenczi. Written by an associate of Freud, this volume presents countless insights on such topics as impotence, transference, analysis and children, dreams, symbols, obscene words, masturbation and male homosexuality, paranoia and psycho-analysis, the sense of reality, hypnotism and therapy, and many others. Also includes full text of THE DEVELOPMENT OF PSYCHO-ANALYSIS by Ferenczi and Otto Rank. Two books bound as one. Total of 406pp. 5⅜ x 8.
T324 Paperbound **$1.85**

BEYOND PSYCHOLOGY, Otto Rank. One of Rank's most mature contributions, focussing on the irrational basis of human behavior as a basic fact of our lives. The psychoanalytic techniques of myth analysis trace to their source the ultimates of human existence: fear of death, personality, the social organization, the need for love and creativity, etc. Dr. Rank finds them stemming from a common irrational source, man's fear of final destruction. A seminal work in modern psychology, this work sheds light on areas ranging from the concept of immortal soul to the sources of state power. 291pp. 5⅜ x 8. T485 Paperbound **$2.00**

ILLUSIONS AND DELUSIONS OF THE SUPERNATURAL AND THE OCCULT, D. H. Rawcliffe. Holds up to rational examination hundreds of persistent delusions including crystal gazing, automatic writing, table turning, mediumistic trances, mental healing, stigmata, lycanthropy, live burial, the Indian Rope Trick, spiritualism, dowsing, telepathy, clairvoyance, ghosts, ESP, etc. The author explains and exposes the mental and physical deceptions involved, making this not only an exposé of supernatural phenomena, but a valuable exposition of characteristic types of abnormal psychology. Originally titled "The Psychology of the Occult." 14 illustrations. Index. 551pp. 5⅜ x 8. T503 Paperbound **$2.00**

THE PRINCIPLES OF PSYCHOLOGY, William James. The full long-course, unabridged, of one of the great classics of Western literature and science. Wonderfully lucid descriptions of human mental activity, the stream of thought, consciousness, time perception, memory, imagination, emotions, reason, abnormal phenomena, and similar topics. Original contributions are integrated with the work of such men as Berkeley, Binet, Mills, Darwin, Hume, Kant, Royce, Schopenhauer, Spinoza, Locke, Descartes, Galton, Wundt, Lotze, Herbart, Fechner, and scores of others. All contrasting interpretations of mental phenomena are examined in detail — introspective analysis, philosophical interpretation, and experimental research. "A classic," JOURNAL OF CONSULTING PSYCHOLOGY. "The main lines are as valid as ever," PSYCHO-ANALYTICAL QUARTERLY. "Standard reading . . . a classic of interpretation," PSYCHIATRIC QUARTERLY. 94 illustrations. 1408pp. 2 volumes. 5⅜ x 8. Vol. 1, T381 Paperbound **$2.50**
Vol. 2, T382 Paperbound **$2.50**

THE DYNAMICS OF THERAPY IN A CONTROLLED RELATIONSHIP, Jessie Taft. One of the most important works in literature of child psychology, out of print for 25 years. Outstanding disciple of Rank describes all aspects of relationship or Rankian therapy through concise, simple elucidation of theory underlying her actual contacts with two seven-year olds. Therapists, social caseworkers, psychologists, counselors, and laymen who work with children will all find this important work an invaluable summation of method, theory of child psychology. xix + 296pp. 5⅜ x 8. T325 Paperbound **$1.75**

Puzzles, Mathematical Recreations

SYMBOLIC LOGIC and THE GAME OF LOGIC, Lewis Carroll. "Symbolic Logic" is not concerned with modern symbolic logic, but is instead a collection of over 380 problems posed with charm and imagination, using the syllogism, and a fascinating diagrammatic method of drawing conclusions. In "The Game of Logic" Carroll's whimsical imagination devises a logical game played with 2 diagrams and counters (included) to manipulate hundreds of tricky syllogisms. The final section, "Hit or Miss" is a lagniappe of 101 additional puzzles in the delightful Carroll manner. Until this reprint edition, both of these books were rarities costing up to $15 each. Symbolic Logic: Index. xxxi + 199pp. The Game of Logic: 96pp. 2 vols. bound as one. 5⅜ x 8. T492 Paperbound **$1.50**

PILLOW PROBLEMS and A TANGLED TALE, Lewis Carroll. One of the rarest of all Carroll's works, "Pillow Problems" contains 72 original math puzzles, all typically ingenious. Particularly fascinating are Carroll's answers which remain exactly as he thought them out, reflecting his actual mental process. The problems in "A Tangled Tale" are in story form, originally appearing as a monthly magazine serial. Carroll not only gives the solutions, but uses answers sent in by readers to discuss wrong approaches and misleading paths, and grades them for insight. Both of these books were rarities until this edition, "Pillow Problems" costing up to $25, and "A Tangled Tale" $15. Pillow Problems: Preface and Introduction by Lewis Carroll. xx + 109pp. A Tangled Tale: 6 illustrations. 152pp. Two vols. bound as one. 5⅜ x 8. T493 Paperbound **$1.50**

AMUSEMENTS IN MATHEMATICS, Henry Ernest Dudeney. The foremost British originator of mathematical puzzles is always intriguing, witty, and paradoxical in this classic, one of the largest collections of mathematical amusements. More than 430 puzzles, problems, and paradoxes. Mazes and games, problems on number manipulation, unicursal and other route problems, puzzles on measuring, weighing, packing, age, kinship, chessboards, joiners', crossing river, plane figure dissection, and many others. Solutions. More than 450 illustrations. vii + 258pp. 5⅜ x 8. T473 Paperbound **$1.25**

THE CANTERBURY PUZZLES, Henry Dudeney. Chaucer's pilgrims set one another problems in story form. Also Adventures of the Puzzle Club, the Strange Escape of the King's Jester, the Monks of Riddlewell, the Squire's Christmas Puzzle Party, and others. All puzzles are original, based on dissecting plane figures, arithmetic, algebra, elementary calculus and other branches of mathematics, and purely logical ingenuity. "The limit of ingenuity and intricacy," The Observer. Over 110 puzzles. Full Solutions. 150 illustrations. vii + 225pp. 5⅜ x 8. T474 Paperbound **$1.25**

MATHEMATICAL EXCURSIONS, H. A. Merrill. Even if you hardly remember your high school math, you'll enjoy the 90 stimulating problems contained in this book and you will come to understand a great many mathematical principles with surprisingly little effort. Many useful shortcuts and diversions not generally known are included: division by inspection, Russian peasant multiplication, memory systems for pi, building odd and even magic squares, square roots by geometry, dyadic systems, and many more. Solutions to difficult problems. 50 illustrations. 145pp. 5⅜ x 8. T350 Paperbound **$1.00**

MAGIC SQUARES AND CUBES, W. S. Andrews. Only book-length treatment in English, a thorough non-technical description and analysis. Here are nasik's, overlapping, pandiagonal, serrated squares; magic circles, cubes, spheres, rhombuses. Try your hand at 4-dimensional magical figures! Much unusual folklore and tradition included. High school algebra is sufficient. 754 diagrams and illustrations. viii + 419pp. 5⅜ x 8. T658 Paperbound **$1.85**

CALIBAN'S PROBLEM BOOK: MATHEMATICAL, INFERENTIAL AND CRYPTOGRAPHIC PUZZLES, H. Phillips (Caliban), S. T. Shovelton, G. S. Marshall. 105 ingenious problems by the greatest living creator of puzzles based on logic and inference. Rigorous, modern, piquant; reflecting their author's unusual personality, these intermediate and advanced puzzles all involve the ability to reason clearly through complex situations; some call for mathematical knowledge, ranging from algebra to number theory. Solutions. xi + 180pp. 5⅜ x 8. T736 Paperbound **$1.25**

MATHEMATICAL PUZZLES FOR BEGINNERS AND ENTHUSIASTS, G. Mott-Smith. 188 mathematical puzzles based on algebra, dissection of plane figures, permutations, and probability, that will test and improve your powers of inference and interpretation. The Odic Force, The Spider's Cousin, Ellipse Drawing, theory and strategy of card and board games like tit-tat-toe, go moku, salvo, and many others. 100 pages of detailed mathematical explanations. Appendix of primes, square roots, etc. 135 illustrations. 2nd revised edition. 248pp. 5⅜ x 8. T198 Paperbound **$1.00**

MATHEMAGIC, MAGIC PUZZLES, AND GAMES WITH NUMBERS, R. V. Heath. More than 60 new puzzles and stunts based on the properties of numbers. Easy techniques for multiplying large numbers mentally, revealing hidden numbers magically, finding the date of any day in any year, and dozens more. Over 30 pages devoted to magic squares, triangles, cubes, circles, etc. Edited by J. S. Meyer. 76 illustrations. 128pp. 5⅜ x 8. T110 Paperbound **$1.00**

CATALOGUE OF DOVER BOOKS

MATHEMATICAL RECREATIONS, M. Kraitchik. One of the most thorough compilations of unusual mathematical problems for beginners and advanced mathematicians. Historical problems from Greek, Medieval, Arabic, Hindu sources. 50 pages devoted to pastimes derived from figurate numbers, Mersenne numbers, Fermat numbers, primes and probability. 40 pages of magic, Euler, Latin, panmagic squares. 25 new positional and permutational games of permanent value: fairy chess, latruncles, reversi, jinx, ruma, lasca, tricolor, tetrachrome, etc. Complete rigorous solutions. Revised second edition. 181 illustrations. 333pp. 5⅜ x 8.
T163 Paperbound **$1.75**

MATHEMATICAL PUZZLES OF SAM LOYD, selected and edited by M. Gardner. Choice puzzles by the greatest American puzzle creator and innovator. Selected from his famous collection, "Cyclopedia of Puzzles," they retain the unique style and historical flavor of the originals. There are posers based on arithmetic, algebra, probability, game theory, route tracing, topology, counter, sliding block, operations research, geometrical dissection. Includes the famous "14-15" puzzle which was a national craze, and his "Horse of a Different Color" which sold millions of copies. 117 of his most ingenious puzzles in all, 120 line drawings and diagrams. Solutions. Selected references. xx + 167pp. 5⅜ x 8. T498 Paperbound **$1.00**

MATHEMATICAL PUZZLES OF SAM LOYD, Vol. II, selected and edited by Martin Gardner. The outstanding 2nd selection from the great American innovator's "Cyclopedia of Puzzles": speed and distance problems, clock problems, plane and solid geometry, calculus problems, etc. Analytical table of contents that groups the puzzles according to the type of mathematics necessary to solve them. 166 puzzles, 150 original line drawings and diagrams. Selected references. xiv + 177pp. 5⅜ x 8. T709 Paperbound **$1.00**

ARITHMETICAL EXCURSIONS: AN ENRICHMENT OF ELEMENTARY MATHEMATICS, H. Bowers and J. Bowers. A lively and lighthearted collection of facts and entertainments for anyone who enjoys manipulating numbers or solving arithmetical puzzles: methods of arithmetic never taught in school, little-known facts about the most simple numbers, and clear explanations of more sophisticated topics; mysteries and folklore of numbers, the "Hin-dog-abic" number system, etc. First publication. Index. 529 numbered problems and diversions, all with answers. Bibliography. 60 figures. xiv + 320pp. 5⅜ x 8. T770 Paperbound **$1.65**

CRYPTANALYSIS, H. F. Gaines. Formerly entitled ELEMENTARY CRYPTANALYSIS, this introductory-intermediate level text is the best book in print on cryptograms and their solution. It covers all major techniques of the past, and contains much that is not generally known except to experts. Full details about concealment, substitution, and transposition ciphers; periodic mixed alphabets, multafid, Kasiski and Vigenere methods, Ohaver patterns, Playfair, and scores of other topics. 6 language letter and word frequency appendix. 167 problems, now furnished with solutions. Index. 173 figures. vi + 230pp. 5⅜ x 8.
T97 Paperbound **$2.00**

CRYPTOGRAPHY, L. D. Smith. An excellent introductory work on ciphers and their solution, the history of secret writing, and actual methods and problems in such techniques as transposition and substitution. Appendices describe the enciphering of Japanese, the Baconian biliteral cipher, and contain frequency tables and a bibliography for further study. Over 150 problems with solutions. 160pp. 5⅜ x 8. T247 Paperbound **$1.00**

PUZZLE QUIZ AND STUNT FUN, J. Meyer. The solution to party doldrums. 238 challenging puzzles, stunts and tricks. Mathematical puzzles like The Clever Carpenter, Atom Bomb; mysteries and deductions like The Bridge of Sighs, The Nine Pearls, Dog Logic; observation puzzles like Cigarette Smokers, Telephone Dial; over 200 others including magic squares, tongue twisters, puns, anagrams, and many others. All problems solved fully. 250pp. 5⅜ x 8.
T337 Paperbound **$1.00**

101 PUZZLES IN THOUGHT AND LOGIC, C. R. Wylie, Jr. Brand new problems you need no special knowledge to solve! Take the kinks out of your mental "muscles" and enjoy solving murder problems, the detection of lying fishermen, the logical identification of color by a blindman, and dozens more. Introduction with simplified explanation of general scientific method and puzzle solving. 128pp. 5⅜ x 8. T367 Paperbound **$1.00**

MY BEST PROBLEMS IN MATHEMATICS, Hubert Phillips ("Caliban"). Only elementary mathematics needed to solve these 100 witty, catchy problems by a master problem creator. Problems on the odds in cards and dice, problems in geometry, algebra, permutations, even problems that require no math at all—just a logical mind, clear thinking. Solutions completely worked out. If you enjoy mysteries, alerting your perceptive powers and exercising your detective's eye, you'll find these cryptic puzzles a challenging delight. Original 1961 publication. 100 puzzles, solutions. x + 107pp. 5⅝ x 8. T91 Paperbound **$1.00**

MY BEST PUZZLES IN LOGIC AND REASONING, Hubert Phillips ("Caliban"). A new collection of 100 inferential and logical puzzles chosen from the best that have appeared in England, available for first time in U.S. By the most endlessly resourceful puzzle creator now living. All data presented are both necessary and sufficient to allow a single unambiguous answer. No special knowledge is required for problems ranging from relatively simple to completely original one-of-a-kinds. Guaranteed to please beginners and experts of all ages. Original publication. 100 puzzles, full solutions. x + 107pp. 5⅜ x 8. T119 Paperbound **$1.00**

CATALOGUE OF DOVER BOOKS

THE BOOK OF MODERN PUZZLES, G. L. Kaufman. A completely new series of puzzles as fascinating as crossword and deduction puzzles but based upon different principles and techniques. Simple 2-minute teasers, word labyrinths, design and pattern puzzles, logic and observation puzzles — over 150 braincrackers. Answers to all problems. 116 illustrations. 192pp. 5⅜ x 8.
T143 Paperbound **$1.00**

NEW WORD PUZZLES, G. L. Kaufman. 100 ENTIRELY NEW puzzles based on words and their combinations that will delight crossword puzzle, Scrabble and Jotto fans. Chess words, based on the moves of the chess king; design-onyms, symmetrical designs made of synonyms; rhymed double-crostics; syllable sentences; addle letter anagrams; alphagrams; linkograms; and many others all brand new. Full solutions. Space to work problems. 196 figures. vi + 122pp. 5⅜ x 8.
T344 Paperbound **$1.00**

MAZES AND LABYRINTHS: A BOOK OF PUZZLES, W. Shepherd. Mazes, formerly associated with mystery and ritual, are still among the most intriguing of intellectual puzzles. This is a novel and different collection of 50 amusements that embody the principle of the maze: mazes in the classical tradition; 3-dimensional, ribbon, and Möbius-strip mazes; hidden messages; spatial arrangements; etc.—almost all built on amusing story situations. 84 illustrations. Essay on maze psychology. Solutions. xv + 122pp. 5⅜ x 8.
T731 Paperbound **$1.00**

MAGIC TRICKS & CARD TRICKS, W. Jonson. Two books bound as one. 52 tricks with cards, 37 tricks with coins, bills, eggs, smoke, ribbons, slates, etc. Details on presentation, misdirection, and routining will help you master such famous tricks as the Changing Card, Card in the Pocket, Four Aces, Coin Through the Hand, Bill in the Egg, Afghan Bands, and over 75 others. If you follow the lucid exposition and key diagrams carefully, you will finish these two books with an astonishing mastery of magic. 106 figures. 224pp. 5⅜ x 8. T909 Paperbound **$1.00**

PANORAMA OF MAGIC, Milbourne Christopher. A profusely illustrated history of stage magic, a unique selection of prints and engravings from the author's private collection of magic memorabilia, the largest of its kind. Apparatus, stage settings and costumes; ingenious ads distributed by the performers and satiric broadsides passed around in the streets ridiculing pompous showmen; programs; decorative souvenirs. The lively text, by one of America's foremost professional magicians, is full of anecdotes about almost legendary wizards: Dede, the Egyptian; Philadelphia, the wonder-worker; Robert-Houdin, "the father of modern magic;" Harry Houdini; scores more. Altogether a pleasure package for anyone interested in magic, stage setting and design, ethnology, psychology, or simply in unusual people. A Dover original. 295 illustrations; 8 in full color. Index. viii + 216pp. 8⅜ x 11¼.
T774 Paperbound **$2.25**

HOUDINI ON MAGIC, Harry Houdini. One of the greatest magicians of modern times explains his most prized secrets. How locks are picked, with illustrated picks and skeleton keys; how a girl is sawed into twins; how to walk through a brick wall — Houdini's explanations of 44 stage tricks with many diagrams. Also included is a fascinating discussion of great magicians of the past and the story of his fight against fraudulent mediums and spiritualists. Edited by W.B. Gibson and M.N. Young. Bibliography. 155 figures, photos. xv + 280pp. 5⅜ x 8.
T384 Paperbound **$1.25**

MATHEMATICS, MAGIC AND MYSTERY, Martin Gardner. Why do card tricks work? How do magicians perform astonishing mathematical feats? How is stage mind-reading possible? This is the first book length study explaining the application of probability, set theory, theory of numbers, topology, etc., to achieve many startling tricks. No-technical, accurate, detailed! 115 sections discuss tricks with cards, dice, coins, knots, geometrical vanishing illusions, how a Curry square "demonstrates" that the sum of the parts may be greater than the whole, and dozens of others. No sleight of hand necessary! 135 illustrations. xii + 174pp. 5⅜ x 8.
T335 Paperbound **$1.00**

EASY-TO-DO ENTERTAINMENTS AND DIVERSIONS WITH COINS, CARDS, STRING, PAPER AND MATCHES, R. M. Abraham. Over 300 tricks, games and puzzles will provide young readers with absorbing fun. Sections on card games; paper-folding; tricks with coins, matches and pieces of string; games for the agile; toy-making from common household objects; mathematical recreations; and 50 miscellaneous pastimes. Anyone in charge of groups of youngsters, including hard-pressed parents, and in need of suggestions on how to keep children sensibly amused and quietly content will find this book indispensable. Clear, simple text, copious number of delightful line drawings and illustrative diagrams. Originally titled "Winter Nights Entertainments." Introduction by Lord Baden Powell. 329 illustrations. v + 186pp. 5⅜ x 8½.
T921 Paperbound **$1.00**

STRING FIGURES AND HOW TO MAKE THEM, Caroline Furness Jayne. 107 string figures plus variations selected from the best primitive and modern examples developed by Navajo, Apache, pygmies of Africa, Eskimo, in Europe, Australia, China, etc. The most readily understandable, easy-to-follow book in English on perennially popular recreation. Crystal-clear exposition; step-by-step diagrams. Everyone from kindergarten children to adults looking for unusual diversion will be endlessly amused. Index. Bibliography. Introduction by A. C. Haddon. 17 full-page plates. 960 illustrations. xxiii + 401pp. 5⅜ x 8½.
T152 Paperbound **$2.00**

Entertainments, Humor

ODDITIES AND CURIOSITIES OF WORDS AND LITERATURE, C. Bombaugh, edited by M. Gardner. The largest collection of idiosyncratic prose and poetry techniques in English, a legendary work in the curious and amusing bypaths of literary recreations and the play technique in literature—so important in modern works. Contains alphabetic poetry, acrostics, palindromes, scissors verse, centos, emblematic poetry, famous literary puns, hoaxes, notorious slips of the press, hilarious mistranslations, and much more. Revised and enlarged with modern material by Martin Gardner. 368pp. 5⅜ x 8. **T759 Paperbound $1.50**

A NONSENSE ANTHOLOGY, collected by Carolyn Wells. 245 of the best nonsense verses ever written, including nonsense puns, absurd arguments, mock epics and sagas, nonsense ballads, odes, "sick" verses, dog-Latin verses, French nonsense verses, songs. By Edward Lear, Lewis Carroll, Gelett Burgess, W. S. Gilbert, Hilaire Belloc, Peter Newell, Oliver Herford, etc., 83 writers in all plus over four score anonymous nonsense verses. A special section of limericks, plus famous nonsense such as Carroll's "Jabberwocky" and Lear's "The Jumblies" and much excellent verse virtually impossible to locate elsewhere. For 50 years considered the best anthology available. Index of first lines specially prepared for this edition. Introduction by Carolyn Wells. 3 indexes: Title, Author, First lines. xxxiii + 279pp. **T499 Paperbound $1.35**

THE BAD CHILD'S BOOK OF BEASTS, MORE BEASTS FOR WORSE CHILDREN, and A MORAL ALPHABET, H. Belloc. Hardly an anthology of humorous verse has appeared in the last 50 years without at least a couple of these famous nonsense verses. But one must see the entire volumes—with all the delightful original illustrations by Sir Basil Blackwood—to appreciate fully Belloc's charming and witty verses that play so subacidly on the platitudes of life and morals that beset his day—and ours. A great humor classic. Three books in one. Total of 157pp. 5⅜ x 8. **T749 Paperbound $1.00**

THE DEVIL'S DICTIONARY, Ambrose Bierce. Sardonic and irreverent barbs puncturing the pomposities and absurdities of American politics, business, religion, literature, and arts, by the country's greatest satirist in the classic tradition. Epigrammatic as Shaw, piercing as Swift, American as Mark Twain, Will Rogers, and Fred Allen, Bierce will always remain the favorite of a small coterie of enthusiasts, and of writers and speakers whom he supplies with "some of the most gorgeous witticisms of the English language" (H. L. Mencken). Over 1000 entries in alphabetical order. 144pp. 5⅜ x 8. **T487 Paperbound $1.00**

THE PURPLE COW AND OTHER NONSENSE, Gelett Burgess. The best of Burgess's early nonsense, selected from the first edition of the "Burgess Nonsense Book." Contains many of his most unusual and truly awe-inspiring pieces: 36 nonsense quatrains, the Poems of Patagonia, Alphabet of Famous Goops, and the other hilarious (and rare) adult nonsense that place him in the forefront of American humorists. All pieces are accompanied by the original Burgess illustrations. 123 illustrations. xiii + 113pp. 5⅜ x 8. **T772 Paperbound $1.00**

MY PIOUS FRIENDS AND DRUNKEN COMPANIONS and MORE PIOUS FRIENDS AND DRUNKEN COMPANIONS, Frank Shay. Folksingers, amateur and professional, and everyone who loves singing: here, available for the first time in 30 years, is this valued collection of 132 ballads, blues, vaudeville numbers, drinking songs, sea chanties, comedy songs. Songs of pre-Beatnik Bohemia; songs from all over America, England, France, Australia; the great songs of the Naughty Nineties and early twentieth-century America. Over a third with music. Woodcuts by John Held, Jr. convey perfectly the brash insouciance of an era of rollicking unabashed song. 12 illustrations by John Held, Jr. Two indexes (Titles and First lines and Choruses). Introductions by the author. Two volumes bound as one. Total of xvi + 235pp. 5⅜ x 8½. **T946 Paperbound $1.00**

HOW TO TELL THE BIRDS FROM THE FLOWERS, R. W. Wood. How not to confuse a carrot with a parrot, a grape with an ape, a puffin with nuffin. Delightful drawings, clever puns, absurd little poems point out far-fetched resemblances in nature. The author was a leading physicist. Introduction by Margaret Wood White. 106 illus. 60pp. 5⅜ x 8. **T523 Paperbound 75¢**

PECK'S BAD BOY AND HIS PA, George W. Peck. The complete edition, containing both volumes, of one of the most widely read American humor books. The endless ingenious pranks played by bad boy "Hennery" on his pa and the grocery man, the outraged pomposity of Pa, the perpetual ridiculing of middle class institutions, are as entertaining today as they were in 1883. No pale sophistications or subtleties, but rather humor vigorous, raw, earthy, imaginative, and, as folk humor often is, sadistic. This peculiarly fascinating book is also valuable to historians and students of American culture as a portrait of an age. 100 original illustrations by True Williams. Introduction by E. F. Bleiler. 347pp. 5⅜ x 8. **T497 Paperbound $1.35**

CATALOGUE OF DOVER BOOKS

THE HUMOROUS VERSE OF LEWIS CARROLL. Almost every poem Carroll ever wrote, the largest collection ever published, including much never published elsewhere: 150 parodies, burlesques, riddles, ballads, acrostics, etc., with 130 original illustrations by Tenniel, Carroll, and others. "Addicts will be grateful . . . there is nothing for the faithful to do but sit down and fall to the banquet," N. Y. Times. Index to first lines. xiv + 446pp. 5⅜ x 8.
T654 Paperbound **$1.85**

DIVERSIONS AND DIGRESSIONS OF LEWIS CARROLL. A major new treasure for Carroll fans! Rare privately published humor, fantasy, puzzles, and games by Carroll at his whimsical best, with a new vein of frank satire. Includes many new mathematical amusements and recreations, among them the fragmentary Part III of "Curiosa Mathematica." Contains "The Rectory Umbrella," "The New Belfry," "The Vision of the Three T's," and much more. New 32-page supplement of rare photographs taken by Carroll. x + 375pp. 5⅜ x 8.
T732 Paperbound **$1.65**

THE COMPLETE NONSENSE OF EDWARD LEAR. This is the only complete edition of this master of gentle madness available at a popular price. A BOOK OF NONSENSE, NONSENSE SONGS, MORE NONSENSE SONGS AND STORIES in their entirety with all the old favorites that have delighted children and adults for years. The Dong With A Luminous Nose, The Jumblies, The Owl and the Pussycat, and hundreds of other bits of wonderful nonsense. 214 limericks, 3 sets of Nonsense Botany, 5 Nonsense Alphabets, 546 drawings by Lear himself, and much more. 320pp. 5⅜ x 8.
T167 Paperbound **$1.00**

THE MELANCHOLY LUTE, The Humorous Verse of Franklin P. Adams ("FPA"). The author's own selection of light verse, drawn from thirty years of FPA's column, "The Conning Tower," syndicated all over the English-speaking world. Witty, perceptive, literate, these ninety-six poems range from parodies of other poets, Millay, Longfellow, Edgar Guest, Kipling, Masefield, etc., and free and hilarious translations of Horace and other Latin poets, to satiric comments on fabled American institutions—the New York Subways, preposterous ads, suburbanites, sensational journalism, etc. They reveal with vigor and clarity the humor, integrity and restraint of a wise and gentle American satirist. Introduction by Robert Hutchinson. vi + 122pp. 5⅜ x 8½.
T108 Paperbound **$1.00**

SINGULAR TRAVELS, CAMPAIGNS, AND ADVENTURES OF BARON MUNCHAUSEN, R. E. Raspe, with 90 illustrations by Gustave Doré. The first edition in over 150 years to reestablish the deeds of the Prince of Liars exactly as Raspe first recorded them in 1785—the genuine Baron Munchausen, one of the most popular personalities in English literature. Included also are the best of the many sequels, written by other hands. Introduction on Raspe by J. Carswell. Bibliography of early editions. xliv + 192pp. 5⅜ x 8.
T698 Paperbound **$1.00**

THE WIT AND HUMOR OF OSCAR WILDE, ed. by Alvin Redman. Wilde at his most brilliant, in 1000 epigrams exposing weaknesses and hypocrisies of "civilized" society. Divided into 49 categories—sin, wealth, women, America, etc.—to aid writers, speakers. Includes excerpts from his trials, books, plays, criticism. Formerly "The Epigrams of Oscar Wilde." Introduction by Vyvyan Holland, Wilde's only living son. Introductory essay by editor. 260pp. 5⅜ x 8.
T602 Paperbound **$1.00**

MAX AND MORITZ, Wilhelm Busch. Busch is one of the great humorists of all time, as well as the father of the modern comic strip. This volume, translated by H. A. Klein and other hands, contains the perennial favorite "Max and Moritz" (translated by C. T. Brooks), Plisch and Plum, Das Rabennest, Eispeter, and seven other whimsical, sardonic, jovial, diabolical cartoon and verse stories. Lively English translations parallel the original German. This work has delighted millions, since it first appeared in the 19th century, and is guaranteed to please almost anyone. Edited by H. A. Klein, with an afterword. x + 205pp. 5⅝ x 8½.
T181 Paperbound **$1.00**

HYPOCRITICAL HELENA, Wilhelm Busch. A companion volume to "Max and Moritz," with the title piece (Die Fromme Helena) and 10 other highly amusing cartoon and verse stories, all newly translated by H. A. Klein and M. C. Klein: Adventure on New Year's Eve (Abenteuer in der Neujahrsnacht), Hangover on the Morning after New Year's Eve (Der Katzenjammer am Neujahrsmorgen), etc. English and German in parallel columns. Hours of pleasure, also a fine language aid. x + 205pp. 5⅝ x 8½.
T184 Paperbound **$1.00**

THE BEAR THAT WASN'T, Frank Tashlin. What does it mean? Is it simply delightful wry humor, or a charming story of a bear who wakes up in the midst of a factory, or a satire on Big Business, or an existential cartoon-story of the human condition, or a symbolization of the struggle between conformity and the individual? New York Herald Tribune said of the first edition: ". . . a fable for grownups that will be fun for children. Sit down with the book and get your own bearings." Long an underground favorite with readers of all ages and opinions. v + 51pp. Illustrated. 5⅜ x 8½.
T939 Paperbound **75¢**

RUTHLESS RHYMES FOR HEARTLESS HOMES and MORE RUTHLESS RHYMES FOR HEARTLESS HOMES, Harry Graham ("Col. D. Streamer"). Two volumes of Little Willy and 48 other poetic disasters. A bright, new reprint of oft-quoted, never forgotten, devastating humor by a precursor of today's "sick" joke school. For connoisseurs of wicked, wacky humor and all who delight in the comedy of manners. Original drawings are a perfect complement. 61 illustrations. Index. vi + 69pp. Two vols. bound as one. 5⅜ x 8½.
T930 Paperbound **75¢**

Fiction

FLATLAND, E. A. Abbott. A science-fiction classic of life in a 2-dimensional world that is also a first-rate introduction to such aspects of modern science as relativity and hyperspace. Political, moral, satirical, and humorous overtones have made FLATLAND fascinating reading for thousands. 7th edition. New introduction by Banesh Hoffmann. 16 illustrations. 128pp. 5⅜ x 8. T1 Paperbound **$1.00**

THE WONDERFUL WIZARD OF OZ, L. F. Baum. Only edition in print with all the original W. W. Denslow illustrations in full color—as much a part of "The Wizard" as Tenniel's drawings are of "Alice in Wonderland." "The Wizard" is still America's best-loved fairy tale, in which, as the author expresses it, "The wonderment and joy are retained and the heartaches and nightmares left out." Now today's young readers can enjoy every word and wonderful picture of the original book. New introduction by Martin Gardner. A Baum bibliography. 23 full-page color plates. viii + 268pp. 5⅜ x 8. T691 Paperbound **$1.45**

THE MARVELOUS LAND OF OZ, L. F. Baum. This is the equally enchanting sequel to the "Wizard," continuing the adventures of the Scarecrow and the Tin Woodman. The hero this time is a little boy named Tip, and all the delightful Oz magic is still present. This is the Oz book with the Animated Saw-Horse, the Woggle-Bug, and Jack Pumpkinhead. All the original John R. Neill illustrations, 10 in full color. 287 pp. 5⅜ x 8. T692 Paperbound **$1.45**

FIVE GREAT DOG NOVELS, edited by Blanche Cirker. The complete original texts of five classic dog novels that have delighted and thrilled millions of children and adults throughout the world with their stories of loyalty, adventure, and courage. Full texts of Jack London's "The Call of the Wild"; John Brown's "Rab and His Friends"; Alfred Ollivant's "Bob, Son of Battle"; Marshall Saunders's "Beautiful Joe"; and Ouida's "A Dog of Flanders." 21 Illustrations from the original editions. 495pp. 5⅜ x 8. T777 Paperbound **$1.75**

TO THE SUN? and OFF ON A COMET!, Jules Verne. Complete texts of two of the most imaginative flights into fancy in world literature display the high adventure that have kept Verne's novels read for nearly a century. Only unabridged edition of the best translation, by Edward Roth. Large, easily readable type. 50 illustrations selected from first editions. 462pp. 5⅜ x 8. T634 Paperbound **$1.75**

FROM THE EARTH TO THE MOON and ALL AROUND THE MOON, Jules Verne. Complete editions of 2 of Verne's most successful novels, in finest Edward Roth translations, now available after many years out of print. Verne's visions of submarines, airplanes, television, rockets, interplanetary travel; of scientific and not-so-scientific beliefs; of peculiarities of Americans; all delight and engross us today as much as when they first appeared. Large, easily readable type. 42 illus. from first French edition. 476pp. 5⅜ x 8. T633 Paperbound **$1.75**

THE CRUISE OF THE CACHALOT, Frank T. Bullen. Out of the experiences of many years on the high-seas, First Mate Bullen created this novel of adventure aboard an American whaler, shipping out of New Bedford, Mass., when American whaling was at the height of its splendor. Originally published in 1899, the story of the round-the-world cruise of the "Cachalot" in pursuit of the sperm whale has thrilled generations of readers. A maritime classic that will fascinate anyone interested in reading about the sea or looking for a solid old-fashioned yarn, while the vivid recreation of a brief but important chapter of Americana and the British author's often biting commentary on nineteenth-century Yankee mores offer insights into the colorful era of America's coming of age. 8 plates. xiii + 271pp. 5⅜ x 8½. T774 Paperbound **$1.00**

28 SCIENCE FICTION STORIES OF H. G. WELLS. Two full unabridged novels, MEN LIKE GODS and STAR BEGOTTEN, plus 26 short stories by the master science-fiction writer of all time! Stories of space, time, invention, exploration, future adventure—an indispensable part of the library of everyone interested in science and adventure. PARTIAL CONTENTS: Men Like Gods, The Country of the Blind, In the Abyss, The Crystal Egg, The Man Who Could Work Miracles, A Story of the Days to Come, The Valley of Spiders, and 21 more! 928pp. 5⅜ x 8. T265 Clothbound **$4.50**

DAVID HARUM, E. N. Westcott. This novel of one of the most lovable, humorous characters in American literature is a prime example of regional humor. It continues to delight people who like their humor dry, their characters quaint, and their plots ingenuous. First book edition to contain complete novel plus chapter found after author's death. Illustrations from first illustrated edition. 192pp. 5⅜ x 8. T580 Paperbound **$1.15**

GESTA ROMANORUM, trans. by Charles Swan, ed. by Wynnard Hooper. 181 tales of Greeks, Romans, Britons, Biblical characters, comprise one of greatest medieval story collections, source of plots for writers including Shakespeare, Chaucer, Gower, etc. Imaginative tales of wars, incest, thwarted love, magic, fantasy, allegory, humor, tell about kings, prostitutes, philosophers, fair damsels, knights, Noah, pirates, all walks, stations of life. Introduction. Notes. 500pp. 5⅜ x 8. T535 Paperbound **$1.85**

CATALOGUE OF DOVER BOOKS

3 ADVENTURE NOVELS by H. Rider Haggard. Complete texts of "She," "King Solomon's Mines," "Allan Quatermain." Qualities of discovery, desire for immortality, search for the primitive, for what is unadorned by civilization, have kept these novels of African adventure excitingly alive-to readers from R. L. Stevenson to George Orwell. 636pp. 5⅜ x 8.
T584 Paperbound **$2.00**

THE CASTING AWAY OF MRS. LECKS AND MRS. ALESHINE, F. R. Stockton. A charming light novel by Frank Stockton, one of America's finest humorists (and author of "The Lady, or the Tiger?"). This book has made millions of Americans laugh at the reflection of themselves in two middle-aged American women involved in some of the strangest adventures on record. You will laugh, too, as they endure shipwreck, desert island, and blizzard with maddening tranquillity. Also contains complete text of "The Dusantes," sequel to "The Casting Away." 49 original illustrations by F. D. Steele. vii + 142pp. 5⅜ x 8. T743 Paperbound **$1.00**

THREE PROPHETIC NOVELS OF H. G. WELLS. Complete texts of 3 timeless science fiction novels by the greatest master of the art, with remarkable prophecies of technological and social changes that are really taking place!—"When the Sleeper Wakes" (first printing in 50 years), "A Story of the Days to Come," and "The Time Machine" (only truly complete text available). Introduction by E. F. Bleiler. "The absolute best of imaginative fiction," N. Y. Times. 335pp. 5⅜ x 8. T605 Paperbound **$1.45**

SEVEN SCIENCE FICTION NOVELS, H. G. Wells. Full unabridged texts of 7 science-fiction novels of the master. Ranging from biology, physics, chemistry, astronomy, to sociology and other studies, Mr. Wells extrapolates whole worlds of strange and intriguing character. "One will have to go so far to match this for entertainment, excitement, and sheer pleasure . . ." NEW YORK TIMES. Contents: The Time Machine, The Island of Dr. Moreau, The First Men in the Moon, The Invisible Man, The War of the Worlds, The Food of the Gods, In The Days of the Comet. 1015pp. 5⅜ x 8. T264 Clothbound **$4.50**

THE PRISONER OF ZENDA and RUPERT OF HENTZAU, Anthony Hope. The first edition to contain the complete story of the English diplomat who becomes King for a Day in the ancient aristocratic Kingdom of Ruritania. Long a favorite of devotees of high adventure, romance, grand intigue. Intelligent thrills presented with verve and elegant excitement. Unabridged reprints. Two volumes bound as one. 14 illustrations by Charles Dana Gibson. 420pp. 5⅜ x 8. T69 Paperbound **$1.35**

TWO LITTLE SAVAGES, Ernest Thompson Seton. A lively narrative of the adventures of two real boys who decide to go Indian, combined with a storehouse of survival information: how to make a fire without matches, use an axe expertly, smudge mosquitoes, distinguish animal tracks, make mocassins, bows and arrows, learn the stars, etc. A classic of nature and boyhood, certain to awaken nature-interest in any youngster—or oldster. Highly recommended to Scouts, hunters, campers, bird-watchers or even city-dwellers who like to learn about the ways of nature. 293 illustrations by the author. x + 286pp. 5⅜ x 8½.
T985 Paperbound **$1.50**

THREE MARTIAN NOVELS, Edgar Rice Burroughs. Complete unabridged reprinting, in one volume, of Thuvia, Maid of Mars; Chessmen of Mars; The Master Mind of Mars. Hours of science-fiction adventure by a modern master storyteller. Reset in large clear type for easy reading. 16 illustrations by J. Allen St. John, vi + 490 pp. 5⅜ x 8½. T39 Paperbound **$1.75**

THE LAND THAT TIME FORGOT, and THE MOON MAID, Edgar Rice Burroughs. Two of Burroughs's rarest novels, considered by most authorities to be his best work. The first is adventure on a lost island where evolution is an individual matter and rapid, rather than slow and in terms of species; the second is the story of the first exploration of the Moon, the weird cultures that inhabit its interior, the conquest of the Earth by the Moon, and the millennia of struggle between the invaders and the earthmen. Packed full of thrills, thought-provoking. 5 illustrations by J. Allan St. John. 5⅜ x 8½.
T358 Paperbound **$2.00**
T1020 Clothbound **$3.75**

PIRATES OF VENUS, LOST ON VENUS, Edgar Rice Burroughs. These are the first two novels describing the adventures of Carson Napier on mysterious Venus. Thrilling adventures and exciting science-fiction situations among the towering jungles, monster-filled seas, and fantastic cities of the Second Planet. Complete and unabridged. Illustrations from original periodical publications. Illustrations by Matania. vi + 340pp. 5⅜ x 8½.
T1053 Paperbound **$1.75**

A PRINCESS OF MARS, A FIGHTING MAN OF MARS, Edgar Rice Burroughs. Two fantastic novels of Mars. "A Princess of Mars" explains how John Carter first came to Mars, and his adventures among the dying civilizations. "A Fighting Man of Mars", an independent novel set in the same adventurous environment, provides hours of thrills among lost cities and monsters. Illustrated by J. Allan St. John. 5⅜ x 8½. T1055 Paperbound **$1.75**

History of Science and Mathematics

THE STUDY OF THE HISTORY OF MATHEMATICS, THE STUDY OF THE HISTORY OF SCIENCE, G. Sarton. Two books bound as one. Each volume contains a long introduction to the methods and philosophy of each of these historical fields, covering the skills and sympathies of the historian, concepts of history of science, psychology of idea-creation, and the purpose of history of science. Prof. Sarton also provides more than 80 pages of classified bibliography. Complete and unabridged. Indexed. 10 illustrations. 188pp. 5⅜ x 8. T240 Paperbound **$1.25**

A HISTORY OF PHYSICS, Florian Cajori, Ph.D. First written in 1899, thoroughly revised in 1929, this is still best entry into antecedents of modern theories. Precise non-mathematical discussion of ideas, theories, techniques, apparatus of each period from Greeks to 1920's, analyzing within each period basic topics of matter, mechanics, light, electricity and magnetism, sound, atomic theory, etc. Stress on modern developments, from early 19th century to present. Written with critical eye on historical development, significance. Provides most of needed historical background for student of physics. Reprint of second (1929) edition. Index. Bibliography in footnotes. 16 figures. xv + 424pp. 5⅜ x 8. T970 Paperbound **$2.00**

A HISTORY OF ASTRONOMY FROM THALES TO KEPLER, J. L. E. Dreyer. Formerly titled A HISTORY OF PLANETARY SYSTEMS FROM THALES TO KEPLER. This is the only work in English which provides a detailed history of man's cosmological views from prehistoric times up through the Renaissance. It covers Egypt, Babylonia, early Greece, Alexandria, the Middle Ages, Copernicus, Tycho Brahe, Kepler, and many others. Epicycles and other complex theories of positional astronomy are explained in terms nearly everyone will find clear and easy to understand. "Standard reference on Greek astronomy and the Copernican revolution," SKY AND TELESCOPE. Bibliography. 21 diagrams. Index. xvii + 430pp. 5⅜ x 8. S79 Paperbound **$1.98**

A SHORT HISTORY OF ASTRONOMY, A. Berry. A popular standard work for over 50 years, this thorough and accurate volume covers the science from primitive times to the end of the 19th century. After the Greeks and Middle Ages, individual chapters analyze Copernicus, Brahe, Galileo, Kepler, and Newton, and the mixed reception of their startling discoveries. Post-Newtonian achievements are then discussed in unusual detail: Halley, Bradley, Lagrange, Laplace, Herschel, Bessel, etc. 2 indexes. 104 illustrations. 9 portraits. xxxi + 440pp. 5⅜ x 8. T210 Paperbound **$2.00**

PIONEERS OF SCIENCE, Sir Oliver Lodge. An authoritative, yet elementary history of science by a leading scientist and expositor. Concentrating on individuals—Copernicus, Brahe, Kepler, Galileo, Descartes, Newton, Laplace, Herschel, Lord Kelvin, and other scientists—the author presents their discoveries in historical order, adding biographical material on each man and full, specific explanations of their achievements. The full, clear discussions of the accomplishments of post-Newtonian astronomers are features seldom found in other books on the subject. Index. 120 illustrations. xv + 404pp. 5⅜ x 8. T716 Paperbound **$1.65**

THE BIRTH AND DEVELOPMENT OF THE GEOLOGICAL SCIENCES, F. D. Adams. The most complete and thorough history of the earth sciences in print. Geological thought from earliest recorded times to the end of the 19th century—covers over 300 early thinkers and systems: fossils and hypothetical explanations of them, vulcanists vs. neptunists, figured stones and paleontology, generation of stones, and similar topics. 91 illustrations, including medieval, renaissance woodcuts, etc. 632 footnotes and bibliographic notes. Index. 511pp. 5⅜ x 8. T5 Paperbound **$2.25**

THE STORY OF ALCHEMY AND EARLY CHEMISTRY, J. M. Stillman. "Add the blood of a red-haired man"—a recipe typical of the many quoted in this authoritative and readable history of the strange beliefs and practices of the alchemists. Concise studies of every leading figure in alchemy and early chemistry through Lavoisier, in this curious epic of superstition and true science, constructed from scores of rare and difficult Greek, Latin, German, and French texts. Foreword by S. W. Young. 246-item bibliography. Index. xiii + 566pp. 5⅜ x 8. S628 Paperbound **$2.45**

HISTORY OF MATHEMATICS, D. E. Smith. Most comprehensive non-technical history of math in English. Discusses the lives and works of over a thousand major and minor figures, from Euclid to Descartes, Gauss, and Riemann. Vol. I: A chronological examination, from primitive concepts through Egypt, Babylonia, Greece, the Orient, Rome, the Middle Ages, the Renaissance, and up to 1900. Vol. 2: The development of ideas in specific fields and problems, up through elementary calculus. Two volumes, total of 510 illustrations, 1355pp. 5⅜ x 8. Set boxed in attractive container. T429,430 Paperbound the set **$5.00**

CATALOGUE OF DOVER BOOKS

A CONCISE HISTORY OF MATHEMATICS, D. Struik. A lucid, easily followed history of mathematical ideas and techniques from the Ancient Near East up to modern times. Requires no mathematics but will serve as an excellent introduction to mathematical concepts and great mathematicians through the method of historical development. 60 illustrations including Egyptian papyri, Greek mss., portraits of 31 eminent mathematicians. Bibliography. xix + 299pp. 5⅜ x 8.   T255 Paperbound **$1.75**

A SHORT ACCOUNT OF THE HISTORY OF MATHEMATICS, W. W. Rouse Ball. Last previous edition (1908) hailed by mathematicians and laymen for lucid overview of math as living science, for understandable presentation of individual contributions of great mathematicians. Treats lives, discoveries of every important school and figure from Egypt, Phoenicia to late nineteenth century. Greek schools of Ionia, Cyzicus, Alexandria, Byzantium, Pythagoras; primitive arithmetic; Middle Ages and Renaissance, including European and Asiatic contributions; modern math of Descartes, Pascal, Wallis, Huygens, Newton, Euler, Lambert, Laplace, scores more. More emphasis on historical development, exposition of ideas than other books on subject. Non-technical, readable text can be followed with no more preparation than high-school algebra. Index. 544pp. 5⅜ x 8.   S630 Paperbound **$2.00**

ON MATHEMATICS AND MATHEMATICIANS, R. E. Moritz. A ten year labor of love by the discerning and discriminating Prof. Moritz, this collection has rarely been equalled in its ability to convey the full sense of mathematics and the personalities of great mathematicians. A collection of anecdotes, aphorisms, reminiscences, philosophies, definitions, speculations, biographical insights, etc., by great mathematicians and writers: Descartes, Mill, De Morgan, Locke, Berkeley, Kant, Coleridge, Whitehead, Sylvester, Klein, and many others. Also, glimpses into the lives of mathematical giants from Archimedes to Euler, Gauss, and Weierstrass. To mathematicians, a superb book for browsing; to writers and teachers, an unequalled source of quotation; to the layman, an exciting revelation of the fullness of mathematics. Extensive cross index. 410pp. 5⅜ x 8.   T489 Paperbound **$1.95**

SIR ISAAC NEWTON: A BIOGRAPHY, Louis Trenchard More. Standard, definitive biography of Newton, covering every phase of his life and career in its presentation of the renowned scientific genius as a living man. Objective, critical analysis of his character as well as a careful survey of his manifold accomplishments in many areas of science, and in theology, history, politics, finance. Text includes letters by Newton and acquaintances, many other papers, some translated from Latin to English by the author. Scientists, teachers of science will especially be interested in this book, which will appeal to all readers concerned with history of ideas, development of science. Republication of original (1934) edition. 1 full-page plate. Index. xii + 675pp. 5⅜ x 8½.   S79 Paperbound **$2.50**

GUIDE TO THE LITERATURE OF MATHEMATICS AND PHYSICS, N. G. Parke III. Over 5000 entries included under approximately 120 major subject headings, of selected most important books, monographs, periodicals, articles in English, plus important works in German, French, Italian, Spanish, Russian (many recently available works). Covers every branch of physics, math, related engineering. Includes author, title, edition, publisher, place, date, number of volumes, number of pages. A 40-page introduction on the basic problems of research and study provides useful information on the organization and use of libraries, the psychology of learning, etc. This reference work will save you hours of time. 2nd revised edition. Indices of authors, subjects. 464pp. 5⅜ x 8.   S447 Paperbound **$2.49**

Prices subject to change without notice.

Dover publishes books on art, music, philosophy, literature, languages, history, social sciences, psychology, handcrafts, orientalia, puzzles and entertainments, chess, pets and gardens, books explaining science, intermediate and higher mathematics, mathematical physics, engineering, biological sciences, earth sciences, classics of science, etc. Write to:

Dept. catrr.
Dover Publications, Inc.
180 Varick Street, N.Y. 14, N.Y.